GRADUATE ENGINEERING EDUCATION
GENESYS

I0329368

OPTICAL
CRYSTALLOGRAPHY

OPTICAL
CRYSTALLOGRAPHY

John Wiley & Sons, Inc.
New York · London · Sydney

ERNEST E. WAHLSTROM

Department of Geology
University of Colorado
Boulder, Colorado

3rd edition

WITH PARTICULAR REFERENCE
TO THE USE AND THEORY OF
THE POLARIZING MICROSCOPE

GENESYS-ORLANDO

BOOKS BY E. E. WAHLSTROM

Optical Crystallography. Third Edition
Introduction to Theoretical Igneous Petrology
Petrographic Mineralogy

THIRD EDITION
Fourth Printing, October, 1966

COPYRIGHT, 1943, 1951 BY ERNEST E. WAHLSTROM
COPYRIGHT © 1960 BY JOHN WILEY & SONS, INC.

LIBRARY OF CONGRESS CATALOG CARD NUMBER: 60-6461
PRINTED IN THE UNITED STATES OF AMERICA

PREFACE

As in previous editions of *Optical Crystallography,* I have directed my treatment of the subject to the student who is becoming interested in the theory and practice of optical crystallography for the first time and to more advanced investigators who may wish to review basic theory. I have made no attempt to include extensive mathematical derivations or detailed descriptions of many of the elegant techniques that have been developed by laboratory workers in this country and abroad. The book is designed as a textbook and not as a handbook or manual, although the student will find it convenient in the laboratory to refer to many of the charts and diagrams.

The theory of optical crystallography has been developed extensively over the last sixty years, and a great mass of literature on the subject has accumulated in books and journals. As in most theoretical subjects, there are several avenues of reasoning that lead to quantitative explanation and understanding of basic and derived concepts. I have chosen the approach that seems to me not only to be logical but also to permit easy two-dimensional and three-dimensional pictorial representation. In the several years that I have taught a course in optical crystallography I have experimented with a wide variety of methods of presentation of theory and applications, and the contents of this book reflect the methods that seem to give students the quickest appreciation of the subject.

In preparing this edition I have made extensive revisions of both text material and illustrations, but, at the same time, I have tried deliberately to avoid expansion of the book into a comprehensive treatise on all aspects of optical crystallography. This approach required arbitrary elimination of certain theoretical treatments and practical applications. I have resisted the temptation to include problems and laboratory exercises because a survey indicates little or no uniformity in teaching the methods of optical crystallography to students.

It is the main purpose of this textbook to review the basic principles of optical crystallographic theory. I feel that, once a student has firmly grasped fundamental concepts, he will be able to meet any problem related to the field. However, considerable space is given to the techniques for the measurement of refractive indices, for these techniques are very widely used in most laboratories. The final chapter contains descriptions of crystal rotation methods, with emphasis placed on the theory and use of the four-axis universal stage.

The reader will observe that the text is profusely illustrated. Much of the text was written after the illustrations were prepared. Three-dimensional visualization is required of the student who wishes to master the theory of optical crystallography. All diagrams in which the third dimension has been indicated are drawn in clinographic projection, a type of projection that is familiar to the crystallographer but may present a slightly distorted appearance to one who is familiar only with block diagrams drawn in perspective.

No effort was made to include descriptive tables of minerals or crystalline chemicals. Descriptions of the optical properties of most natural and artificial compounds may be found in many standard references in mineralogy and chemistry.

I have gathered the materials for this book from many sources. The illustrations are for the most part original, but, of course, many of the diagrams were suggested by illustrations appearing in other published works in the field of optical crystallography.

I wish to extend thanks to the numerous individuals who have offered criticisms and suggestions. Many of the improvements in this edition are the result of friendly collaboration with students and professional colleagues. It is difficult for me to appraise all the influences that have contributed to the evolution of the present approach to the subject. It is with a deep feeling of obligation that I acknowledge the indispensable assistance given to me by my coworker, Kathryn

Kemp Wahlstrom, who patiently worked at my side in all stages of preparation of the manuscript.

Finally, I wish to express my sincere appreciation to Professor John L. Rosenfeld of the University of California who made a very thorough analysis and criticism of the preliminary manuscript and made many suggestions that were incorporated into the book.

ERNEST E. WAHLSTROM

December 1959

CONTENTS

1 CRYSTALLOGRAPHY 1

2 LIGHT 20

3 OPTICS OF OPTICALLY ISOTROPIC SUBSTANCES 33

4 THE POLARIZING MICROSCOPE 45

5 CALCULATION AND MEASUREMENT OF INDEX OF REFRACTION 55

6 THE UNIAXIAL INDICATRIX 87

7 POLARIZED LIGHT 109

8 UNIAXIAL CRYSTALS IN PLANE–POLARIZED LIGHT 126

9 UNIAXIAL CRYSTALS IN CONVERGENT POLARIZED LIGHT 160

10 OPTICAL ACCESSORIES 189

ix

11 OPTIC SIGN DETERMINATION IN UNIAXIAL CRYSTALS 196

12 BIAXIAL CRYSTALS—THE BIAXIAL INDICATRIX 207

13 BIAXIAL CRYSTALS IN CONVERGENT POLARIZED LIGHT 245

14 DETERMINATION OF OPTIC SIGN IN BIAXIAL CRYSTALS 269

15 DISPERSION IN BIAXIAL CRYSTALS 287

16 SYSTEMATIC MICROSCOPIC EXAMINATION OF NONOPAQUE SUBSTANCES 301

17 CRYSTAL ROTATION METHODS 308

INDEX 343

CHAPTER 1 CRYSTALLOGRAPHY

Nature of Crystals

A *crystal* may be defined as a polyhedral solid bounded by plane faces which express an orderly internal arrangement of atoms or molecules. In the study of the internal structure of substances by X-ray techniques, less emphasis is placed on crystal faces; a *crystal* is regarded as a body characterized by a more or less undisturbed three-dimensional space extension of a characteristic unit of internal structure. A distinction is made between *crystalline substances* and *amorphous substances*. Amorphous substances display random arrangement of atoms or molecules.

If emphasis is placed on the presence or absence of crystal faces, the following distinctions apply: *euhedral* crystals possess a completely developed array of faces; *subhedral* crystals show a partial development of faces; no crystal faces are present on *anhedral* grains.

A *perfect* or *ideal crystal* is a regular repetition in three dimensions of a unit of structure called the *unit cell*, which, for a particular crystalline substance at a specified temperature and pressure, always has the same size and contains the same number and kinds of atoms in a characteristic arrangement. Practically all crystals are imperfect in one or more respects. Analysis of the intensity of reflection of

1

X-rays for various angles of incidence on the surfaces of crystals indicates the common presence of a *mosaic structure* in which the crystal appears to be built up of blocks about 10^{-5} cm on a side. The blocks are not perfectly aligned and make angles of a few minutes or seconds of arc with each other. In addition to imperfections resulting from mosaic structure so-called *lattice defects* may be present within the blocks. The lattice is a three-dimensional pattern of identical points in space, and each point, in a perfect crystal, is characterized by a certain definite array of atoms or molecules about it. In *defect lattices* there may be vacant positions, rotated or dislocated atoms or groups of atoms, interstitial atoms, or a random arrangement of atoms of one or more kinds. In mixed crystals of isomorphous substances, defect structures result from substitution of atoms for other atoms of different size and, in some instances, of different valence.

The physical properties of a perfect crystal, in which the ratio of the atoms can be expressed in simple whole numbers, are constant for specified conditions of temperature and pressure. Crystal defects, whatever their nature, cause departures in the physical properties, including the optical properties, from those for the perfect crystal.

Law of Constancy of Interfacial Angles

The vast majority of crystals are malformed. Growth conditions cause crystals to develop unsymmetrically. Crystals precipitated simultaneously from the same solution rarely look exactly alike. *However, in a given chemical or mineral species, no matter what growth irregularities are present, the angles between similarly chosen adjacent or projected faces are essentially constant.*

Crystal Axes and Crystal Systems

Crystal faces are conveniently referred to imaginary lines or directions which may be used to describe the position of a face or group of faces in space. These lines or directions are called *crystal axes* (Fig. 1). All crystals naturally fall into six systems, based on six simple geometric groupings of the crystal axes. The six systems are as follows:

I. Isometric system. Crystals in this system are referred to three mutually perpendicular, equal axes. The axes are designated as a_1, a_2, and a_3.

II. Tetragonal system. All crystals that are referable to three mutually perpendicular axes, two equal and one either longer or shorter, belong in this system. The axes are designated as a_1, a_2, and c.

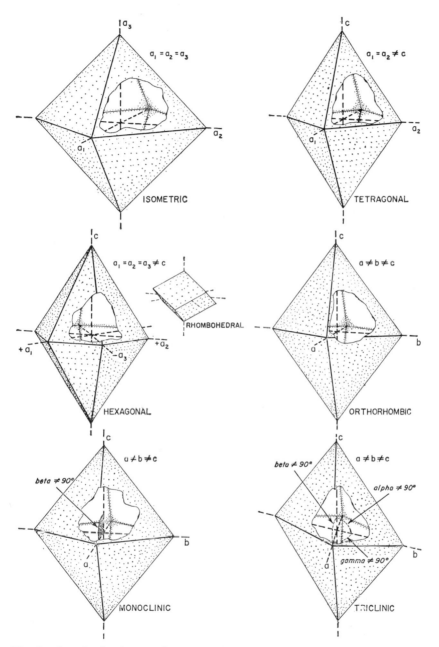

Fig. 1. Axes in the six crystal systems. All faces on the crystals intercept the axes at unit distances.

III. Hexagonal system.   This system includes what some crystallographers call the *trigonal system.*   It embraces all crystals which are referred to four axes: three of these lie in a plane, intersect at 60- and 120-degree angles, and are equal in length; the fourth axis is perpendicular to the plane including the other three and is either longer or shorter than the other axes.   The axis designation is a_1, a_2, a_3, and c.   The hexagonal system has been subdivided into the *hexagonal division* and the *rhombohedral division.*

IV. Orthorhombic system.   This system includes all crystals referable to three unequal, mutually perpendicular axes.   The axes are designated as a, b, and c.   By convention, orthorhombic crystals are oriented so that the unit intercept on the a axis is shorter than the unit intercept on the b axis.

V. Monoclinic system.   This system contains crystals referred to three unequal axes: two are in a plane and intersect at acute and obtuse angles; the third axis is perpendicular to the plane including the other two.   The axes are designated as a, b, and c.   The obtuse angle between the positive ends of the a and c axes is identified as β (*beta*).

VI. Triclinic system.   This system contains all crystals that cannot be placed in the above systems.   Its three unequal axes intersect at acute and obtuse angles.   The axes are designated as a, b, c.   The angles between the positive ends of b and c, c and a, and a and b are designated as α, β, and γ (*alpha, beta, and gamma*), respectively.

Axial Ratio

The axial ratio of a mineral or crystalline chemical is characteristic for each species.   Commonly the axial ratio is determined by choosing a prominent crystal face that cuts all three axes and then calculating the relative intercepts on the axes.   Figure 1 shows crystal faces which cut each crystal axis at unity and define the unit intercept on each axis.   Modern X-ray technique assists in the choice of the proper face for the computation of the axial ratio.   As a matter of fact, the axial ratio may be determined in certain substances by the X-ray method without considering the external form of the crystal.

In the isometric system all axes are equal; hence the axial ratio for all isometric crystals is the same.   In tetragonal crystals the lateral axes are equal, but the vertical axis is longer or shorter.   All that is necessary is a statement of the intercept on the vertical axis relative to the intercept on the lateral axes; for example, $c = 1.1321$ indicates that the intercept on the c axis is to the intercept on a lateral axis as 1.1321 is to 1. The same type of reasoning applies to the hexagonal system. In the orthorhombic system the intercept on the b axis is set equal to unity, and the axial ratio is stated thus: $a:b:c = 0.8131:1:1.2034$.

In the monoclinic and triclinic systems, it is necessary to state not only the axial ratio but also the angular relationships of the axes.

Law of Rational Intercepts

Once the unit intercepts have been established, the position of any face on a crystal may be described by ascertaining its intercepts on each of the axes as related to the unit intercepts. In making this evaluation, the *law of rational intercepts* is useful. This law states that *the ratios between the intercepts for crystal faces must be rational numbers,* that is, $1:2, 3:3/2, 4:2/3$, etc., but never $1:\sqrt{2}$, etc.

Parameters and Indices

The *parameters* of a crystal face express by a series of numbers the relative intercepts by that face on the crystallographic axes. The relative intercepts are expressed in terms of the unit intercepts. For example, the parameters of the unit pyramid in the orthorhombic system are $a:b:c$. Another pyramid might have the parameters $1/3a : 1/4b : c$.

Miller indices are the reciprocals of the parameters cleared of fractions. The relationships between parameters and indices are indicated in the following examples.

Parameters	Miller Indices
$a_1:a_2:a_3$	111
$\infty a_1: \infty a_2:c$	001
$a_1: \infty a_2: -a_3:c$	$10\bar{1}1$
$\frac{1}{2}a:\frac{2}{3}b:c$	432
$\infty a:\frac{3}{5}b:c$	053
$\frac{1}{3}a_1:\frac{1}{3}a_2:c$	331
$a_1:a_2:3c$	331

Crystal faces are more easily represented by indices than by parameters; hence indices are used almost exclusively. The indices, in generalized form, may be designated by the letters $h, k, i,$ and l.

Crystal Forms

Crystallographically, a *form* is a face or group of faces which bear like relationships to the crystallographic axes. For example, a cube is a form consisting of six similar faces, each of which is perpendicular to one axis of the isometric system and parallel to the other two. When two or more forms are present on a crystal, it is said to be a *combination*.

Figure 2 shows simple forms and combinations in the six crystal systems.

When indices are used to designate individual faces, the indices are enclosed in parentheses. Thus $(1\bar{2}1)$, $(h0l)$, (hkl) designate individual faces. If the indices are enclosed in braces thus, $\{0kl\}$, $\{120\}$, $\{hkl\}$, $\{hk\bar{\imath}l\}$, they refer to a complete form rather than to an individual face of a form.

Forms which enclose space and can exist alone, for example a cube, are called *closed forms*. *Open forms* do not enclose space and can exist only in combination with other forms.

The best method for assigning names to forms, except for the simplest forms, is in dispute. However, a crystal face or form can be described adequately and unequivocally by its parameters and indices, without reference to any particular scheme of form nomenclature.

Symmetry Elements

The elements of symmetry include center of symmetry, planes of symmetry, and axes of symmetry. A crystal is said to have a *center of symmetry* if a line passed from any point on the surface of the crystal through the center of the crystal emerges at a similar point on the opposite side at the same distance from the center. A *plane of symmetry* is present if an imaginary plane can be passed through a crystal so as to divide it into symmetrical halves, each the mirror image of the other. A *symmetry axis* is an imaginary line about which a crystal may be rotated so as to bring identical faces, lines, or angles into view at least twice during a complete rotation. The symmetry elements are best visualized in perfectly formed symmetrical crystals (Fig. 3).

A fourth element of symmetry, the *axis of rotary inversion,* is a composite element which combines rotation about an axis with inversion about the center. This element is required to explain the symmetry of only a few crystals of very low symmetry.

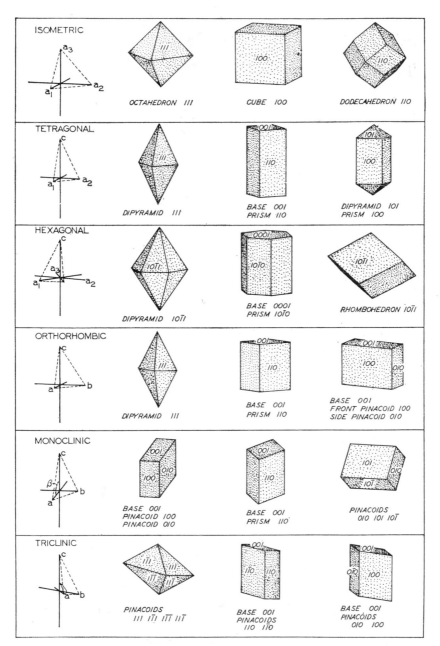

Fig. 2. Axes, simple forms, and combinations in the six crystal systems.

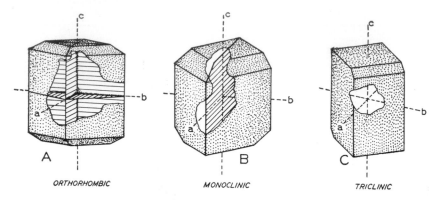

ORTHORHOMBIC   MONOCLINIC   TRICLINIC

Fig. 3. Elements of symmetry in selected crystals.

A. Orthorhombic crystal showing three planes of symmetry (ruled), three axes of twofold symmetry, each parallel to a crystallographic axis, and a center of symmetry.

B. Monoclinic crystal with one plane of symmetry (ruled), a twofold axis parallel to the *b* axis, and a center of symmetry.

C. Triclinic crystal having a center of symmetry only.

There are 32 possible combinations of symmetry elements, which give rise to 32 crystal classes.

Cleavage, Parting, and Fracture

In the absence of crystal faces, cleavage may assist in placing a substance in the proper crystal system and is of help in locating important planes and directions in crystals for optical crystallographic measurements. *Cleavage* is the tendency of a crystalline substance to split along one or more crystal directions. Plane surfaces resulting from splitting along cleavage directions ordinarily are parallel to common crystal faces. Cleavage in a crystal species is a constant property which expresses a characteristic internal structure.

A crystal may possess several cleavages or none. The quality of cleavage may range from poor to perfect. The number of cleavages and the quality of each do not vary in a given mineral or chemical species no matter what the external form or occurrence may be. Figures 4 to 7 illustrate several types of cleavage commonly seen in crystalline substances.

Parting is the tendency of certain crystalline substances to split along smooth planes which do not necessarily parallel crystal planes or faces. Parting is not a constant property but is often controlled by regularly oriented inclusions which cause planes of weakness to form. External causes may induce a tendency to split which was not originally present.

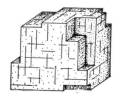

Fig. 4. Cubic cleavage.

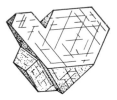

Fig. 5. Octahedral cleavage.

Fig. 6. Rhombohedral cleavage.

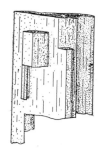

Fig. 7. Prismatic cleavage.

Fracture defines the manner in which a substance breaks in any direction that is not a cleavage direction. Commonly used terms denoting fracture are *conchoidal, subconchoidal, uneven, splintery,* and *hackly.*

Habit

The shape acquired by a crystal depends on many factors, such as the temperature, pressure, and the composition of the parent solutions. Moreover, impurities, movements of solvents, differences in concentration from place to place, and the rate of precipitation from solution contribute to the variations observed in crystals. However, precipitation of a given compound generally results in a characteristic shape or outline, or *habit.* Expressions commonly used to denote habit are the following: *tabular, platy, micaceous, equant* or *equidimensional, stubby, prismatic, acicular,* and *fibrous.*

Twins

Twin crystals result from the intergrowth of two or more crystals of a particular substance according to some definite law. One part

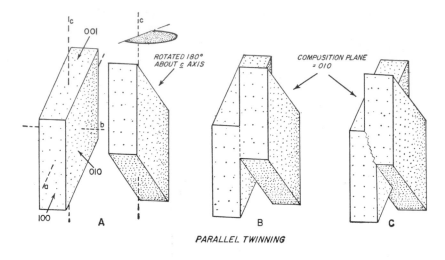

PARALLEL TWINNING

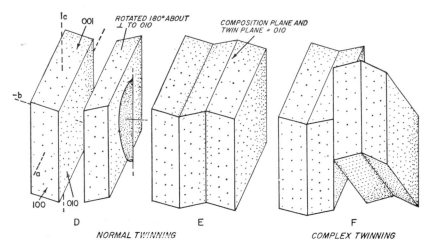

NORMAL TWINNING   COMPLEX TWINNING

Fig. 8. Twinning in monoclinic and triclinic crystals.

A. Relationship of twinned segments in a parallel twin. Composition plane {010}.
B. Contact twin formed as in *A.*
C. Penetration twin with twinning as in *A.*
D. Normal twinning in triclinic crystal. Composition plane {010}.
E. Repeated normal twin (trill) with twinning as in *D.*
F. Complex twin showing type of twinning in *A* combined with type of twinning shown in *D.* Composition plane for both types of twinning is {010}.

of a twinned crystal is related to another part as if it were rotated 180 degrees about a crystal direction common to both parts. The axis about which the rotation appears to have taken place is called the *twin axis;* the plane involved, perpendicular to the twin axis, is called the *twin plane.* The plane along which the twin segments unite is called the *composition plane.* Twins in which the twin axis lies in the composition plane are described as *parallel twins.* Twinned crystals in which the twin axis is perpendicular to the composition

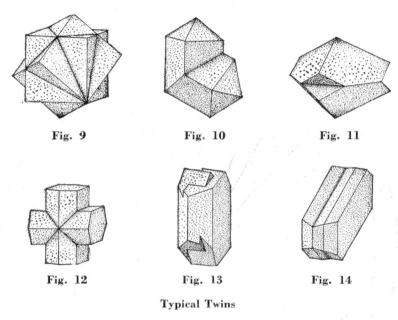

Fig. 9   Fig. 10   Fig. 11

Fig. 12   Fig. 13   Fig. 14

Typical Twins

Fig. 9. Penetration twin. Composition plane and twin plane {111}. Isometric.

Fig. 10. Tetragonal crystal. Composition plane and twin plane {101}.

Fig. 11. Rhombohedron in normal contact twin. Composition plane and twin plane {0001}. Hexagonal.

Fig. 12. Orthorhombic penetration twin. Composition plane and twin plane {032}.

Fig. 13. Carlsbad penetration twin of monoclinic feldspar. Parallel twin (see Fig. 8). Twin axis parallel to *c* axis. Composition plane {010}.

Fig. 14. Albite trill. Normal contact twin (see Fig. 8). Composition plane and twin plane {010}. Triclinic.

plane (and the twin plane) are classified as *normal twins.* Twins which combine parallel and normal twinning in the same crystal are called *complex twins.* Examples of parallel, normal, and complex twinning are shown in Fig. 8. Figures 9 through 14 illustrate twins in each of the six crystal systems.

Twinned crystals may be either *contact* or *penetration twins.* A *simple twin* is twinned once; *repeated* or *polysynthetic twins* are twinned two or more times and are described as *trills, fourlings, five-lings,* etc.

Projections

Projections play an important part in the graphic depiction of space relationships of crystal faces and directions. Projections have an

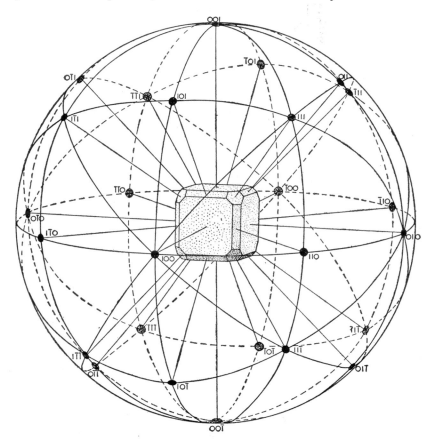

Fig. 15. Spherical projection of cube {100}, octahedron {111}, and dodecahedron {110}.

increasingly important use in optical crystallography. There are various types, each serving best a specific purpose.

Figure 15 shows the *spherical projection* of an isometric crystal—a combination of cube, octahedron, and dodecahedron. To construct the spherical projection the crystal is enveloped by a sphere whose center is coincident with that of the crystal, and normals to each crystal face are drawn out from the center until they intersect the surface of the sphere. The points of intersection of the normals and the sphere locate the *poles* of the faces. Crystal faces whose edges of intersection are parallel have poles which lie on a great circle of the sphere. Great circles which contain two or more poles are designated

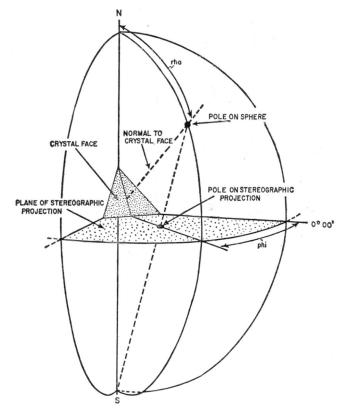

Fig. 16. Location of a pole of a crystal face in stereographic projection.

as *zones*. The spherical projection is three dimensional and cannot be used with ease for routine portrayal of crystal faces or directions.

In ordinary work the poles are projected into a plane for two-dimensional representation. The choice of the position of the plane and the manner of projection into it are determined by the use to which the projection is to be put.

The angles between crystal faces can be measured accurately by a *reflecting goniometer,* an optical device with graduated arcs in which

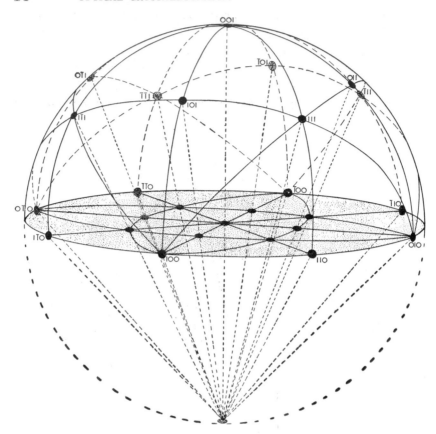

Fig. 17. Diagram showing relationship of spherical projection to stereographic projection (stippled plane).

crystals are rotated about one or more axes into positions such that light from a collimator is reflected from successive faces into a telescope. Approximate angles between crystal faces may be measured with a *contact goniometer,* a protractor with an attached straight-edge which rotates about a pin at the center of the protractor. The normal to a crystal face or its pole on a projection is described conveniently by an angle of azimuth (phi) measured from an arbitrarily selected zero azimuth, and the angle with respect to a vertical axis (rho) (Fig. 16). Commonly the azimuth of an {010} face is taken as zero, and azimuth angles are measured clockwise (+) and counterclockwise (−) from zero azimuth.

In the *stereographic projection* the plane of projection is the equatorial plane of the spherical projection. The location of each pole

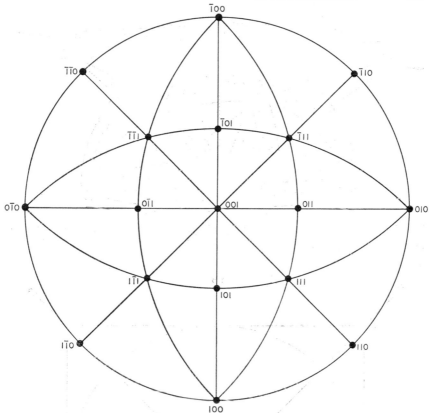

Fig. 18. Stereographic plot of poles of cube {100}, octahedron {111}, and dodecahedron {110}.

in the stereographic projection is obtained by determining the location of the point of intersection with the equatorial plane of a line drawn from the pole of a crystal face or direction on the spherical projection to the south pole (Fig. 16) of the spherical projection. The construction of the stereographic projection of a combination of cube, octahedron, and dodecahedron is shown in Fig. 17. Figure 18 shows the stereographic projection in plan.

North-south meridian zones of the spherical projection appear as radial lines in the stereographic projection, and other great circles or arcs of circles are transferred to the stereographic projection as arcs of true circles. The latter property permits easy geometric construction.

Stereographic projections are particularly useful in the representation of the geometric relations between crystal directions and optical

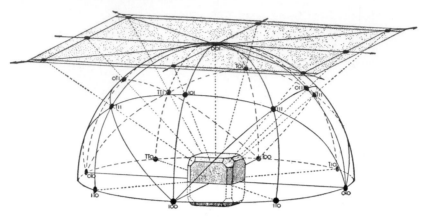

Fig. 19. Diagram showing relationship of spherical projection to gnomonic projection (stippled plane).

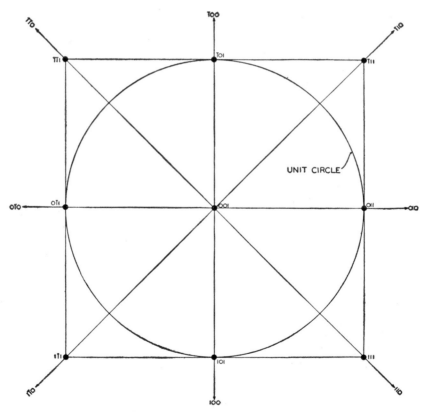

Fig. 20. Gnomonic projection of poles of cube, octahedron, and dodecahedron.

properties. For example, in the triclinic system the stereographic projection may be used to indicate the orientation of the optical indicatrix with respect to the crystallographic axes or certain crystal faces.

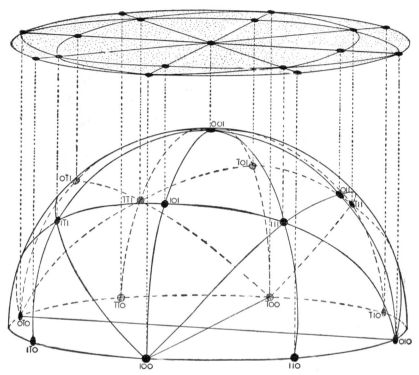

Fig. 21. Diagram showing relationship of spherical projection to orthographic projection (stippled plane).

Like the stereographic projection, the *gnomonic projection* is derived from the spherical projection. The plane of projection, however, is tangent to the north pole of the sphere. Figure 19 shows the relations of the gnomonic projection to the spherical projection. It will be noted that all zonal lines in the gnomonic projection are straight lines. Poles of faces parallel to the vertical axis of the sphere lie at infinity in the gnomonic projection and are designated by straight lines terminated by arrows. Figure 20 shows the gnomonic projection of a cube, octahedron, and dodecahedron.

The gnomonic projection is widely used to plot data obtained by measurements of crystals with a two-circle goniometer. The projection readily lends itself to computation of axial ratios and crystal drawing.

The *orthographic projection* is obtained by dropping normals from the poles in the spherical projection to the plane of projection as in Fig. 21, in which the plane of projection is normal to the north-south

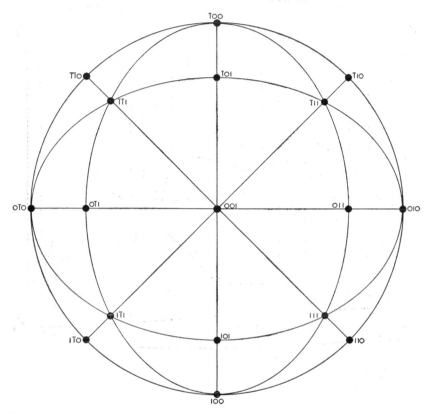

Fig. 22.   Orthographic projection of poles of cube, octahedron, and dodecahedron.

axis of the sphere.   However, the plane may be put into any desired position with respect to the spherical projection in order to serve special requirements.

The orthographic projection is constructed with difficulty because, in general, great circles or arcs of great circles on the spherical projection in the orthographic projection become ellipses or arcs of ellipses.   Figure 22 shows an orthographic projection of a cube, octahedron, and dodecahedron.

The orthographic projection is particularly useful in study of the origin of interference phenomena under the polarizing microscope.

All the line drawings showing three-dimensional relationships in this book have been drawn in *clinographic projection*. The clinographic projection is used almost exclusively for construction of three-dimensional crystal drawings from gnomonic, stereographic, or orthographic projections. Unlike perspective drawings all directions, edges, or faces that are parallel in the crystal are also parallel in the clinographic projection. Commonly the crystal is shown as if it had been rotated somewhat to the left and viewed from above.

CHAPTER 2 LIGHT

The Nature of Light

Light is a form of radiant energy. The exact nature of light is not fully understood, but it is known that light constitutes the visible portion of a spectrum extending from high-frequency gamma radiation at one end to low-frequency radio waves at the other end. Just beyond the range of visibility are ultraviolet radiation, of higher frequency, and infrared radiation, of lower frequency.

The process of emission of energy from a substance is called *radiation,* and the emitted energy is also described as *radiation.* Maxwell regarded light as consisting of electromagnetic ether waves of superimposed electric and magnetic fields transmitted with a velocity of approximately 186,000 miles/sec. His theory, brought up to date, is called the *electromagnetic theory of light;* it is supported by a vast amount of experimentation and calculation leading to the conclusion that light energy actually travels through space in continuous waves. However, analysis of radiant energy in terms of the *quantum theory* has yielded an impressive body of evidence that seems to be in direct contradiction to the electromagnetic theory. According to the quantum theory, light travels through space as discontinuous, indivisible particles or bundles of energy called *quanta* or *photons.* In the face

20

of a dilemma, modern theory combines the electromagnetic-wave concept and the particle concept and recognizes them as not necessarily contradictory but as complementary.

Figure 1 shows a simple electromagnetic wave. The electric vector oscillates in a plane, and the magnetic vector oscillates in a perpendicular plane. Both vectors vibrate, at any instant, in a plane which

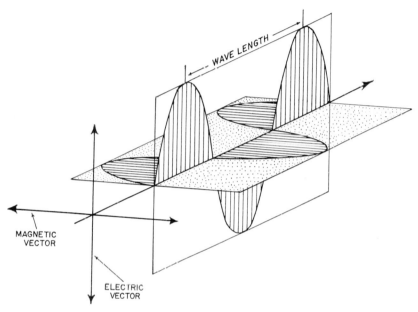

Fig. 1. Conventional representation of a simple, plane-polarized electromagnetic wave.

is perpendicular to the direction of propagation. The magnitudes of the vectors vary so as to reach maximums and minimums simultaneously. Such a wave is said to be *linearly polarized* or *plane polarized*. In the passage of light through crystals, emphasis is placed on the oscillation of the electric vector, it being understood that there is synchronous oscillation of a magnetic vector in another direction. Experiments with reflecting surfaces indicate that the electrical vector is the vector that is important in optical phenomena, and, for most purposes, light waves are analyzed in terms of the electrical components only.

The theory of optical crystallography can be developed cogently and consistently if light is regarded as an electrical wave phenomenon. In this book, light is treated as continuous wave motion, and all con-

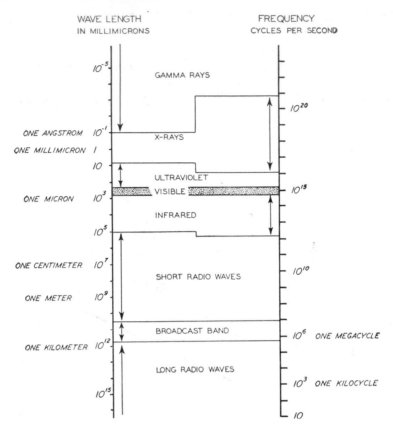

Fig. 2. The electromagnetic spectrum. Diagram shows wave lengths and corresponding frequencies of waves in the interval extending from short gamma rays at one end to long radio waves at the other end of the spectrum.

structions and derivations are based on this fundamental if somewhat inadequate concept. Radiation of all types is treated as comprising a gradational spectrum which can be analyzed in terms of wave lengths and frequencies.

The following equation is basic:

$$f = \frac{v}{\lambda}$$

where f is the frequency expressed in cycles per second; v is the velocity of propagation of energy waves in vacuum, a value near 3.0×10^{10} cm/sec (approximately 186,000 miles/sec); and λ is the wave length. The frequency of the pulses or oscillations of light waves does not change when the waves pass through media other than vacuum. Imagine a glass plate suspended in vacuum and assume that light of a specified frequency is passing through the vacuum and the glass plate. Although the velocity of the light waves is less in the glass plate than in the vacuum, as many waves must leave the plate as entered it. Accordingly, a change in the velocity must be accompanied by a change in the wave length in the glass plate, and the frequency can be regarded as a constant that does not vary with the nature of the medium transmitting the light. Figure 2 shows wave lengths and corresponding frequencies of waves in the electromagnetic spectrum. Note that visible light waves comprise a very limited segment of the spectrum and have wave lengths in vacuum of the order of 400 to 700 millimicrons (approximately 16 to 32 millionths of an inch).

In optical crystallography, wave lengths are commonly expressed in terms of millimicrons, but occasionally one may encounter other units. Following is an expression of equivalence among several units of linear measurement.

$$1 \text{ millimicron } (m\mu) = 10 \text{ angstroms } (\text{Å}) = 10^{-3} \text{ micron } (\mu)$$
$$= 10^{-7} \text{ cm} = 10^{-9} \text{ m} = 3.937 \times 10^{-8} \text{ in.}$$

The Visible Spectrum

White light embraces a gradational series of wave lengths and frequencies. At one extreme is violet light with a minimum wave length in vacuum of about 390 $m\mu$; at the other extreme is red light with a maximum wave length in vacuum near 770 $m\mu$. Many devices are available for separating white light into its component colors. White light passed through a colorless triangular glass prism or a ruled diffraction grating is resolved into a color spectrum which is red at one end and grades through orange, yellow, green, blue, and indigo to violet at the other end. Measurement of the wave lengths by means of calibrated diffraction gratings or similar instruments gives the range and average wave lengths for the more important components of white light shown in the accompanying table. Light of a particular wave length is described as *monochromatic light*.

Waves and Wave Fronts

A *wave* is a single pulse or disturbance advancing through a medium. The disturbance, as it passes an arbitrarily selected point in the line

Wave Lengths of Light in the Visible Spectrum in Vacuo

(in millimicrons)

	Range	Average
Violet	390–430	410
Indigo	430–460	445
Blue	460–500	480
Green	500–570	535
Yellow	570–590	580
Orange	590–650	620
Red	650–770	710

of advance, has an intensity which increases from zero to a maximum, decreases to zero, decreases still more to a minimum, and then increases to zero. Sound waves are *longitudinal waves* in which the oscillations or vibrations are in the line of advance of the waves and the waves move forward by alternate compression and decompression of air or some other medium. Light waves and other electromagnetic waves are *transverse waves* and, in isotropic media, vibrate or oscillate at right angles to the line or direction along which they advance.

Closely related to the concept of waves is the concept of *wave fronts*. As the waves are pulsating or vibrating systematically and repetitively, points in the waves that are in comparable positions in both space and time can be said to be *in the same phase*. For example, sinusoidal waves are in phase if, after an instant of time, the crests and troughs are in the same actual or relative positions. A *wave front* is a surface passing through all points in the same phase in the waves generated at a particular instant. In Fig. 3*A* suppose that a small spherical body is generating periodic disturbances that move with constant velocity outward along all radii of a sphere. In a plane passing through the center of the sphere equally spaced circles may be drawn to indicate the movement of disturbances in all directions away from the source. The solid circles might represent wave fronts passing through points corresponding to maximum compression in sound waves or the crests of transverse waves, and the dashed lines might indicate wave fronts drawn through points of maximum decompression in sound waves or through the troughs of transverse waves. Where waves are moving outward along all radii of a sphere the wave front corresponding to the movement of a wave along any particular radius can be obtained by drawing a tangent plane, *FF'*, to the spherical wave front at the point of intersection of the radius and the wave front. The radius, perpendicular to the tangent plane, is the *wave-front normal, ON,* for the wave as it moves along the radius. The wave front normal commonly is designated as the *wave normal,* a usage that will be adopted in this book.

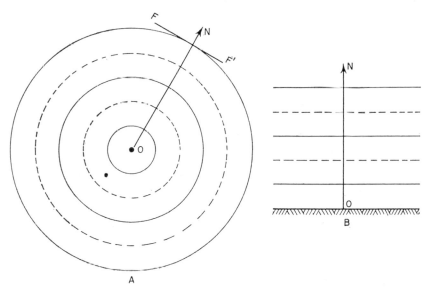

Fig. 3. Wave movement.

A. Waves generated by a point source in a homogeneous medium.
B. Waves generated by a flat surface and traveling through a homogeneous medium.

In Fig. *3B* the waves are generated at points in a flat surface and travel with uniform velocity in a direction normal to the surface. The wave fronts are indicated by solid and dashed lines as in Fig. *3A* and pass through points in the same phase. *ON* is the wave normal (wave front normal). Some confusion may result if the terms *wave* and *wave front* are used synonymously, although such usage is common. The wave front passes through points in the same phase in a family of waves, and the total disturbance in an advancing wave front is the sum of the disturbances of all the individual waves that are participating in the advance of the wave front. An individual wave advances along a *ray,* but a wave front advances in the direction of the *wave normal.*

Sinusoidal Waves

Oscillatory wave motion in its simplest form consists of a combination of uniform forward movement and simple-harmonic oscillation at right angles to the direction of movement. In subsequent sections of this book, oscillations of the magnetic vector will be omitted from discussions, and attention will be given only to waves generated by a

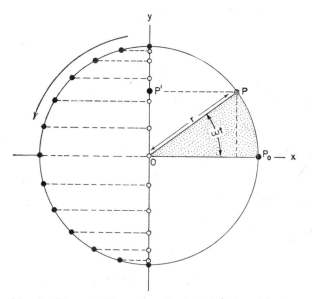

Fig. 4. Diagram illustrating simple-harmonic oscillation.

combination of oscillation of the electric vector and forward movement. The electric vector can be described also as the *light vector*.

Simple-harmonic oscillation is understood by reference to Fig. 4. Imagine a point P moving with uniform velocity ω around a circle of radius r. If the starting point P_0 is on the x-coordinate axis and ω is expressed in degrees or radians per second, the angle through which the point has moved from P_0 to P in time t is ωt. The displacement of P', the projection of P on the diameter of the circle as measured from the center of the circle along the y axis is

$$v = r \sin \omega t$$

The movement of the projection of P back and forth along the diameter as P moves around the circle is *simple-harmonic motion*. The time T that it takes P to travel 360 degrees or 2π radians around the circle is the *period* and is measured in seconds. The maximum displacement from the center of the circle of the projection of *P* on the diameter is equal to the radius of the circle and is the *amplitude* of the simple-harmonic oscillation. The velocity *v* of movement of *P′* along the diameter at any particular instant is

$$v = \omega\sqrt{r^2 - y^2}$$

where *y* is the distance from the center of the circle to the projection of *P* on the diameter. When *y* equals zero, the velocity is at a maximum; and, when *y* equals *r*, the velocity is zero.

The generation of a sinusoidal wave is indicated in Fig. 5. The wave originates at *O* and consists of a combination of movement toward *U* and simple-harmonic oscillation parallel to *AM*. Combination of oscillation and movement yields the wave *ANPQRSTU*. The *wave length* is *NS* and is the distance between like points in the wave. Wave length commonly is designated by the Greek letter λ. *OA* is the amplitude of the wave, and the time that it takes for the wave to travel from *N* to *S* is the *period* of the wave. The number of whole wave lengths that pass a given point in a given time is the *frequency*. The plane in which the wave oscillates is the *plane of vibration,* and the wave in Fig. 5 may be described as *plane polarized.*

Phase, Phasal Difference, and Path Difference

In Fig. 4 the position of the point *P* at any time relative to the time that motion started at P_0 is the *phase* of the point. Similarly, the location of point *P′* on the diameter of the circle defines the phase of the simple-harmonic oscillation. For both *P* and *P′* the phase relative to the starting point of circular motion at P_0 is given in angular measure (degrees) or in radians. For example, if point *P* were 45 degrees of arc removed from P_0, the angle would indicate the phase of point *P*, or, in terms of the motion of the point all the way around the circle, the phase could be expressed as a fraction of the period, in this instance 45°/360°, or one-eighth period. For an angle of 45 degrees the phase expressed in radians is $\pi/4$, in which a movement of the point around 360 degrees of the circle corresponds to 2π radians.

Phasal difference or *phase difference* is a dimensionless quantity defining the position of a point in circular motion, simple-harmonic oscillation, or sinusoidal wave motion with respect to some other arbitrarily selected point. Again, the phasal difference can be expressed in angular measure in degrees, angular measure as a fraction of 360 degrees, or in radians. In Fig. 6 the phasal difference between

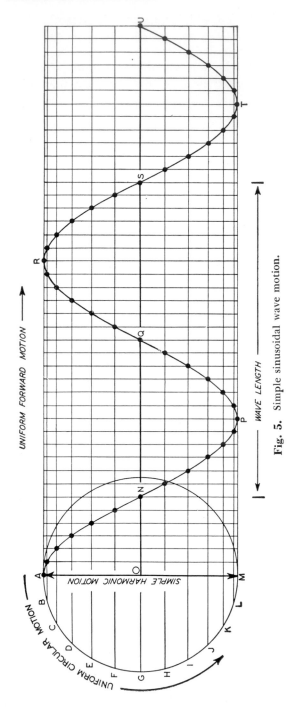

Fig. 5. Simple sinusoidal wave motion.

the two sinusoidal waves is 45 degrees, one-eighth (45°/360°) period, or $\pi/4$ radian.

The *path difference* between the two waves moving in the same direction along the same path as in Fig. 6 is the distance in the direction of movement between similar points in each wave and has a dimension of length. The path difference is given by the equation

$$\text{Path difference} = \frac{(\text{phasal difference in radians})}{2\pi} \lambda$$

where λ is the wave length. In Fig. 6 the phasal difference is $\pi/4$, and substitution in the above equation gives a path difference of $\lambda/8$ wave

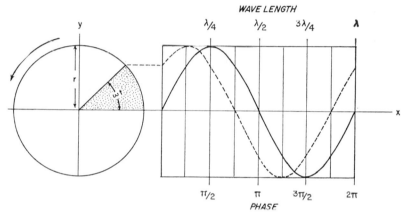

Fig. 6. Two sinusoidal waves with a phasal difference of $\pi/4$ and a path difference of $\lambda/8$.

lengths. Because the path difference expressed in whole or fractional wave lengths also defines the phasal difference, there is a tendency to use the expressions synonymously and to express both phasal difference and the path difference in wave lengths. The path difference between two waves is sometimes called the *retardation*, a term which refers to the fact that one wave has fallen behind or has advanced ahead of the other wave by a certain number of whole or fractional wave lengths.

Rays and Wave Normals (Wave Front Normals)

A *ray* is the line or direction along which pulsating energy is propagated. A *light ray* is the path that a light wave follows in traveling from one point to another in a medium. As the term is used here, a ray is *not* the light energy that travels a linear path, but it is the *path* that the light energy follows. A *beam of light* may be considered as having a finite cross section and as consisting of a bundle of rays, each of infinitesimal cross section. In a homogeneous substance or vacuum, light rays are straight lines; however, light energy moving along rays may be bent or *refracted* on passing from one substance to another of different properties.

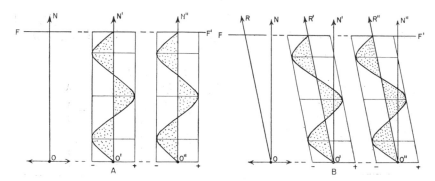

Fig. 7. Plane-polarized electromagnetic waves. Magnetic vector not shown.

A. In an isotropic medium.
B. In an anisotropic medium.

In optically *isotropic* media, such as isometric crystals, and unstressed glass, liquid, and gas, a light wave moving along any ray may be considered as consisting of forward movement along a ray combined with oscillation at right angles to the direction of movement. In Fig. 7 plane-polarized light waves are being emitted from several points *O, O′,* and *O″* and are moving away from the points of emission with constant velocity. Only the light vector is shown. *ON, O′N′,* and *O″N″* are rays. The direction of vibration is at right angles to the rays and is parallel to a wave front *FF′*. Inasmuch as the wave front advances in the direction of the rays, this direction is also the wave normal, and it may be said that the direction of the rays coincides with the wave normal direction.

In many substances light waves travel with different velocities in different directions. This is true for crystals in the tetragonal, hexagonal, orthorhombic, monoclinic, and triclinic systems and in stressed isometric crystals or stressed noncrystalline substances. Media in which the velocity of light waves varies with the direction of transmission are described as *optically anisotropic*.

The theory of transmission of electromagnetic waves by crystals

includes the assumption that certain waves passing through anisotropic crystals do not vibrate at right angles to the direction of travel
of the waves, that is, the vibrations are not normal to the rays. It
is assumed, moreover, that the vibrations of all waves lie in their
associated wave fronts. In this particular situation the quantum
theory of photon transmission provides a more rational explanation of
the observed phenomena in that there is no particular need for consideration of vibrations transverse to the direction of energy propagation. In Fig. 7B as in Fig. 7A, O, O', and O'' are points of emission
of plane-polarized light waves, but the waves emitted at the points
do not travel in a direction perpendicular to the direction of vibration.
As in Fig. 7A, OR, O'R', and O''R'' are rays. The light waves are
travelling along the rays with the same velocity as in Fig. 7A, but
the wave front, FF', has not advanced in the direction of its normal
as far as the wave front in Fig. 7A. The direction of the rays and
the wave normal direction do not coincide, and the velocity of light
waves in the direction of the rays is greater than the velocity of
propagation of the wave front in the direction of its normal. Thus,
in anisotropic substances there is a basis for distinguishing between
ray velocity and *wave-normal velocity*. The *ray velocity* is the velocity
of transmission of light energy, whether as photons or as transverse
wave oscillations, in the direction of a ray. The *wave-normal velocity*
is the velocity with which a wave front advances in the direction of
its normal. The two velocities are the same only when the ray
direction coincides with the direction of the normal to the wave front.

Ray-Velocity Surfaces

The surface to which individual light waves have spread along the
rays in a given time interval variously has been identified as the
wave, the *wave front,* the *wave surface,* the *ray surface,* and the *ray-
velocity surface.* In this book the surface shall be designated as the
ray-velocity surface, and it is regarded as the surface to which light
waves have spread along the rays in a given interval of time, regardless of the nature of the waves. The emphasis is placed on the velocity of light waves in the particular directions of the rays. In
optically isotropic substances the ray-velocity surfaces coincide exactly
with the wave fronts.

In Fig. 8A, O and O' are point sources of light in a medium which
transmits light waves with equal velocity in all directions. Suppose
that in a given instant each point has generated in the plane of the
drawing a circular ray-velocity surface such as the one about O.
The radii of the circles are the rays. If consideration is given to the

rays in a particular direction, such as OR and $O'R'$, certain relationships between the rays and the wave fronts become apparent. The
light energy moving along OR and $O'R'$ travels as waves, and the
wave front, which passes through all points in like phase, is obtained
by drawing the tangent FF' to the ray velocity surface at R. FF'

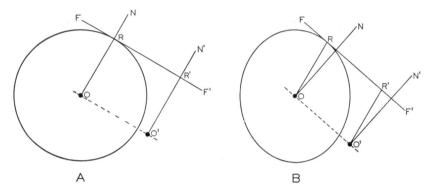

Fig. 8. Ray-velocity surfaces.

A. Ray-velocity surface in an isotropic medium.
B. Ray-velocity surface in an anisotropic medium.

indicates the position the wave front for light waves generated at O
and O' and moving in the direction OR has reached in the same
instant that a light wave moving from O to R along the ray has
reached R.

The *wave normal, ON,* perpendicular to the wave front, is the
direction of propagation of the wave front of the waves moving along
rays OR and $O'R'$ and is parallel to the rays. That is, in media
which transmit light with equal velocity in all directions, each ray and
its associated wave normal are coincident.

In Fig. 8*B*, O and O' are point sources of light waves in an anisotropic medium. In a given interval of time, light waves traveling
along all possible rays reach surfaces (the ray-velocity surfaces) which,
in the two dimensions of the drawing, are ellipses such as the one
about O. For light waves traveling along rays OR and $O'R'$, in a particular direction, a *wave front, FF',* is obtained by drawing a tangent
to the ellipse at point R where the ray OR intersects it. The *wave
normal* is ON, perpendicular to the wave front. Note that whereas
the light waves traveling along the rays move in one direction, the
wave front, which moves in a direction parallel to its normal, moves in
a different direction.

CHAPTER 3 OPTICS OF OPTICALLY ISOTROPIC SUBSTANCES

Isotropic substances transmit light waves with equal velocity in all directions. The ray-velocity surface for a point source in an isotropic medium is a sphere coincident with the wave front. Geometric constructions showing how light is reflected or refracted are based on *Huygens' principle,* which states that any point or particle excited by the impact of wave energy becomes a new point source of energy. Thus every point in a reflecting surface may be considered as a secondary source of radiation having its own spherical ray-velocity surface.

According to *Fermat's principle,* first stated in 1658, light energy traveling along a ray from one point to another in a medium follows the path that requires the least time. In an optically isotropic medium and in any particular direction in a crystalline anisotropic medium such a path is a straight line. All derivations based on Huygens' principle can be treated with equal success by using Fermat's principle, although this procedure has not been adopted in this book.

Reflection

A fundamental law of reflection states that the *angles of incidence and reflection, measured from a normal to the reflecting surface, are equal and lie in the same plane.* This plane is called the *plane of incidence.* Figure 1*A* shows light in several parallel rays falling with inclined incidence on a reflecting surface *gg'*. The wave front for the light in these rays is *bb'*. The light in each ray sets up a secondary

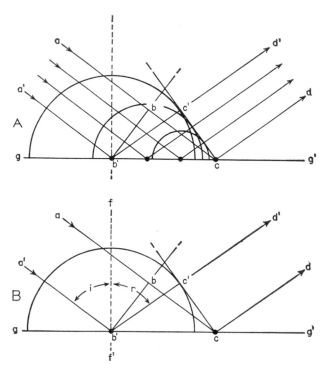

Fig. 1. Reflection by a plane surface.

A. Huygenian construction.
B. Simplified version of *A*.

point of radiation with a spherical ray-velocity surface (circles in the plane of the diagram). For example, light traveling along *a'b'* sets up a new point source at *b'*, and, while light in ray *abc* is traveling from *b* to *c*, the light emitted from *b'* travels out to a ray-velocity surface with radius equal to *bc*. Light moving along other rays behaves similarly, so that it becomes possible to determine the wave front for the light in the reflected rays by drawing a line from *c* tangent to the ray-velocity surfaces generated in the reflecting surface by the points of impact of the light in each incident ray. The wave front obtained in this manner is *cc'*. The rays for the reflected light are drawn perpendicular to this wave front and are parallel to the wave normal.

In Fig. 1B only two rays for the incident light are shown so that the geometric and trigonometric relationships can be seen more easily. Angle i is the angle of incidence and angle r is the angle of reflection. Both are measured from ff', a normal to the reflecting surface gg'. Right triangles $bb'c$ and $b'c'c$ are similar because, by construction, bc equals $b'c'$. Therefore angles $c'cb'$ and $bb'c$ are equal. Now, angles $bb'c$ and i are equal because their sides are mutually perpendicular, and angles $c'cb'$ and r are equal for the same reason. Hence, angles i and r are equal.

The extent to which light is reflected from a surface depends upon the nature of the surface. If the surface is flat and highly polished, none of the light seems to come from the surface, and the reflected object seems to lie beyond the surface. This type of reflection may be called *regular* reflection. If the reflecting surface is rough, it seems to be a source of the light. This results in *diffuse* reflection.

Luster depends upon the manner and quality of light reflection.

That light penetrates reflecting bodies is shown by the fact that the intensity of reflected light is less than that of the incident light.

Refraction

In general, light passing from one isotropic medium to another is bent or refracted. This is not true when the light falls with perpendicular incidence on the contact between the media. In Fig. 2, suppose that gg' is the trace of a plane contact between two substances which transmit light with different velocities. Let V_1 and V_2 be the respective velocities, and suppose that V_1 is greater than V_2; bb' is the wave front for the light striking the contact gg' with an angle of incidence i. Part of the light is reflected (not shown), and part of the light enters the substance of velocity V_2. The points of impact of light in the rays on the contact gg' serve as point sources of light in medium V_2, so that the wave front in medium V_2 can be obtained by drawing cc' tangent to the ray-velocity surfaces for each of the point sources in the plane gg'. The rays in medium V_2 are drawn perpendicular to cc', normal to the wave front.

Figure 2B is a simplified version of Fig. 2A and shows the important elements of the construction. The ray-velocity surface about point b' in medium V_2 is drawn with a radius somewhat less than the distance bc because light travels faster in medium V_1 than in medium V_2. The angle r is the *angle of refraction*.

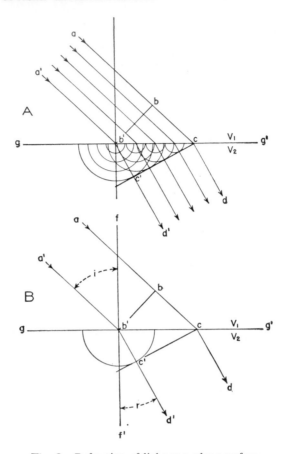

Fig. 2. Refraction of light at a plane surface.

A. Huygenian construction for several rays.
B. Simplified version of *A.*

Index of Refraction

In Fig. 2, by construction $V_1/V_2 = bc/b'c'$, where V_1 and V_2 are the velocities of light in the two media. In right triangles $bb'c$ and $b'c'c$

$$bc = b'c \sin \angle bb'c$$

and

$$b'c' = b'c \sin \angle b'cc'$$

Now

angle $bb'c$ = angle i (mutually perpendicular sides)

and

$$\text{angle } b'cc' = \text{angle } r \text{ (mutually perpendicular sides)}$$

so

$$bc = b'c \sin i$$

and

$$b'c' = b'c \sin r$$

Therefore

$$\frac{V_1}{V_2} = \frac{b'c \sin i}{b'c \sin r} = \frac{\sin i}{\sin r} = n$$

where n is the *index of refraction*, a constant.

That is, in isotropic media the ratio between the velocities in the two media is equal to the ratio between the sine of the angle of incidence and the sine of the angle of refraction. This relationship commonly is referred to as *Snell's law*. The constant n is the *index of refraction* of the medium of light velocity V_2 with respect to the medium of light velocity V_1.

If the angle of incidence is zero, sin i equals zero, and the angle of refraction, r, becomes zero. That is, light normally incident on a plane surface is not refracted. Light passing obliquely from air into a solid is refracted toward the normal, and light passing from a solid into air is refracted away from the normal. This rule also holds when light passes from an optically rarer to an optically denser medium or when the reverse is true.

The index of refraction of a substance differs for the various colors comprising white light. This fact can be demonstrated by the familiar prism experiment shown in Fig. 3. A narrow beam of white light falling on the wall of a prism cut from glass or some other colorless transparent substance is split into the individual colors that comprise the visible spectrum; this proves that the prism has a different refractive index for each of the colors. Normally light of short wave length has a lower velocity and is refracted more than light of longer wave length, thus permitting the generalization that, in colorless substances, the *index of refraction varies inversely as the wave length of light.* Substances for which this relation obtains are said to exhibit *normal dispersion of the refractive indices.* Substances that strongly absorb light waves of certain frequencies may show *abnormal dispersion,* and the above generalization is not valid. A general relationship between refractive index and the wave length of the incident light is expressed by a complex equation, such as the Ketteler-Helmholtz equation, which includes consideration of the manner and amount of absorption of the transmitted light. Discussions of abnormal dispersion are found in several modern textbooks on physical optics.

When the index of refraction for a medium is given for a particular wave length of light the student should understand that the stated wave length is the wave length in vacuum (or air) of the light that enters, is refracted, and leaves the medium. The wave length in the

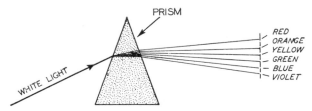

Fig. 3. Formation of color spectrum by a beam of white light passing through a colorless prism.

refracting medium is *less* than the wave length in vacuum of the incident light, because a decrease in velocity must be accompanied by a decrease of the wave length in the medium, if the frequency is to remain constant.

The power of a substance to refract light waves is sometimes described as *refringence*. Substances of high refractive index have high refringence; those of low index, low refringence.

A generalized formula for the index of refraction may be written as

$$n = \frac{c}{v}$$

in which n is the index of refraction, c is a constant, and v is the velocity of light waves for a particular wave length in a specified medium. The constant c is generally regarded as the velocity of light waves in a vacuum and is arbitrarily assigned a value of unity.

The average index of refraction of air at sea level pressure is 1.00029, indicating that the velocity of light waves in air is only slightly less than their velocity in vacuum. Thus a very small, and for most purposes, an insignificant error is introduced in refractive-index measurements in air.

The index of refraction, as defined above, applies without qualification to optically isotropic substances, but in anisotropic substances having two or three principal refractive indices the definition should be phrased more precisely. In isotropic substances light waves transmitted along rays move in the same direction and with the same velocity as the associated wave front. However, in anisotropic substances the velocity of the wave front in the direction of its normal is not necessarily the same as the ray velocity.

In the equation

$$n = \frac{\sin i}{\sin r}$$

i is regarded as the angle of incidence in vacuum or air, and r, unless otherwise stated, is the angle of refraction of the wave front as it moves in the direction of the wave normal in the refracting medium.

The Isotropic Indicatrix

If it is assumed that a light wave vibrates at right angles to the direction of its propagation, the passage of light through an isotropic medium can be related to a sphere called an *isotropic indicatrix*

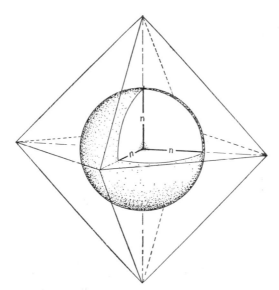

Fig. 4. The isotropic indicatrix.

(Fig. 4). All radii of the sphere are equal to n, the index of refraction of the medium for a particular wave length; the radii give the refractive indices in the directions of their vibration for all waves originating at a point source. The wave corresponding to a particular radius of the sphere travels at right angles to the radius with a velocity proportional to $1/n$.

Total Reflection and Critical Angle

Light traveling from one medium to another of higher refractive index is refracted toward the normal in the medium of higher index. Conversely, light traveling in the opposite direction is bent away from the normal in the medium of lower index.

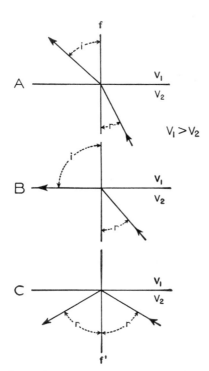

Figure 5 shows light passing from a medium of velocity V_2 to a medium of velocity V_1. Inasmuch as in the derivation of the formula for the index of refraction i is used to designate the angle of incidence in the medium of higher velocity, it will be retained here with the understanding that the light is actually moving in the opposite direction, that is, from medium of velocity V_2 into medium of velocity V_1. In Fig. 5A, light entering a medium of velocity V_1 is refracted away from the normal ff', and, if V_1 is the velocity in air or vacuum,

$$n = \frac{\sin i}{\sin r}$$

Fig. 5. Refraction and reflection of light at plane contact of two isotropic media.

In Fig. 5B, the angle r is such that the angle i is 90 degrees; that is, the light entering air just grazes the surface of contact between the two media. The angle r when this condition obtains is called the *critical angle*. The following relation now holds:

$$n = \frac{1}{\sin r} \quad (\sin 90° = 1)$$

For example, diamond has a refractive index of 2.42, and 2.42 = $1/\sin r$, from which it follows that the critical angle is 24° 24′. When the critical angle is exceeded, all the light is internally reflected as in

Fig. 5C. This type of reflection is described as *total internal reflection*. The refractive indices of two substances are related by the equation

$$\frac{n_1}{n_2} = \frac{\sin i}{\sin r}$$

where n_1 is greater than n_2, and i is measured in the medium of lower index. Thus, a critical angle r can be determined for any substance in contact with another of lower refractive index. At this critical angle

$$\frac{n_1}{n_2} = \frac{1}{\sin r}$$

where r is measured in the medium of higher index. In air or vacuum, n_2 becomes unity.

Lenses

Lenses are optical devices for refracting light and are made of transparent isotropic substances. The surfaces of lenses are generally spherical, and the curvatures of the two surfaces are equal or different

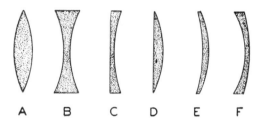

Fig. 6. Simple lenses.

A. Biconvex.   *D*. Plano-convex.
B. Biconcave.   *E*. Concave-convex.
C. Plano-concave.   *F*. Convex-concave.

depending upon the intended use of the lens. The line passing through the centers of curvature is the *axis* of a lens.

Figure 6 illustrates various types of simple lenses. Depending on the manner in which it refracts light, a lens may be said to be *converging* (positive) or *diverging* (negative). Refraction by a biconvex converging lens is illustrated in Fig. 7. Light moving along a ray *abcd,* incident at *b,* is refracted toward the normal *N',* and as it leaves the lens is refracted again, this time away from the normal.

Light in a ray, *a'b'c'd,* parallel to the axis, is not refracted. Light in ray *a''b''c''d* is refracted so as to intersect refracted light in other rays at *F,* the *focal point* or *focus.* The distance *f* from the center of the lens to the focal point is termed the *focal distance* or *focal length.*

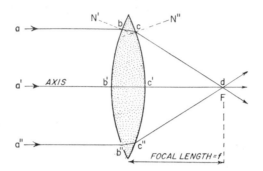

Fig. 7. Passage of light through a biconvex lens.

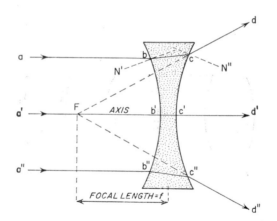

Fig. 8. Passage of light through a biconcave lens.

The focus at *F* is a *real focus,* and the image at that point is a *real image.*

A biconcave lens is shown in Fig. 8. This lens causes light to diverge. The rays for light passing through the lens, if projected backward, intersect at point *F,* the *virtual focus,* and it is said that a *virtual image* is formed at *F.*

Lenses reverse images as shown in Fig. 9. Light from the tip of the arrow passes through the lens and comes to a focus on the opposite side in such a way that the image of the tip is reversed. Light in

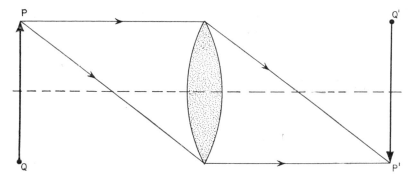

Fig. 9. Reversal of image by a lens.

other rays behaves similarly, resulting in the reversal of the image of the whole arrow.

Defects of Lenses

Lenses suffer from certain inherent defects called *aberrations*. *Chromatic aberrations* result from the fact that a lens has different refractive indices for the various component colors of white light. Other defects, present even in monochromatic light, are called *mono-chromatic aberrations*.

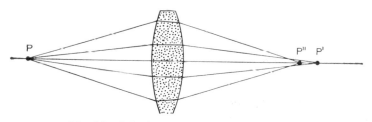

Fig. 10. Spherical aberration in a simple lens.

Spherical aberration is illustrated in Fig. 10. The point P yields an image at P' or P'', depending upon the path followed by the light through the lens. Light passing through the central portion of the lens produces an image at P', and that passing through the lens near its edge forms an image at P''. Evidently, there is no single plane in which a sharp image of P will be formed. This type of aberration is reduced by employing a diaphragm so that only the central portion of the lens transmits light.

Chromatic aberration, shown in Fig. 11, results from the fact that the lens has different refractive indices for different wave lengths of light. In white light, an arrow OA will produce a series of reversed images corresponding to each of the colors of the visible spectrum. The images $O'A'$ for violet and $O''A''$ for red are at the extremes of the spectrum and indicate the maximum limits of aberration. Note

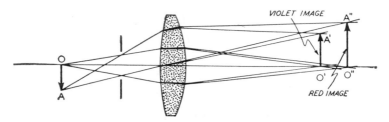

Fig. 11. Chromatic aberration in a simple lens.

in Fig. 11 that not only are the images of the arrow corresponding to the various colors at different focal distances, but they are of different size.

Other types of aberrations are *coma, astigmatism,* and *distortion*. *Coma* affects the image of a point not lying in the axis of a lens and tends to spread the image out over a plane at right angles to the lens axis. *Astigmatism* affects the image of a point not on the lens axis and tends to spread the image in a direction along the axis. *Distortion* arises not from a lack of sharpness of the image but from a variation of magnification with axial distance.

Balancing of Aberrations

The inherent defects of simple lenses may be partly or completely nullified by constructing *compound lenses*. A compound lens consists of two or more individual lenses assembled in such a manner that the aberrations of one part of the system are balanced against those of another part. However, as a practical matter, it is almost impossible to construct a compound lens which overcomes all the various types of aberrations, and so, in general, a lens is constructed in such a manner as to remove or considerably reduce the aberrations that are detrimental to a specific use.

CHAPTER 4 THE POLARIZING MICROSCOPE

The polarizing microscope originally was constructed for the petrographic examination of thin slices of rocks, but in recent years it has assumed increasing importance in the fields of chemistry, ceramic technology, metallography, crime detection, military intelligence, and medicine. Many branches of industry make advantageous use of the polarizing microscope. Because of widely varying applications, the polarizing microscope has undergone many modifications, but in principle all types do not differ essentially from the original petrographic microscope. Accordingly, the descriptions here will be limited to the type of microscope ordinarily employed by the petrographer or the chemical microscopist. The polarizing microscope will perform all the functions of an ordinary microscope. Moreover, it permits the evaluation of properties and characteristics that can not be measured by other means.

The Polarizing Microscope

The polarizing microscope differs from an ordinary compound microscope in that it has a revolving, graduated circular stage, a polarizing device below the stage, called the *polarizer,* and a similar device above the objective, called the *analyzer.* The polarizer and

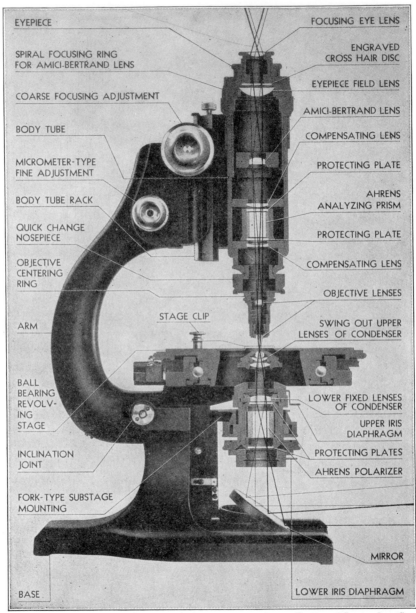

EYEPIECE

SPIRAL FOCUSING RING
FOR AMICI-BERTRAND LENS

COARSE FOCUSING ADJUSTMENT

BODY TUBE

MICROMETER-TYPE
FINE ADJUSTMENT

BODY TUBE RACK

QUICK CHANGE
NOSEPIECE

OBJECTIVE
CENTERING
RING

ARM

BALL
BEARING
REVOLV-
ING
STAGE

INCLINATION
JOINT

FORK-TYPE SUBSTAGE
MOUNTING

BASE

STAGE CLIP

FOCUSING EYE LENS

ENGRAVED
CROSS HAIR DISC

EYEPIECE FIELD LENS

AMICI-BERTRAND LENS

COMPENSATING LENS

PROTECTING PLATE

AHRENS
ANALYZING PRISM

PROTECTING PLATE

COMPENSATING LENS

OBJECTIVE LENSES

SWING OUT UPPER
LENSES OF CONDENSER

LOWER FIXED LENSES
OF CONDENSER

UPPER IRIS
DIAPHRAGM

PROTECTING PLATES

AHRENS POLARIZER

MIRROR

LOWER IRIS DIAPHRAGM

Courtesy of Spencer Lens Co.

Fig. 1. Cross section of a polarizing microscope.

analyzer may be referred to simply as the *upper* and *lower polars*[1] and are made of cut and recemented clear calcite prisms or of discs of Polaroid or a similar material. Calcite polarizing prisms commonly are called *Nicol prisms*, but the calcite prisms used in most modern polarizing microscopes differ radically in design from the prisms originally constructed by Nicol. Each polar transmits light waves vibrating in one direction only, and, for most purposes, the polars are oriented so that their planes of vibration are mutually perpendicular and are parallel to the cross hairs of the microscope ocular. When the polars are crossed, no light is transmitted by the microscope unless the light passes through an optically anisotropic substance somewhere in the optical system. In addition to the revolving stage and the polars, most polarizing microscopes contain a swing-out auxiliary condensing lens below the microscope stage and a removable Amici-Bertrand lens between the upper polar and the ocular. Figure 1 shows a cross section of a polarizing microscope with all lenses in use and identifies the component parts.

Certain kinds of measurements with the polarizing microscope require optical accessories, such as the quartz wedge, mica plate, or gypsum plate. The accessories are used for producing various effects on the light transmitted by the microscope and serve mainly to produce path differences under controlled conditions. Most accessories are plates or wedges of anisotropic substances mounted in metal plates that can be inserted into the microscope in a slot just above the objective or in a slot in a specially constructed ocular. The use of some of the common accessories is described in subsequent chapters. For certain purposes the microscope is made more versatile by adding a multiaxis universal stage to the microscope stage so as to permit rotation of a preparation into any desired orientation. The theory and use of the universal stage is summarized in Chapter 17.

The passage of light through a polarizing microscope when it is used as an orthoscope to look at an object on the stage of the microscope is indicated in Figs. 2 and 3. Figure 2 is a diagram of a microscope in which the light is polarized by polarizing filters; the compensating lenses that are commonly present have been omitted. Two sets of parallel inclined rays pass through the lower polarizing filter and are focused on an object on the stage by the condensing lenses. If the upper polarizing filter is present in the optical system with its plane of vibration perpendicular to that of the lower polarizer and the object on the stage is isotropic, no light will be transmitted through

[1] The useful term *polar* was suggested by A. F. Hallimond, *Manual of the Polarizing Microscope,* Cooke, Troughton, and Simms. Ltd., York, England, 1953.

the microscope to the eye. If the upper polarizing filter is removed from the optical system or if the object on the stage is anisotropic, light is transmitted to the eye and an image of the object on the stage

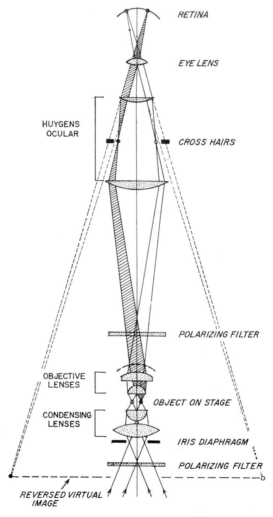

Fig. 2. Passage of light through an orthoscope containing polarizing filters.

will be seen. The objective lens system refracts light from an object on the stage in somewhat the same manner as an ordinary hand mag-nifier. However, before the light can come to a focus above the objective to form a real image it is intercepted by the ocular lens system and brought to a focus in a plane including the cross hairs of the microscope. On passing through the upper lens of the ocular the light is refracted again, enters the eye, and is focused on the retina by the eye lens. A reversed enlarged virtual image of the object on the stage is seen by the observer. The ocular in effect enlarges the image produced by the objective, and the magnifying power of the microscope is obtained by multiplying the magnifying power of the ocular by that of the objective, as the lenses are designed for a microscope of particular tube length.

Figure 3 shows a microscope with calcite polarizing prisms and compensating lenses. The elements of the compound lenses are not shown. The drawing indicates all components in their correct relative positions and shows the light passing through the microscope along different paths from those indicated in Fig. 2. The rays entering the microscope are not parallel and are numbered so that they can be traced through the microscope to the eye and back into the plane of the virtual image of the magnified object on the stage. Angles for the entering rays were selected so that the rays

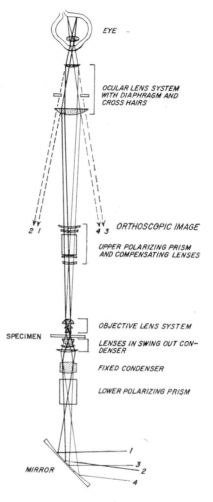

Fig. 3. Passage of light through a polarizing microscope with lenses arranged for orthoscopic observation. Based on a diagram prepared by E. Leitz, Inc.

projected from the eye into the plane of the virtual image are parallel rather than converging as in Fig. 2. Points 1, 2, 3, and 4 in the virtual image correspond to four different points in the object on the microscope stage.

In Figs. 4 and 5 the orthoscope has been converted into a *conoscope* by the insertion of an Amici-Bertrand lens into the optical system.

In the conoscope the observer looks *through* rather than *at* an object on the stage of the microscope. Figure 4 is a schematic drawing of a conoscope with polarizing filters, and Fig. 5 is a drawing of a cono-

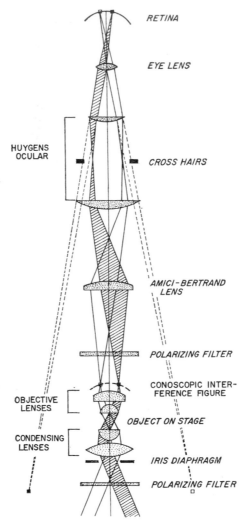

Fig. 4. Passage of light through a conoscope containing polarizing filters.

scope employing calcite polarizing prisms. The Amici-Bertrand lens converts the microscope into a low-power telescope focused at infinity. With the upper polarizer removed and with no obstructions on the stage, distant objects in the line of sight of the microscope can be seen, or, if an undiffused light source is used, the image of the lamp filament may be observed. If the object on the stage is isotropic or there is nothing on the stage, practically no light will pass through the cono-scope when the polars are crossed. If there is an anisotropic substance on the stage, double refraction with the polars crossed will cause an *interference figure* to appear in a curved surface just above the objective lens system, above the lower lens of the ocular in the plane of the cross hairs, and again on the retina of the eye. Interference figures are discussed in later sections of this book. The Amici-Bertrand lens brings the ocular and eye-lens system to a focus on the inter-ference figure in the curved sur-face above the objective and produces an enlarged virtual image. The light rays intersect-ing in the curved surface *do not* produce an image of the object on the stage of the microscope. The interference figure just above the objective can be ob-served directly by looking down the microscope tube after remov-ing the Amici-Bertrand lens and the ocular lenses, although it is smaller than when viewed with the help of these lenses. Some microscopes are equipped with a special combination of auxiliary lenses which may be inserted in the microscope tube to produce an enlarged image of the inter-ference figure.

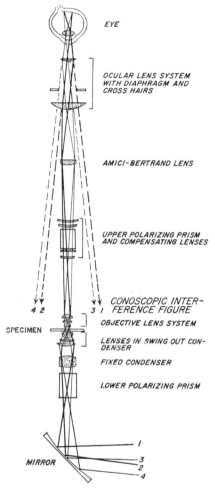

Fig. 5. Passage of light through a polar-izing microscope with lenses arranged for conoscopic observation. Based on dia-gram prepared for E. Leitz, Inc.

To view the interference figure satisfactorily it is necessary to use condensing and objective lenses of large *angular aperture*. Preferably the angular apertures should be nearly equal. The angular aperture measures the angle between the directions followed by light waves passing through lenses with maximum obliquity.

It is instructive to compare the refraction of the numbered rays in Fig. 5 with the numbered rays in Fig. 3. Note that there is a different disposition of the rays that form an orthoscopic image as compared with the rays that form the image of the conoscopic interference figure.

Objectives

Microscope objectives produce a magnified image of an object on the microscope stage. The ratio of the size of this image to the size of the object is termed the *initial magnification of the objective*. The magnification increases with an increase in the tube length and with a decrease in the focal length of the objective lens system.

The *resolving power* of an objective is an important property which measures its ability to show as distinctly separated in the structure of an object two small elements which are a small distance apart. Resolving power is a function of the numerical aperture (N.A.) and wave length and increases with an increase in the numerical aperture. The following relationship holds:

$$\text{N.A.} = n \sin u$$

where n is the lowest refractive index between the object and the objective, and u is half the angular aperture of the objective. With most objectives n is the index of air, which is slightly greater than unity.

The application of the principle discussed above is well illustrated by the oil-immersion objective. At high magnifications, the resolving power of a lens may be increased by displacing the air space between a magnified object and the objective with a liquid layer which has an index of refraction considerably higher than that of air.

The *depth of focus* of an objective measures the vertical interval for which the image of an object on the microscope stage is clearly seen and depends on the numerical aperture and magnification; it is inversely proportional to both. Thus, as the numerical aperture and magnification increase, the depth of focus decreases. Any effort to increase depth of focus by means of diaphragms results in decreased resolving power.

Various types of objectives are available. *Apochromatic objectives* are constructed so as to reduce color aberration to a minimum. Such lenses, however, may suffer from a decided lack of flatness of field and do not produce flat images. This condition is corrected in part by careful construction.

Achromatic objectives are not corrected for spherical and chromatic aberration to the same extent as apochromatic objectives but are satisfactory for most purposes. These objectives should be used for exact optical measurements because they do not rotate the plane of vibration of transmitted light as much as other types of objectives.

For special types of work *fluorite objectives* may be useful. They consist of a combination of glass and fluorite lenses and have better resolving power than achromatic objectives. Fluorite and apochromatic objectives find wide use in photomicrography at high magnifications.

The focal length, numerical aperture, and magnification usually are engraved on the barrel of an objective and have been determined for specified microscope tube lengths (commonly 16–18 cm). For high magnifications objectives may be corrected for a specified thickness of the cover glass on a glass slide.

Objectives are mounted on the microscope tube in various ways. In some microscopes several objectives of different magnifications are mounted on a revolving objective holder. In other microscopes the objectives are mounted separately and are attached to the microscope tube with adapters and clutches. For accurate work the objectives must be centered so that as the microscope stage is rotated the

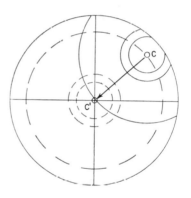

Fig. 6. Adjustment required to center a microscope objective.

center of the rotation in the field coincides with the intersection of the cross hairs of the microscope. In Fig. 6 rotation of the microscope stage might cause particles on a glass slide on the stage of the microscope to rotate off-center about *C*. To correct this condition the image of point *C* is moved to *C'* by manipulation of the centering screws on the objective holder.

Oculars

Oculars, also called *eyepieces,* magnify the image produced by the objective, and, if properly designed, increase the field of view and reduce the aberrations produced by the objective. In the *Ramsden ocular* the lenses are placed above the focal plane for the objective. In the *Huygens ocular,* shown in Figs. 2 to 5, the converging light from the objective is brought to a focus between the upper and lower lenses of the ocular. Cross hairs or a ruled micrometer scale may be placed in the focal plane of either type of ocular and will be seen superimposed over the magnified image of an object on the stage of the microscope or over an interference figure produced by an anisotropic substance on the stage.

Compensating oculars are constructed primarily for use with apochromatic objectives and eliminate color fringes which are seen when other types of oculars are used. The *Huygens oculars* are used more than any other type and give good results in combination with achromatic objectives at low to medium magnifications. *Hyperplane oculars* have a color compensation midway between that of compensating and Huygens oculars and are used for high magnification and in photomicrography.

Substage Condensers

Substage condensers are lenses that serve to focus light from below the stage on an object on the stage. For best results the numerical aperture of the condensing lens should approximate the numerical aperture of the objective that is being employed. A typical polarizing microscope has a condensing lens of low numerical aperture for use with objectives of low magnification. For higher magnifications and observation of interference phenomena under the conoscope a swing-out condensing lens can be introduced into the lens system below the stage to increase the numerical aperture and to increase the intensity of illumination. Many condensing lenses contain built-in iris diaphragms that can be used to vary the angular aperture or to control the amount and intensity of the transmitted light.

CHAPTER 5 CALCULATION AND MEASUREMENT OF INDEX OF REFRACTION

Measurement of the refractive indices of solids is a very useful procedure in determinative mineralogy or chemistry. There are many methods of index measurement, each suited to a certain purpose and yielding results within certain limits of accuracy. The method most widely employed is the immersion method, in which the index of a solid is compared with that of a liquid of known index. Many variations of the immersion method have been devised: some are adaptable to routine laboratory work with a minimum of equipment; others require expensive and complicated apparatus and are not widely used.

The discussion of index determination presented in this chapter is based on the assumption that the measured substance has only one index of refraction for a particular color (wave length) of incident light; that is, it is *optically isotropic*. It should be understood that uniaxial crystals have two principal indices of refraction and that biaxial crystals have three. The measurement of all indices of refraction of optically anisotropic crystals is discussed in subsequent chapters.

Interrelations of Index of Refraction, Density, and Chemical Composition

The rule of Gladstone and Dale states: "Every liquid has a specific refractive energy composed of the specific refractive energies of its component elements, modified by the manner of combination, and which is unaffected by changes of temperature and accompanies it when mixed with other liquids. The product of this specific refractive energy and the density is, when added to unity, the refractive index."

Mathematically, this rule, which is very primitive from a theoretical standpoint, is expressed as follows:

$$K = \frac{n - 1}{d}$$

where K is the specific refractive energy of a substance, n is its index of refraction, and d is its density. Put another way, the rule states that

$$K = k_1 \cdot \frac{p_1}{100} + k_2 \cdot \frac{p_2}{100} + \cdots$$

where k_1, k_2, etc., are the specific refractive energies of the components of the substance and p_1, p_2, etc., are the weight percentages of the components of the subtance.

Lorentz and Lorenz independently derived a formula based on the electromagnetic theory of light. Their formula is

$$K = \frac{n^2 - 1}{n^2 + 2} \cdot \frac{1}{d}$$

Lichtenecker proposed the empirical formula

$$K = \frac{\log n}{d}$$

All the above equations give calculated refractive indices which agree more or less with experimentally measured refractive indices. It is known, however, that for many substances the manner in which the components enter into crystal structures has an important influence upon the magnitude of the calculated index. In uniaxial crystals (tetragonal and hexagonal) the calculated index is compared with the mean index $(2n_O + n_E)/3$, where n_O is the measured refractive index for light vibrating perpendicular to the c crystallographic axis and n_E

is the measured index for light vibrating parallel to the c axis. In biaxial crystals (orthorhombic, monoclinic, and triclinic) the calculated index is compared with the mean index $(n_X + n_Y + n_Z)/3$, where n_X, n_Y, and n_Z are the principal refractive indices as determined by measurement. For anisotropic substances with a large difference between the maximum and minimum measured refractive indices the calculated index should be compared with

$$\sqrt[3]{(n_O)^2 \cdot n_E} \quad \text{or} \quad \sqrt[3]{n_X \cdot n_Y \cdot n_Z}.$$

A tabulation of specific refractive energies is given by Larsen and Berman,[1] and a discussion of the application of the rule of Gladstone and Dale to minerals and some additional values for specific refractive energies are presented by Jaffe.[2] Calculations by Jaffe for data for 121 minerals demonstrate a surprisingly close agreement between calculated and measured mean refractive indices.

Molecular refractivity is the specific refractive energy, sometimes called the *specific refractivity,* multiplied by the molecular weight and is useful in structural studies of crystals.

Allen[3] proposed the equation

$$\frac{\alpha\beta\gamma}{d} = K$$

which, in the symbolism adopted in this book, **is**

$$\frac{n_X \cdot n_Y \cdot n_Z}{d} = K$$

The product $n_X \cdot n_Y \cdot n_Z$ is designated as the *refractive capacity* and K as the *specific refractive capacity.* He tabulates the specific refractive capacities of common oxides in minerals, glasses, and chemical compounds. For uniaxial crystals the mean index of refraction, n, equals $\sqrt[3]{n_O^2 \cdot n_E}$, and for biaxial crystals the mean index equals $\sqrt[3]{n_X \cdot n_Y \cdot n_Z}$.

As for the rule of Gladstone and Dale the specific refractive capacity for a substance is obtained by multiplying the weight percent of each component of the substance by its individual specific refractive capacity and adding the results.

[1] E. S. Larsen and H. Berman, "The Microscopic Determination of the Nonopaque Minerals," *U. S. Geol. Surv. Bull.* 848, pp. 11–18, 1934.

[2] H. W. Jaffe, "Application of the Rule of Gladstone and Dale to Minerals," *Am. Mineralogist,* Vol. 41, pp. 757–777, 1956.

[3] R. D. Allen, "A New Equation Relating Index of Refraction to Specific Gravity," *Am. Mineralogist,* Vol. 41, pp. 245–257, 1956.

Light Sources

The accurate measurement of the refractive index requires a light source of known characteristics. For routine measurements where only approximate determinations will suffice, a white-light source, such as daylight, light from a tungsten lamp passed through a blue filter, or light from a carbon arc may be employed. For precise measurements an essentially monochromatic light source with a known wave length is required, and the refractive index as measured is specified for the particular wave length. Most refractive index measurements are made for wave lengths (frequencies) in the visible portion of the spectrum, and the most commonly used single wave length is that emitted by a sodium flame or a sodium vapor lamp. The wave length of sodium light in vacuum is 589.3 mμ. For special purposes refractive indices may be measured for wave lengths in the ultraviolet or in the infrared, but special equipment is needed to detect the radiation in these portions of the spectrum.

Certain well-spaced and easily obtained monochromatic radiations in the visible spectrum have been used as standards for specifying refractive index in terms of the wave length of light. Many of these wave lengths correspond to absorption lines in the sun's spectrum and have been called *Fraunhofer lines.* The accompanying table gives the letter designations, wave lengths in millimicrons, and common sources for many of the standard wave lengths.

The mercury arc and the hydrogen discharge tube contain several prominent spectral lines, and, by proper use of filters, lines for particular wave lengths may be isolated. More useful as a source of monochromatic light is a *monochromator,* a device that may be similar to a prism or grating spectrometer. If an intense source of white light is used, rotation of the prism or grating or movement of a narrow slit across the spectrum produced by a prism or grating permits isolation of narrow segments of the spectrum. If a mercury arc or a hydrogen tube is used as the light source, the monochromator may be used to isolate each of the characteristic spectral lines. Colored filters used with a white-light source permit isolation of narrow bands of wave lengths in the spectrum. There is limited use for so-called *interference filters,* glass plates on which semitransparent metallic films separated by thin layers of a transparent medium have been deposited.[4]

---

[4] Interference filters with a wide range of characteristics are manufactured by the Bausch and Lomb Optical Co., Rochester, N. Y.

Reference Wavelengths in the Visible Spectrum

Letter Designation	Wavelength, mμ	Source
A[1]	766.5	Potassium flame
C	656.3	Hydrogen discharge
D	589.3	Sodium flame
d	587.6	Helium discharge
e	546.1	Mercury arc
E	527.0	Sun
F	486.1	Hydrogen discharge
g	435.9	Mercury arc
G[1]	434.1	Hydrogen discharge
h	404.7	Mercury arc

When a white-light source is used in optical crystallographic measurements, including refractive-index measurements, color phenomena of one kind or another commonly are observed and result from separation of white light into the colors of its component wave lengths by refraction and reflection or by double refraction and interference. Many color phenomena depend on the fact that certain segments of the visible spectrum are subtracted from the light that reaches the eye through the microscope because of nonrefraction of light of certain wave lengths incident on an object on the microscope stage or because of destructive interference of light of certain wave lengths transmitted by anisotropic substances. A particular color that may be seen is, then, commonly the result of subtraction of light in narrow to wide bands of wave lengths from some portion of the spectrum of white light.

White light, sometimes called *omnichromatic* or *achromatic light* (as opposed to *chromatic* or *colored light*), is not usually defined precisely. White light can be produced by uniform emission of radiant energy for all of the wave lengths of the visible spectrum or can be generated by several kinds of mixing and balancing of bands of wave lengths of different characteristics. The colors that result from subtraction of bands of wave lengths depend, accordingly, on the nature of the white light from which they are subtracted and upon the width and position of the subtracted bands in the spectrum.

Another factor that is of importance is the response of the eye to various portions of the spectrum of white light. The eye is more sensitive to wave lengths in the middle of the spectrum than to colors at either end, and subtraction from white light of colors to which the eye is especially sensitive produces effects which differ in magnitude from those produced by subtraction of wave lengths to which the eye is not particularly sensitive. Moreover, there is a wide variation in the sensitivities of various observers to colors in different portions of the spectrum.

A comprehensive analysis of the factors contributing to the formation of colors by mixing or subtraction is beyond the scope of this book. The color phenomena that are associated with certain methods of refractive-index measurement will be described qualitatively, but no attempt will be made to explain the colors in terms of the quantitative aspects of colorimetry. Many of the problems that attend the use of a white-light source are eliminated when a monochromatic-light source is substituted.

Refractive-Index Dispersion

The index of refraction of an isotropic substance varies progressively with the wave length of light provided by the source of illumination. Its value generally increases as the wave length decreases; also, the principal indices of refraction of most anisotropic substances vary individually in the same manner. The index variation is expressed by the fact that for a single angle of incidence the angles of refraction differ for the different wave lengths of incident light. This inequality of refraction of the progressively varying wave lengths differs in amount in different media. The degree of inequality of refraction of light of various colors is a measure of the *dispersion*. The dispersion dependent on variation of the refractive indices with the wave length of the incident light might be called *wave-length dispersion of the refractive indices*. *Total dispersion* is expressed as the difference between the refractive indices for red and violet light, at opposite ends of the visible spectrum. *Partial dispersion* measures the difference between the indices for specified wave lengths, and commonly is specified for the C (656.3 mμ) and F (486.1 mμ) reference wave lengths. *Relative dispersion* or *dispersive power* is expressed as

$$\delta = \frac{n_2 - n_1}{n - 1}$$

where n_1 and n_2 are the refractive indices for wave lengths λ_1 and λ_2, and n is the mean index or the refractive index for sodium light (589.3 mμ). Commonly the relative dispersion is determined by the equation

$$\delta = \frac{n_F - n_C}{n_D - 1}$$

where n_F, n_C, and n_D are the indices for the F, C, and D reference wave lengths. For certain types of calculations the reciprocal of the relative dispersion is more useful than the direct relationship. In whatever manner the dispersion is expressed, it is characteristic for each homogeneous substance.

A simple relationship between refractive index and wave length of visible light is given by the empirical formula known as Cauchy's equation which follows:

$$n = A + \frac{B}{\lambda^2} + \frac{C}{\lambda^4} \cdots$$

where n is the refractive index, λ is the wave length, and A, B, and C are constants. The equation works well with most substances that do not strongly absorb certain colors of the transmitted light.

Now, if the refractive indices of a substance for three different wave lengths are determined and if each of the values is substituted in the above equation, three simultaneous equations which permit evaluation of A, B, and C are obtained. When these constants are determined for a given substance, it becomes possible to compute the index for any wave length of the visible spectrum.

Hartmann equations show an empirical relationship between refractive index and wave length, as follows:

$$n = n_0 + \frac{c}{(\lambda_0 - \lambda)^{1.2}}$$

and

$$n = n_0 + \frac{c}{\lambda - \lambda_0}$$

where c is a constant characteristic of each substance.

Refractive index is a function not only of the wave length of the incident light but also of temperature, chemical composition, and the physical state of matter. Changes of refractive indices with temperature may be described as *temperature dispersion of the refractive indices*. The change of refractive index per degree of temperature change is the *temperature coefficient of refraction*. In general, refractive indices decrease as temperature is elevated. The indices of liquids change much more rapidly with temperature than the indices of solids. Accordingly, both temperature and the wave length of light should be specified in stating the results of precise index measurement.

Figure 1 shows the variation of refractive index with temperature and wave length for ethyl salicylate, a liquid, and the variation of the index with wave length for a borosilicate glass. The curves in Fig. 1 may be described as *dispersion curves*. Data plotted on a graph with a uniform wave-length scale yield curved lines, but the same data plotted on Hartmann nets with a logarithmic wave-length scale as in Fig. 1 commonly yield essentially straight lines that within short intervals permit fairly accurate interpolation and extrapolation.

In Fig. 1 note the wide variation in the refractive indices for the liquid with wave length and temperature. The index of the glass

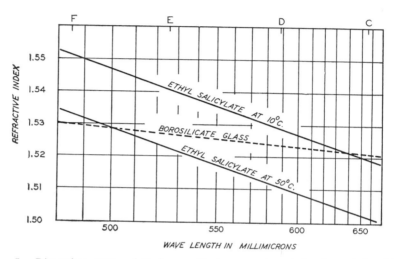

Fig. 1. Dispersion curves plotted on a Hartmann net and showing relationships among index of refraction, wave length, and temperature.

changes appreciably with wave length, but index changes corresponding to temperature changes are so small that for small temperature intervals they are practically negligible. If it is assumed that the refractive index of the glass does not change appreciably in the temperature range between 10° and 50° C, it can be seen that the index of the liquid at either 10° or 50° C can be made to match the index of the glass by changing the wave length of the light emitted by the source of illumination. At 10° C liquid and glass have the same refractive indices for a wave length of 640 mμ; at 50° C the indices are the same at a wave length of 500 mμ.

Immersion Methods of Refractive-Index Measurement

An outstanding method of refractive-index measurement employs liquids of known refractive indices as immersion media. Fragments or crystals are placed in successive immersions until by one or more techniques it is ascertained that the refractive index of the fragment or crystal matches that of the immersion medium. When a monochromatic-light source is used and the refractive index of the fragment lies between those of two liquids in a series, the liquids may be mixed in various proportions to obtain a match.

Several variations of the immersion method are described in subsequent sections of this chapter. The accuracy of the results obtained by any immersion technique depend on several factors such as the numerical apertures and the quality of the lenses of the microscope, the extent to which the light source is rendered monochromatic (where a monochromatic source is desired), the extent to which the temperature of the immersion medium is controlled, and the care with which the observations are made. If a white-light source and immersion media of low dispersion are used, routine measurements will be accurate to about ± 0.003. With a monochromatic-light source and controlled temperatures an accuracy of ± 0.001 can be obtained with almost any immersion technique. With all variables carefully controlled and with a microscope containing high-quality lenses, measurements may be made with an accuracy of $\pm 0.000n$. All techniques are more sensitive if observations are made with objectives of low numerical aperture.

By means of immersion media it is possible to measure refractive indices in the range 1.333 to 3.17_{Li}. Liquids are used in the range 1.333 to about 2.1, and low melting-temperature solids are used to measure indices above 2.1. For work with a white-light source many workers prefer media with low dispersions, but for some techniques media of high dispersion are more desirable. Whatever medium is used, accurate index measurement requires knowledge of the manner of variation of the refractive index with both temperature and the wave length provided by the light source. Desirable immersion media are safe, stable liquids that are inert to all substances placed in them, but, in practice, most liquids do not fulfill all these requirements.

A widely used series of index media is shown in the table on p. 64 by Larsen and Berman.[5] A set of liquids in which both temperature and wave-length dispersions are large is tabulated by Emmons.[6] Highly combustible liquid mixtures of sulfur, phosphorous, and methylene iodide with an index range of 1.74 to 2.06 are described

[5] E. S. Larsen and H. Berman, "The Microscopic Determination of the Nonopaque Minerals," *U. S. Geol. Surv. Bull.* 848, pp. 11–18, 1934.

[6] R. C. Emmons, *The Universal Stage*, Geol. Soc. Amer., Memoir 8, p. 63, 1943.

Refractive Indices of Immersion Media*

(From Larsen and Berman)

	n at 20° C	$-\dfrac{dn}{dt}$	Dispersion	Remarks
Water	1.333	Slight	....	Dissolves many of the minerals with low indices.
Acetone	1.357	....	Slight	Dissolves many of the minerals with low indices.
Ethyl alcohol†	1.362	0.00040	Slight	
Ethyl butyrate	1.381	....	Slight	
Methyl butyrate	1.386	....	Slight	
Ethyl valerate	1.393	....	Slight	
Amyl alcohol‡	1.409	0.00042	Slight	Dissolves many minerals with which it is used.
Kerosene	1.448	0.00035	Slight	
Petroleum oil§				
Russian alboline	1.470	0.0004	Slight	
American alboline	1.477	0.0004	Slight	
α-Monochlornaphtha-lene‖	1.626	....	Moderate	
α-Monobromnaphtha-lene	1.658	0.00048	Moderate	
Methylene iodide	1.737 to 1.741	0.00070	Rather strong	Rather expensive. Discolors on exposure to light, but a little copper or tin in the bottle will prevent this change.
Methylene iodide saturated with sulfur	1.778	....	Rather strong	
Methylene iodide, sulfur, and iodides#	1.868	....	Rather strong	
Piperine and iodides	1.68 to 2.10	....	....	
Sulfur and selenium	1.998_{Na} to 2.716_{Li}	....	Very strong	
Selenium and arsenic selenide	2.72 to 3.17_{Li}	....	Very strong	

* Another list of immersion media has been given by R. C. Emmons (*Am. Mineralogist*, Vol. 14, pp. 482–483, 1929).

† V. T. Harrington and M. S. Buerger used petroleum distillates prepared from kerosene, gasoline, etc., for the range of 1.35 to 1.45; the liquids with the lower indices are very volatile ("Immersion Liquids of Low Refraction," *Am. Mineralogist*, Vol. 16, pp. 45–54, 1931).

‡ Ordinary fusel oil may be used, but on mixing with kerosene it forms a milky emulsion, which settles on standing, and then the clear liquid may be decanted off.

§ Any of the medicinal oils may be used, such as Nujol.

‖ Hallowax oil is satisfactory.

To 100 grams methylene iodide add 35 grams iodoform, 10 grams sulfur, 31 grams SnI_4, 16 grams AsI_3, and 8 grams SbI_3, warm to hasten solution, allow to stand, and filter off undissolved solids. (See H. E. Merwin, "Media of High Refraction," *Washington Acad. Sci. Jour.*, Vol. 3, pp. 35–40, 1913.)

by West,[7] but they are dangerous if not properly used and stored. A compilation and classification of various immersion media of high refractive index (above 1.74) is given by Meyrowitz.[8] Several handbooks of physics and chemistry contain tabulations of immersion media.

The refractive indices of immersion liquids within the range of 1.40 to 1.80 for sodium light are conveniently measured with an Abbe refractometer. Liquids with an index up to 1.85 may be measured on the glass hemisphere of a refractometer of the Pulfrich type, but this instrument is not used widely because of its cost and delicacy. Liquids or low-melting-temperature solids may be measured conveniently and accurately in a hollow glass prism by the method of minimum deviation.

Relief

Under the microscope, crystal sections or fragments generally are characterized by rough, irregular, sometimes pitted surfaces, which result in the phenomenon of *relief*. The relief of a crystal fragment depends upon the relative indices of the fragment and the medium with which it makes contact. As the indices of the fragment and the surrounding medium approach each other, the relief diminishes.

Relief is an expression of the fact that as light passes from a medium of one index to a medium of a different index, the surface of contact acts so as to refract or totally reflect the light. If a crystal is immersed in a medium of considerably higher or lower index, every imperfection or flaw becomes conspicuous, and the relief is said to be high. Relief is absent when the index of the crystal and the immersion medium are the same, because light is not reflected or refracted at the contact and passes without path deviation through solid and immersion medium.

Relief depends on the *difference* in the indices of a substance and the immersion medium and *not* on the fact that the immersion medium has an index higher or lower than the substance. However, *apparent relief* may result from inclusions, alteration products, cleavage, internal fractures, or absorption of transmitted light.

The nature of relief is illustrated by the diagrams in Fig. 2. In each example it is assumed that a corrugated glass plate of index N is placed in an immersion medium of known index. In Fig. 2*A* the

[7] C. D. West, "Immersion Liquids of High Refractive Index," *Am. Mineralogist,* Vol. 21, pp. 245–249, 1936.

[8] R. Meyrowitz, "A Compilation and Classification of Immersion Media of High Index of Refraction," *Am. Mineralogist,* Vol. 40, pp. 298–409, 1955.

index of the immersion medium is considerably less than that of the glass, and, as the light passes from the glass into the immersion medium, it is strongly bent or refracted. In consequence, as indicated by the top view of the glass plate, the relief is high, and each trough and ridge stands out prominently. In Fig. 2B the index of the immersion medium is slightly less than that of the glass plate, and the

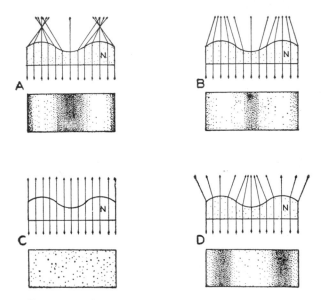

Fig. 2. Relief as exhibited by a corrugated glass plate.

A. Index of plate considerably higher than that of surrounding medium.
B. Index of plate slightly higher than that of surrounding medium.
C. Indices of plate and surrounding medium are the same.
D. Index of plate less than that of surrounding medium.

relief is lower than in Fig. 2A. In Fig. 2C the indices of the glass plate and the immersion medium are the same, and the relief disappears. In Fig. 2D the index of the immersion medium is considerably higher than that of the glass, and the relief again is high.

The diagrams in Fig. 2 do not show the effect of total reflection of light at the surface of contact between the glass and the immersion medium. However, total reflection contributes to relief in fragments which have curved or rough surfaces.

Becke Line Method

The *Becke line,* as originally defined, refers to a phenomenon associated with a vertical contact of two substances of different indices of refraction observed on the stage of a microscope. The Becke line is seen to best advantage under the microscope when a medium-power objective is used and the opening in the substage iris diaphragm is partly closed to render the incident light more nearly parallel and to reduce the total amount of illumination.

The light leaving the low-power condenser just below the microscope stage usually is slightly convergent. In Fig. 3 substances of indices n and N make a vertical contact. N is larger than n. Part of the light in rays 1 and 2, passing through the medium of index n and striking the contact between the two media, is reflected, and part is refracted into the medium of index N. The reflected light in medium of index n is not shown in the diagram. Light in rays 3 and 4 passing through the medium of index N is totally reflected. The effect is a concentration of light above the contact on the side toward the medium of higher index.

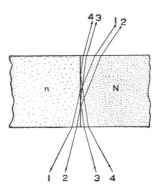

Under the microscope the Becke line may not be seen when the microscope is exactly focused on a fragment. However, if the tube of the microscope is slightly raised, a narrow line of light (the Becke line) appears just inside or outside the contact of the fragment with the surrounding medium. If the Becke line moves into the fragment when the microscope tube is raised, the index of the fragment is higher than that of the surrounding substance. If the Becke line moves out into the surrounding medium when the tube is raised,

Fig. 3. Origin of the Becke line.

the fragment has a lower index than that of the surrounding medium. Lowering the tube reverses the effect in each instance. The greater the difference in the refractive indices between the fragment and immersion, the greater is the displacement of the Becke line as the microscope tube is raised or lowered.

Concentrations of light near the borders of light-transmitting substances may be observed also when the contact between a substance and the medium in which it is immersed is inclined to the axis of the microscope. Plates of nonopaque substances with wedge edges are shown in Fig. 4, and it is assumed that the plates are illuminated by parallel (collimated) light. Note that refraction in both Fig. 4A and B results in a concentration of light above and near and inside the edges of the plates when the refractive index of the plates is greater than the refractive index of the immersion medium. Such concentrations of light produce bright lines that look and behave like

Becke lines associated with vertical contacts. Similar plates with lower refractive indices than the immersion medium produce light concentrations outside the edges of the plates.

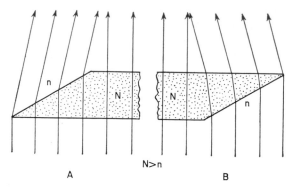

Fig. 4. Plates of nonopaque substances with wedge edges showing effects of refraction and concentration of light above plates.

Thick, irregular fragments or fragments displaying conspicuous cleavages commonly produce a bright line near the edge of a fragment as a result of internal reflection, or, more commonly, from ordinary reflection of light at the contact with the immersion medium. This line which moves in an opposite direction to that of the Becke

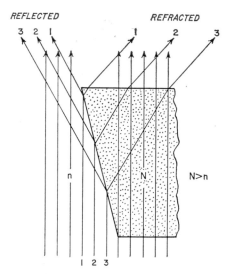

Fig. 5. Reflection of light at inclined contact that produces a "false Becke line."

line as the tube of the microscope is raised or lowered, is called a
false Becke line. The false Becke line is especially conspicuous when
the difference between the refractive indices of the fragment and
immersion medium is considerable and when strongly converging light
from the substage condensing lens passes through and near the fragment and then enters an objective lens of large angular aperture.
In Fig. 5 light traveling along parallel rays is incident on an inclined
surface between two media of different refractive indices. Note a
concentration of reflected light on one side of the contact and a
concentration of refracted light on the other side. The effects illustrated in Fig. 5 become more pronounced in converging incident

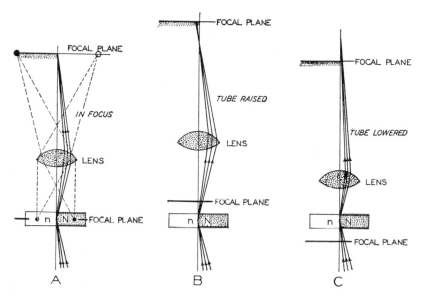

Fig. 6. Diagram illustrating movement of Becke line as microscope is raised or
lowered from position of sharp focus. Light refracted from medium of lower index
into medium of higher index not shown.

     A. Objective lens focused on object on stage of microscope.
     B. Objective lens raised above position of sharp focus.
     C. Objective lens lowered below position of sharp focus.

light. At times it is possible to eliminate or to reduce the intensity
of the false Becke line by reducing the opening in the substage diaphragm so as to produce nearly parallel incident light and by substituting an objective lens of low or moderate angular aperture for
an objective lens of large angular aperture.

The lateral movement of the "true" Becke line as the microscope tube is raised or lowered beyond the position of sharp focus on an object on the stage of the microscope is explained by reference to the diagrams in Fig. 6. In Fig. 6A the objective lens is focused on the vertical contact between two substances of different refractive indices, n and N; n is smaller than N. The light totally reflected at the contact of the medium of higher index with the medium of lower index and the light refracted into the medium of higher index (not shown in the diagram) come to a focus in the upper focal plane of the lens, and the observer is not aware of any concentration of light at the contact. In Fig. 6B the microscope tube is raised slightly above the position of sharp focus. The totally reflected light (and the refracted light) now converges below the upper focal plane of the lens and in the focal plane forms a concentration near the image of the contact on the side of the medium of higher index. In Fig. 6C the microscope tube is lowered, and the concentration of light has moved across the image of the contact into the medium of lower refractive index.

Color Phenomena in Immersion Methods

When the refractive index of a fragment matches the refractive index of the liquid in which it is immersed for a particular color, the transmitted light travels without deviation through the fragment. None of the light for the particular wave length is concentrated into a Becke line. The dispersion for the liquid is generally considerably greater than that for the solid, and, accordingly, the liquid will have a higher index than the solid for colors of shorter wave length than the matching color and a lower index than the solid for colors of longer wave length. For example, for an index match for the yellow color of the D line of sodium, near the middle of the spectrum, the liquid, compared to the solid, will have a higher index for violet and a lower index for red, and separate red and violet (or blue) Becke lines might form on opposite sides of the contact between the solid and the liquid. These lines would move in opposite directions as the tube of the microscope is raised or lowered.

Figure 7 affords a partial explanation of the color effects that might result from placing a fragment of a solid in a succession of liquids and viewing the Becke lines in white-light illumination. For liquid A the matching indices correspond to a wave length near the red end of the spectrum, and the Becke line will not include the colors for a band of wave lengths at and near the point of the intersection of the dispersion curves for the solid and liquid. In effect, these colors are subtracted from the Becke line that is formed by the remaining colors. Similarly, a match between the solid and liquid *B* results in the sub-traction from the Becke line of a more or less wide band of colors near the middle of the spectrum. For solid and liquid *C* colors for short wave lengths are subtracted, and the Becke line contains only colors corresponding to medium and long wave lengths.

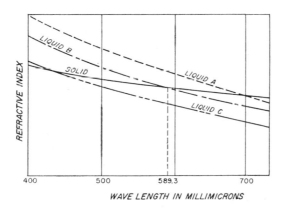

Fig. 7. Dispersion curves for liquids and a solid.

A detailed analysis of the particular effects of subtraction of bands of colors from the various portions of the spectrum of white light requires careful photometric measurements. In succeeding pages various qualitative effects of color subtraction will be noted for various immersion methods, including the Becke line method, but no attempt will be made to explain the effects in quantitative terms.

Emmons and Gates[9] emphasize the desirability of using colors in Becke lines for increasing the accuracy and speed of index measure-ment with a white-light source and describe the use of immersion liquids of moderate to high refractive-index dispersion for refractive-index measurement of crystal fragments. According to Emmons and Gates, for solids with indices near 1.5 in an immersion liquid of moderate dispersion, Becke lines on opposite sides of the interface are medium blue and medium yellow when the refractive indices match for a color near the middle of the spectrum. For matching indices in the short-wave-length portion of the spectrum, subtraction produces rich blue or violet on one side of the interface and very pale yellow

[9] R. C. Emmons and R. M. Gates, "The Use of Becke Line Colors in Refractive Index Determination," *Am. Mineralogist,* Vol. 33, pp. 612–618, 1948.

or yellowish white on the other side. If the index of liquid and solid are the same for long wave lengths in the red portion of the spectrum, a yellowish brown or red Becke line on one side of the contact opposes a pale blue Becke line on the other side. For higher refractive indices (above 1.7), diffuse Becke lines containing most of the colors in the spectrum may be observed. The Becke line for the matching wave length is eliminated, but colored Becke lines for wave lengths on either side of the matching wave length spread out on both sides of the contact of the solid with the liquid. By determining the index of the matching wave length of the liquid by reference to its dispersion curve it is possible to determine the index of the solid for the same wave length and, under favorable circumstances, to estimate the index for adjacent wave lengths.

Best results with the colored Becke line method are obtained if the observer first familiarizes himself with the characteristics of the particular set of immersion liquids that he is using and notes the specific effects for crystals of known refractive index in liquids for which the dispersion curves have been carefully determined.

Central Illumination Method

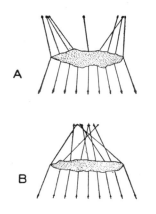

Fig. 8. Refraction of light by lenticular fragments.

A. Fragment has lower index than surrounding medium.
B. Fragment has higher index than surrounding medium.

Fragments of solids commonly are crudely lenticular in cross section and, if embedded in an immersion medium, act as biconvex lenses. The effect of refraction of light under such circumstances is diagrammatically indicated in Fig. 8. In Fig. 8A it is supposed that the fragment is immersed in a medium of higher index. Such a condition results in the dispersal of light passing through the fragment. In Fig. 8B the fragment has a higher index than that of the medium in which it is immersed. The refraction of light produces a concentration of light above the fragment.

By considering central illumination alone, the index of a fragment relative to the medium in which it is immersed may be determined by raising the microscope tube slightly above the position of sharp focus. If its index is higher than that of the immersion medium, the central portion of the fragment is illuminated when the tube is raised. If the fragment has a lower index, its central portion is darkened.

Ordinarily, central illumination is observed when the field of the microscope is somewhat darkened and the light rendered more nearly parallel by reducing the opening in the substage iris diaphragm.

In practice crystal fragments in immersion media show a composite effect. Both central illumination and the Becke line play a part, and each·supplements and reinforces the other.

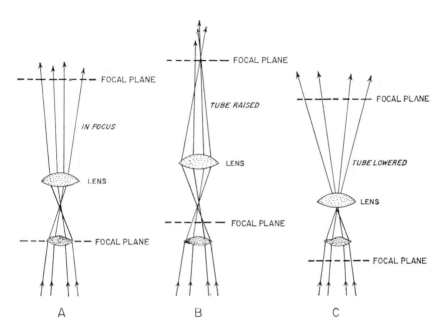

Fig. 9. Central illumination as related to the position of the objective lens of the microscope. Fragment has index higher than that of surrounding medium.

      A. Lens in sharp focus on object on microscope stage.
      B. Objective lens raised above position of sharp focus.
      C. Objective lens lowered below position of sharp focus.

Central illumination as related to the position of the objective lens and a fragment on the microscope stage is shown in Fig. 9. A lenticular fragment of higher refractive index than the surrounding medium causes a concentration of light above the fragment. In Fig. 9*A* the lens is in a position that produces a sharp image of the fragment. The observer is not aware of the concentration of light above the fragment until the tube of the microscope is raised as in Fig. 9*B*. Lowering the objective lens below a position of sharp focus, as in Fig. 9*C*, causes the central portion of the fragment to appear to darken.

Figure 10 shows diagrammatically the composite effect of central illumination and the Becke line. In Fig. 10*A* the microscope is exactly focused on a fragment immersed in a liquid. The light from the condenser is made more nearly parallel by the use of a substage diaphragm. Figure 10*B* illustrates the result of raising the microscope tube when the grain has a higher index than that of the immersion

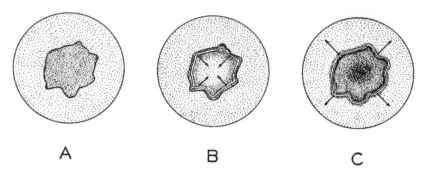

A   B   C

Fig. 10. Central illumination and the Becke line.

A. Microscope focused on grain.
B. Microscope tube slightly raised, index of fragment higher than that of surrounding medium.
C. Microscope tube slightly raised, index of fragment lower than that of surrounding medium.

medium. The center of the grain is illuminated, and a fine line of light (the Becke line) moves from the edge into the grain. In Fig. 10*C* it is assumed that the fragment has a lower index than the material in which it is embedded. When the microscope tube is raised, the center of the fragment is darkened, and the Becke line moves into the immersion medium. The arrows indicate the direction of movement of the Becke line in the two examples.

If the microscope tube is lowered below a sharp focus, the effects are the opposite of those just described.

Oblique Illumination Method

The relative refractive indices of a substance and an immersion medium may be determined satisfactorily by the *method of oblique illumination,* sometimes called the *Schroeder van der Kolk method.* In this method half the field of the microscope is darkened by the partial insertion of an accessory plate or some other opaque object into the optical system of the microscope so as to cut out half of the slightly

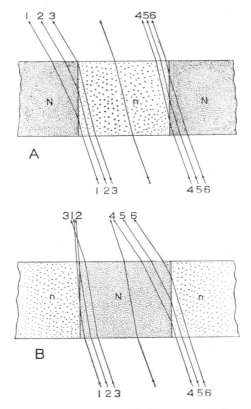

Fig. 11. Oblique illumination with vertical contacts. Reflected light not shown.

A. Index of substance *n* less than that of surrounding medium *N*.
B. Index of substance *N* greater than that of surrounding medium *n*.

converging cone of light that normally forms above the low-power substage condenser.

Figures 11 and 12 illustrate crystal plates or fragments in obliquely incident light. In Fig. 11 the crystal makes a vertical contact with the immersion medium. In Fig. 11*A* it is supposed that the index *n* of the crystal is less than that of the immersion medium *N*. Light in inclined rays 1, 2, and 3 passing from the medium of index *n* into the medium of index *N* is refracted toward the normal and is dispersed. Light in rays 4, 5, and 6, passing from the medium of index *N* to the medium of index *n,* is refracted away from the normal and crowded together (reflected light is not shown). If the fragment is viewed from above, one part appears dark, the other illuminated.

Figure 11*B* illustrates the refraction of light at vertical contacts when a substance has a higher index than that of the immersion medium. The result again will be the darkening of one part of the fragment and the illumination of the other, but the illuminated area is on the opposite side when compared to the example described above, in which the substance has a lower index than that of the immersion medium.

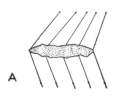

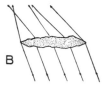

Fig. 12. Oblique illumination of lenticular fragments.

A. Index of fragment lower than that of surrounding medium.
B. Index of fragment higher than that of surrounding medium.

Lenticular fragments produce similar effects, as shown in Fig. 12. Figure 12*A* shows refraction of light by a lenticular fragment when its index is less than that of the immersion medium. Figure 12*B* illustrates the opposite condition.

The total result under the microscope, whether the substance has vertical sides or is lenticular, is the same. If half the field is darkened, the fragments will be illuminated on one side and darkened on the other. The particular result depends on just where in the optical system the opaque object is inserted to darken half the field and on what particular combination of lenses is used.

Best results are obtained with this method if the medium or low-power objective is used and the field is half-darkened in the same manner for each measurement. It is advisable to determine the result in a fragment of known index immersed in a medium of known index. In subsequent determinations the identical arrangement of lenses should be preserved, and the field should be darkened in the same manner.

As in the method of central illumination, relief is a guide to the relative indices of the fragment and immersion medium. As the index of the fragment approaches that of the surrounding medium, the relief becomes less.

Figure 13 illustrates the effect of oblique illumination. In Fig. 13*A* the microscope is focused on two fragments immersed in oil. Figure 13*B* shows the effect of insertion of an accessory plate above a low-power objective when the substance has a higher index than the oil. The fragments have dark borders on the sides toward the dark half of the field and a bright border on the opposite side. In Fig. 13*C* the substance has a lower index than the oil, and the dark and light borders are reversed. In monochromatic light, a transparent substance practically disappears when its index is exactly the same as that of the immersion medium.

Saylor[10] investigated the accuracy of the various immersion techniques of refractive-index measurement. He suggested modifications of the method of oblique illumination outlined above and inserted opaque stops in the lens system of the microscope so as to produce a dimly but uniformly illuminated field rather than a half-dark field. Increased accuracy of index measurement is claimed. The

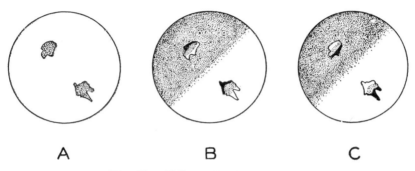

A   **B**   **C**

Fig. 13. Oblique illumination in plan.

A. Entire field illuminated.

B. Field half-darkened at accessory slot. Index of fragments higher than that of immersion medium.

C. Field half-darkened. Index of fragments lower than that of immersion medium. See text discussion.

following procedure is based on Saylor's recommendations: (1) Focus condenser in plane of preparation on microscope stage, and adjust iris diaphragm in condenser so that the angular aperture of the condenser is greater than that of the objective. (2) Remove ocular, and insert an opaque stop, such as a file card or a metal scale, into the condensing lens system at a level such that a sharp image of the edge of the opaque stop is seen on the back (upper) surface of the objective as viewed by looking down the microscope tube. Some microscopes are equipped with a swing-out opaque stop already located at the proper level. (3) Push the opaque stop into the condenser so that all but about a fifth of the back surface of the objective is darkened. (4) Replace the ocular and note a dimly but uniformly illuminated field. (5) Test a fragment of known index in a liquid

[10] C. P. Saylor, "Accuracy of Microscopical Methods for Determining Refractive Index by Immersion," *J. Research, Nat. Bur. Standards,* Vol. 15, pp. 277–294, 1935.

of known index to determine the distribution of light in the fragment under controlled conditions. Subsequent tests should be made with the same combination of lenses and opaque stop.

Saylor[11] describes an additional method, the "double-diaphragm method," in which opaque stops are placed not only in the condenser but also on the upper surface of the objective so as to cover half of the upper lens. Again the effects of oblique illumination are viewed against a uniformly illuminated background.

As in the Becke line method, color fringes may appear when a fragment is immersed in a liquid of moderate to high dispersion. For a match of the refractive indices for the colors near the middle of the spectrum the index of the fragment will be less than that of the liquid for light of shorter wave lengths and greater for light of longer wave lengths. In index measurements in oblique illumination a match for yellow wave lengths in the middle of the spectrum commonly produces a red fringe on one side of the fragment and a blue or bluish violet fringe on the opposing side. For matches in the other portions of the spectrum colors are seen that are similar to the colors in Becke lines observed with a white-light source. Again, the observer should acquaint himself with the technique by comparing substances of known refractive index with immersion media for which the dispersion curves have been carefully ascertained.

Dark-Field Immersion Method

Dodge[12] has described an immersion method for measuring refractive indices which utilizes dark-field illumination and a white-light source. In Fig. 14A a condensing lens of larger angular aperture than the objective lens illuminates a transparent object such as a crystal fragment on the microscope stage. Some of the light enters the objective, and the fragment on the stage is seen in the usual manner. Figure 14B shows the effect of insertion of an opaque disk-shaped dark-field stop below the condenser to cut out some of the light incident on the fragment. The resulting hollow cone of light is more or less reflected and refracted by the fragment so that some of the light enters the objective and reaches the eye. According to Dodge, when the fragment is immersed in a liquid of considerably different refractive index, the fragment will appear white against a dark background. If the indices of the fragment and liquid are close, the

[11] Saylor, *ibid.*

[12] N. B. Dodge, "The Dark-Field Immersion Method," *Am. Mineralogist*, Vol. 33, pp. 541–549, 1948.

fragment will appear to be illuminated by yellow light when its index is higher than that of the liquid and by blue light if its index is lower than that of the liquid. When the index of the liquid for sodium light matches that of the fragment, the fragment will be illuminated a

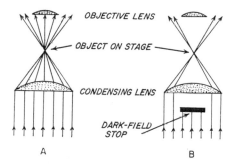

Fig. 14. Ordinary (*A*) and dark-field (*B*) methods of illumination.

purplish blue with irregular deep-red patches near the edges of the fragment. For details of the modifications of the petrographic microscope required by this method the reader should consult the original paper by Dodge.

Dispersion Methods of Index Measurement

Merwin[13] has described a procedure for the accurate determination of index of refraction by the immersion method. A grain of the substance to be measured is embedded in a liquid of a slightly higher index for sodium light. The grain is examined in monochromatic light produced by a monochromatic illuminator, and the wave length is changed until the indices of the grain and the liquid match. The grain is then embedded in a liquid of slightly lower index for sodium light, and the wave length is again varied until the indices are matched. Inasmuch as the curve showing variation of index with the wave length of light as plotted on a logarithmic scale is nearly a straight line (the dispersion curve) for most solids, the index of a substance for any wave length of light is easily determined by interpolation or extrapolation. The indices of immersion oils for the various wave lengths of light may be determined from their dispersion curves or may be measured with a refractometer at the time the grain is measured.

[13] E. Posnjak and H. E. Merwin, "The System Fe_2O_3–SO_3–H_2O," *Am. Chem. Soc. Jour.*, Vol. 44, p. 1970, 1922.

Another method, Emmons' *double variation method*,[14] utilizes the principle illustrated in Fig. 1 and measures index of refraction by embedding crystal fragments in liquids and varying both the wave length of the light source and the temperature of the liquid. A single mount may yield sufficient information to permit determination of all indices of refraction, each for any wave length of light. Emmons' method is especially versatile if used in conjunction with a universal stage modified to permit examination of liquid immersions in various positions of rotation on the microscope stage.

Method of Minimum Deviation

One of the most accurate methods for measuring the index of refraction is the *method of minimum deviation*. This method requires crystals with faces intersecting at an angle somewhat less than 90 degrees or a prism cut from the substance to be measured. Use is made of a spectrometer or a one-circle reflecting goniometer. The prism to be measured is mounted, and the angle α between the faces is determined. A monochromatic-light beam is then passed through the prism, the prism is rotated, and the refracted beam of light is followed with the telescope until it reaches the position of minimum deviation. The angle between the light in the rays in this position and the undeviated light from the source is the angle of minimum deviation δ.

Figure 15 indicates diagrammatically the measurements required in the method of minimum deviation. In Fig. 15*A* the spectrometer is used as a reflecting goniometer. The prism for which the refractive index is measured is rotated until a normal to one of its faces, N', bisects the angle between the directions of passage of light through the collimator and the telescope. In this position light passing through a slit signal in the collimator is reflected so as to be seen in the telescope. The prism is now rotated until the normal to the other face, N'', occupies the same position. Again the reflection of the slit signal from the face will be seen in the telescope. The angle through which the prism was rotated is subtracted from 180 degrees to obtain α, the prism angle. In Fig. 15*B* the angle δ is measured between the undeviated light from the collimator and the refracted light from the prism at the position of minimum deviation. The

[14] R. C. Emmons, "The Double Variation Method of Refractive Index Determination," *Am. Mineralogist,* Vol. 14, pp. 414–426, 441–461, 1929; and *The Universal Stage,* Geol. Soc. Amer., Memoir 8, 1943.

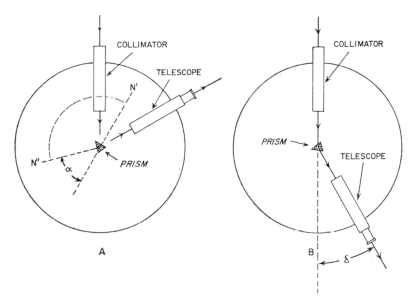

Fig. 15. Method of minimum deviation. Necessary measurements with goniometer.

refractive index of a liquid may be measured by using a hollow prism rather than a solid prism.

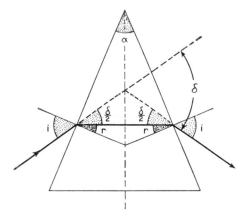

Fig. 16. Method of minimum deviation. Path followed by monochromatic light at position of minimum deviation.

Figure 16 shows in detail the passage of light through a prism in the position of minimum deviation. Note that the angle of incidence of the entering light is the same as the angle of refraction of the emergent light. Now, let n be the index of refraction of the prism; then

$$n = \frac{\sin i}{\sin r}$$

$$r = \tfrac{1}{2}\alpha \quad \text{(mutually perpendicular sides)}$$

and

$$i = r + \tfrac{1}{2}\delta$$

Therefore

$$i = \tfrac{1}{2}\alpha + \tfrac{1}{2}\delta$$

Substituting

$$n = \frac{\sin i}{\sin r} = \frac{\sin \tfrac{1}{2}(\alpha + \delta)}{\sin \tfrac{1}{2}\alpha}$$

Winchell[15] has described a useful alignment chart for calculation of refractive index from angles measured by the method of minimum deviation and the method of perpendicular incidence.

Method of Perpendicular Incidence

This method is not as widely used as the method of minimum deviation but employs the same instrument and gives results of

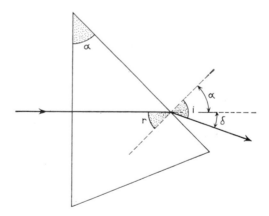

Fig. 17. Method of perpendicular incidence. Necessary measurements.

the same order of accuracy. As in the method of minimum deviation, the angle between two faces of a crystal or a cut and polished prism is used. The angle α (Fig. 17) is measured, and the prism is rotated

15 H. Winchell, "Alignment Chart for Calculation of Refractive Index from the Deviation of Light by a Prism," *Am. Mineralogist*, Vol. 36, pp. 287–290, 1951.

so that one of its faces is perpendicular to the beam of light from the collimating tube. The angular position of the refracted light passing through the telescope is determined, and the angle δ between the refracted light and the undeviated light is measured. Now

$$i = \alpha + \delta$$

and

$$r = \alpha$$

By substituting in the equation,

$$n = \frac{\sin i}{\sin r}$$

we obtain

$$n = \frac{\sin (\alpha + \delta)}{\sin \alpha}$$

It should be remembered that the angle i is the angle between the normal and the path followed by the light in air so that, although the light is refracted as it passes from the prism into air, the angle of refraction at emergence is properly designated as i.

Methods Based on Critical Angle

There are many variations of the method based on measurement of the critical angle. A few will be described here to demonstrate the principles.

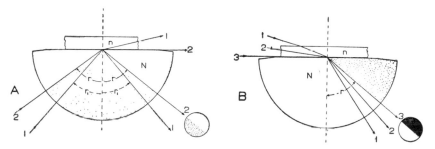

Fig. 18. Measurement of index with glass hemispheres.

A. Method of total reflection.
B. Method of grazing incidence.

The Abbe total reflectometer (Fig. 18) utilizes glass hemispheres of high index of refraction (commonly about 1.85). A flat surface of the substance of unknown index is placed on the flat surface of the hemisphere after a drop of high-index liquid has been used to remove the film of air at the contact. If this method is to be successful, the index of the unknown substance must be less than that of the hemisphere. If a source of slightly converging monochromatic light is placed below and to one side of the hemisphere, the light will pass through the hemisphere and upon striking the contact of the substance with unknown index is refracted or totally reflected, depending upon the critical angle for the hemisphere and the superimposed plate. Suppose that in Fig. 18A the critical angle is r. Light traveling along rays of angle r_1, less than r, is partly refracted and partly reflected. Light in rays of greater angle is completely reflected. The totally reflected light is more intense than that which suffers partial refraction, and a telescope lined up with the reflected light in the critical position reveals a sharp contact between a bright field and one of diminished intensity. The angle r between the reflected light in the critical position and the normal to the flat surface of the hemisphere may be measured. The index of the hemisphere is already known, so that when r is measured, the index of the unknown substance may be computed.

If a monochromatic-light source is placed above the hemisphere as in Fig. 18B, light passing the substance of smaller index n is refracted toward the normal upon entering the hemisphere. Inasmuch as the maximum angle of incidence is 90 degrees (ray 3), no light will pass through the hemisphere with an angle of refraction r greater than that of the light with an angle of incidence of 90 degrees. Accordingly, a telescope lined up with ray 3 will reveal a field which is half dark and half illuminated. The angle r, as measured, yields the index of the superimposed plate by computation.

Another method which utilizes the principles of total reflection and the critical angle employs a prism or a combination of prisms rather than a glass hemisphere. Many modern instruments are constructed with prisms instead of hemispheres.

Figure 19 is a diagrammatic cross section of a Pulfrich refractometer. In practice, if the index n of a solid is to be measured, a flat surface is placed on a face of a prism of higher index. High-index oil is used to exclude the air film. Light passing from the substance of lower index is refracted when entering the prism. No light with an angle of refraction in excess of the critical angle r can pass through the prism. Inasmuch as the angle r varies with the index of the superimposed plate, it is possible to construct an instrument which, by means of a movable telescope and a fixed calibrated scale or conversion tables, gives the index of the superimposed substance directly.

One of the most widely used and versatile refractometers is the Abbe

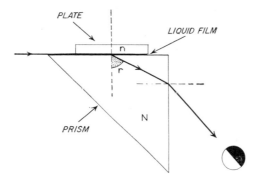

Fig. 19. Diagrammatic section of a Pulfrich refractometer.

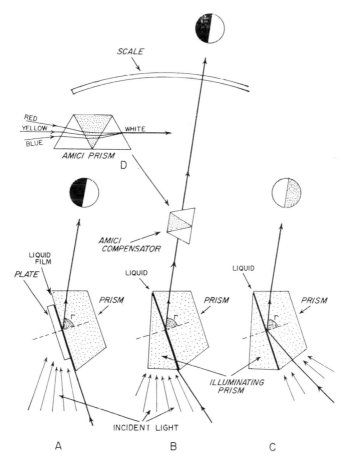

Fig. 20. Diagrammatic cross section of an Abbe refractometer.

refractometer, which is shown diagrammatically in Fig. 20. In Fig. 20*A* light is refracted into a telescope in much the same manner as in a Pulfrich refractometer, and the refractive index of a transparent plate placed on a higher-index oil film on the surface of the prism can be read directly from a calibrated scale after the telescope is rotated to a central position over the refracted light. In Fig. 20*B* the index of a liquid film between the prism and an auxiliary illuminating prism can be read by the same method. In Fig. 20*C* the light is incident in a manner different from that in Fig. 20*B*, and the telescope, as lined up with the refracted light, shows a brightly illuminated half-field opposed by a considerably dimmer half-field.

When a white-light source is used, unequal refraction of light of various wave lengths produces a spectrum. To overcome this difficulty an Amici compensating prism is placed in the tube of the telescope of most Abbe refractometers and can be rotated so as to produce a sharp contact between the dark and light halves of the field as viewed through the telescope. Commonly the Amici compensator is constructed to permit the measurement of refractive index for the *D* line of sodium with a white-light source, and, at the same time, yields data enabling calculation of the $n_F - n_C$ dispersion. Figure 20*D* shows an Amici prism constructed from flint glass (stippled) and crown glass and suggests how the prism can be used to oppose and recombine into white light the spectral colors formed in the refractometer.

To obtain greater accuracy in the measurement of the index for the *D* line of the sodium spectrum some investigators remove the Amici prism from the refractometer and use a sodium-light source rather than a white-light source.

CHAPTER 6 THE UNIAXIAL INDICATRIX

There is conflicting usage of the terms employed by various writers to describe the passage of light through anisotropic crystals. In the interests of clarity of presentation certain terms defined in Chapter 2 are defined again, but with the emphasis placed on the passage of light through optically anisotropic crystals rather than through optically isotropic substances. A *light wave* is a single pulse of energy and, in a plane-polarized wave, is a combination of forward motion and the simple-harmonic vibration specified for a phase change of 0 to 360 degrees (0 to 2π radians). A *ray* is the path followed by a wave or a succession of waves in traveling from one point to another in a medium. A succession of waves moving along a ray constitutes a *wave train*. The *wave front* is a surface passing through all points in phase in a family of waves. The *wave front normal,* or, more briefly, the *wave normal,* is perpendicular to the wave front and, at the same time, according to the electromagnetic wave theory, perpendicular to the direction of vibration of the light vectors in the light waves forming a wave front. The *ray velocity* is the velocity of movement of a light wave along a ray, as opposed to the velocity of movement of a wave front in the direction of the wave normal. The confusing but widespread use of the term *wave* to describe the sum of all energy advancing in a wave front is specifically avoided in the following treatment. Advance of a wave front is regarded as a group phenomenon involving the in-phase advance of the total energy in a family of electromagnetic waves.

In an optically isotropic medium, light waves of the same frequency (or wave length) travel with the same velocity in all directions; moreover, the light waves, except insofar as they are partially polarized by reflection and refraction, are not constrained to vibrate in any particular direction, and, for most purposes, the waves may be considered as being essentially nonpolarized. However, in crystals in the tetragonal and hexagonal systems, light waves are constrained to vibrate in two mutually perpendicular planes in most directions of transmission, and the waves are plane polarized. There is one direction in tetragonal and hexagonal crystals in which all light waves of a particular frequency (or wave length) travel with the same velocity. This direction, which is parallel to the *c* crystallographic axis, is called the optic axis, and, inasmuch as there is only one such direction, such crystals are described as *uniaxial*.

For each color of light, uniaxial crystals have *two principal indices of refraction,* from which it follows that light of a particular color traveling in any direction except the direction of the optic axis consists of two sets of wave trains with different velocities but the same frequency. The change of refractive index with the direction of light propagation or vibration may be visualized by use of a *uniaxial indicatrix,* a three-dimensional geometric figure showing the variation of the indices of refraction of a crystal for light waves in their *directions of vibration.* Each radius vector represents a vibration direction whose length measures the index of refraction of the crystal for waves vibrating parallel to the direction.

Geometric Representation of Index Variation— The Indicatrix

Figure 1 shows indicatrices for positive and negative uniaxial crystals. Figure 1*A* is a prolate spheroid of revolution constructed so that its semimajor and semiminor axes are proportional, respectively, to the maximum and minimum refractive indices of a uniaxial positive crystal. Figure 1*B* portrays a negative uniaxial indicatrix: an oblate spheroid of revolution. Any section passing through and including the optic axis of either indicatrix is an ellipse and is called a *principal section.* Equatorial sections at right angles to the optic axes are circles.

If nonpolarized light is normally incident on a crystal plate cut perpendicular to the optic axis, the light entering the crystal is not refracted and passes through without becoming polarized. This light can be thought of as vibrating within the crystal in all directions parallel to the radii of the circular equatorial section of the indicatrix. In the direction of the optic axis, and in this direction only, all light of a particular color travels through the crystal as if the crystal were optically isotropic. Moreover, for light traveling in any direction

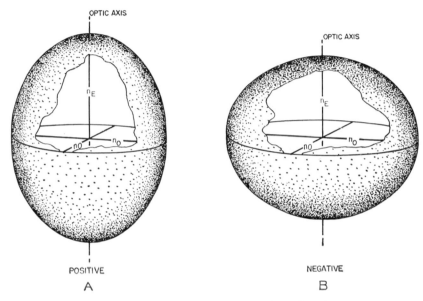

Fig. 1. Positive and negative uniaxial indicatrices.

whatsoever through the crystal and vibrating parallel to a radius of the equatorial section, the crystal has the same refractive index, and the light has a constant velocity. Accordingly, waves which vibrate parallel to the radii of the circular equatorial section (perpendicular to the optic axis) are referred to as *ordinary* or *O waves;* the refractive index of the crystal for these waves is described as the *index for the ordinary waves* and is here designated as n_O.

For waves vibrating in a plane including the optic axis (a principal section) the crystal has refractive indices which depend on the direction of vibration of the waves. Waves vibrating in the principal section are called *extraordinary* or *E waves*. The index of the crystal for waves vibrating parallel to the optic axis in a principal section is at a maximum or minimum, depending upon whether the crystal is positive or negative. The index of the crystal for such waves is designated as n_E. For waves vibrating in a principal section and traveling in a random direction the crystal has a refractive index somewhere between n_O and n_E, the exact index being a function of the direction of vibration and the configuration of the indicatrix. The *refractive index* of the crystal for such waves is designated as n_E'.

The indicatrix gives the values for the refractive indices of the crystal for all waves in their direction of vibration for only *one* color (wave length) of incident light. For each color of the spectrum there is, for each substance, a characteristic indicatrix. In general, n_O and n_E increase as the wave length of the color decreases, but not at the same rate. Exceptions are noted in some substances that show strong differential absorption of the transmitted light.

The use of n_O and n_E to designate the principal refractive indices may cause some confusion because of various usages by different writers. No confusion should result if the equivalent usage shown in the accompanying table is kept in mind.

Various Designations of Principal Refractive Indices of Uniaxial Crystals

Index for ordinary waves	n_O	N_O	O	ω	n_ω	N_ω
Principal index for extraordinary waves	n_E	N_E	E	ϵ	n_ϵ	N_ϵ

From Figs. 1A and 1B it is seen that in positive uniaxial crystals $n_E > n_O$, and in negative crystals $n_E < n_O$. As n_E approaches n_O, the indicatrix approaches the form of a sphere, and, when n_E finally equals n_O, the crystal becomes isotropic.

Optical Orientation of Uniaxial Crystals

Symmetry requirements of tetragonal and hexagonal crystals are such that the optic axis must parallel the c crystallographic axis. Any other orientation would result in disharmony of the symmetry elements of indicatrix and crystal.

Figures 2 and 3 show the orientations of the indicatrices in quartz and calcite. Visualization of these relationships is useful in studying the optics of uniaxial crystals, for similar relationships exist in all uniaxial crystals.

The direction of the c axis of a crystal or fragment under the microscope is determined when the vibration direction corresponding to the n_E index is found. Methods for measuring n_O and n_E are discussed in a subsequent chapter.

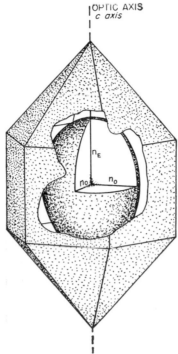

Fig. 2. Uniaxial positive crystal (quartz) showing orientation of the indicatrix. Rotatory polarization disregarded.

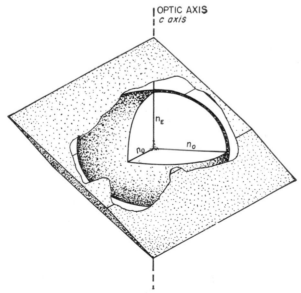

Fig. 3. Uniaxial negative crystal (calcite) showing orientation of the indicatrix.

Dispersion in Uniaxial Crystals

Figure 4 shows the dispersion curves for quartz plotted on a Hartmann net and indicates how n_O and n_E vary with the wave length of light in a particular uniaxial crystal. Wave lengths are plotted on a logarithmic scale to yield straighter curves than would be obtained

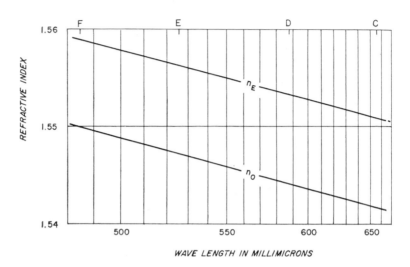

Fig. 4. Dispersion curves for quartz.

with an arithmetic scale. The dispersion curves are not parallel, and the extent of departure from parallelism differs with different substances. The difference between n_O and n_E for a particular color is the *birefringence* for that color. Unless otherwise specified the birefringence usually is expressed as the numerical difference between the refractive indices of a crystal for the D line (589.3 mμ) of sodium light.

Principal Sections of the Uniaxial Indicatrix

Figure 5 shows principal sections of a uniaxial positive indicatrix for which $n_O = 1.5$ and $n_E = 2.0$. In Fig. 5A nonpolarized monochromatic light is normally incident at O and O' on a crystal plate cut parallel to the optic axis (c axis). The incident light, as can be demonstrated by experiment, is resolved into two components in which the light waves vibrate in mutually perpendicular planes. The light

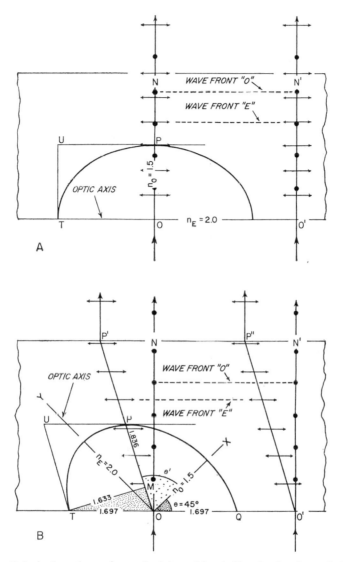

Fig. 5. Principal sections of a uniaxial positive indicatrix showing relationships between rays and wave normals.

A. Nonpolarized light normally incident on a section of a uniaxial positive crystal. Section cut parallel to optic axis.

B. Nonpolarized light normally incident on a section of a uniaxial crystal. Section inclined to optic axis.

waves in one component (the extraordinary component) vibrate in the principal section (the plane of the drawing) and travel through the crystal in the direction of the wave normal, ON. For this component the crystal has a refractive index of n_E, and the waves and the wave fronts travel through the crystal with a velocity proportional to $1/n_E$. Light waves in the other component, the ordinary component, vibrate perpendicular to the principal section and parallel to a radius of the circular equatorial section of the indicatrix. For this component the crystal has a refractive index of n_O, and both the waves and the wave fronts have a velocity in the direction of the wave normal proportional to $1/n_O$. In Fig. 5A the relative velocities and directions of vibration of the O and E waves are indicated by proportionally spaced dots and arrows in the wave trains. Certain wave fronts for both components also are indicated. ON and ON' are the directions of both the rays and the wave normals, and it may be said that the rays and the wave normals coincide.

The amplitude of the light vector shown for the E component, vibrating in the principal section and parallel to the optic axis, is indicated arbitrarily by the lengths of the arrows in Fig. 5. The dimension of the indicatrix parallel to the vibration direction bears no direct relationship to the amplitudes of the light vectors. Instead, the amplitudes depend on the amplitude of the incident light and the manner in which it is resolved by the crystal.

The equation for the uniaxial indicatrix is

$$\frac{x^2 + z^2}{(n_O)^2} + \frac{y^2}{(n_E)^2} = 1$$

and the equation for the ellipse in a principal section is

$$\frac{x^2}{(n_O)^2} + \frac{y^2}{(n_E)^2} = 1$$

where x and y are the coordinates for any point on the ellipse; by convention x is measured in a direction normal to the optic axis, and y is parallel to the optic axis.

The equation for the ellipse in the principal section of the indicatrix also can be expressed in polar coordinates, as

$$r^2 = \frac{(n_O)^2 (n_E)^2}{(n_O)^2 \sin^2 \theta + (n_E)^2 \cos^2 \theta}$$

where r is a radius vector measured from the center of the ellipse to some point on the ellipse and θ (theta) is the angle between the radius vector and a reference axis, the x axis of coordinates. In the following discussions use will be made of the polar-coordinate equation for the indicatrix in principal section to analyze certain conditions in which light waves do not pass through the crystal in the direction of the optic axis or in a direction normal to the optic axis.

In Fig. 5B nonpolarized monochromatic light is normally incident on a crystal plate which, in the principal section, makes an angle of θ (theta) with the x coordinate axis. The value of θ was arbitrarily set at 45 degrees. The incident light is resolved into two components vibrating in mutually perpendicular planes, and, as in Fig. 5A, the waves for the ordinary component are not refracted and pass through the crystal in the direction of the normal to the wave front with a velocity proportional to $1/n_o$. The waves vibrating in the principal section (the extraordinary waves) follow the rays OP' and O'P'', and, upon leaving the crystal plate are refracted so as to move in a direction parallel to that of the incident light. OP' is obtained by drawing a line from O through P, the point of tangency with the ellipse of a line drawn parallel to TQ. The light vectors of the extraordinary waves vibrate parallel to the wave front but obliquely to the direction of movement of the individual waves (the ray direction), and the direction of the rays for the extraordinary component does not coincide with the direction of the normal to the associated wave front. The velocity of movement of the wave front in the direction of its normal is less than the velocity of movement of the individual waves in the direction of the rays, and a distinction can be made between *wave-normal velocity* (wave-front-normal velocity) and *ray velocity*. These *velocities* are the same only when the wave-normal directions are the same as the ray directions as in Fig. 5A.

The velocity of a wave as it moves along the ray OP' in Fig. 5B is proportional to $1/TM$, where TM is obtained by dropping a perpendicular from T to the ray OP'. Calculation of the ray velocity and the velocity of the wave front in the direction of the wave normal is made with the aid of the equation for the ellipse expressed in polar coordinates. Substitution of the values shown in Fig. 5B and a value of 45 degrees for θ yields a refractive index for the crystal of 1.697 for the waves vibrating in the principal section and in the wave front. The velocity of movement of the wave front in the direction of its normal, ON is proportional to $1/1.697$, that is, proportional to $1/OT$. The tangent, UP, is parallel to the wave fronts for the waves vibrating in the principal section. Another radius of the ellipse, OP, is conjugate to the radius OT and fulfills the specification that one radius is conjugate to a second radius if the first radius is parallel to the tangent to the ellipse at the end of the second radius. From the geometry of the ellipse it is known that the area enclosed by conjugate radii and their associated tangents is constant. In Fig. 5A n_O and n_E are conjugate radii, and the enclosed area is $n_O \cdot n_E = 3.0$. In Fig. 5B parallelogram $UTOP$ encloses the same area. The radius OP has a dimension which can be obtained from the equation[1]

$$(r_2)^2 = (n_O)^2 + (n_E)^2 - (r_1)^2$$

where r_2 is the length of a radius that is conjugate to the reference radius, r_1. Computation yields a value of 1.836 for OP. Because the area of a parallelogram is the product of the base by the altitude, dividing the area of the parallelogram by 1.836 yields a value of 1.633 for TM. By construction TM is normal to the ray OP', along which light waves vibrating in the principal section are propagated, and is the *ray index of refraction* of the crystal for this energy. The velocity of the light waves moving along OP' is proportional to $1/TM = 1/1.633$, and in Fig. 5B the arrows in the wave trains are spaced accordingly. The ray index has not been measured experimentally for optically anisotropic crystals and is obtained only by calculation.

The angle θ^1, between OP' and the same reference axis that was used to measure off θ in Fig. 5B (the x axis), can be calculated from the equation[2]

$$\tan \theta^1 = - \frac{(n_E)^2}{(n_O)^2} \cot \theta$$

Accordingly, the direction of the ray OP' relative to the direction of vibration of the light vector can be calculated rather than being obtained by the graphical method outlined above.

Ray-Velocity Surfaces

Ray-velocity surfaces are geometrically and mathematically related to the indicatrix and permit visualization of the velocities of propagation of the light energy in waves along rays in all directions in a crystal. Rays along which ordinary waves are transmitted may be designated as *ordinary rays*. Similarly, *extraordinary rays* are the paths followed by extraordinary waves.

Figure 6 portrays the relationship between the indicatrix and the ray-velocity surfaces in a negative crystal. Light energy following any

---

[1] The derivation of this equation was supplied to the writer by C. A. Hutchinson of the Department of Applied Mathematics, University of Colorado.

[2] C. A. Hutchinson, *Idem*.

ray *OP* consists of two wave trains, one vibrating in the principal section (plane of drawing) and containing extraordinary waves and the other perpendicular to the principal section and containing ordinary waves. In negative crystals, a wave vibrating in the principal section

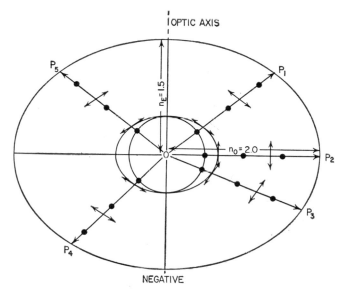

Fig. 6. Principal section of negative uniaxial indicatrix showing relationship of ray-velocity surfaces to indicatrix.

has a greater velocity than the component vibrating normal to it, as is shown by the spacing of the dots and arrows in the wave trains in the diagram. An ordinary wave traveling along ray OP_1, for example, in a given instant will move a distance proportional to $1/n_0$. Along the other paths, OP_2, OP_3, etc., an ordinary wave moves the same distance in the same instant. In two dimensions the velocity of the ordinary waves moving along all the rays is represented by a circle with its center at O. In three dimensions the velocity is represented by a sphere with its center at O.

The velocity of an extraordinary wave traveling along a ray is inversely proportional to the ray index of refraction, and can be obtained by the kind of calculations indicated for Fig. 5B. An extraordinary wave, in negative crystals, moves with maximum velocity in a direction perpendicular to the optic axis (velocity proportional to $1/n_E$). This relationship is reversed in positive crystals. The variation in the velocities of waves moving along the extraordinary rays

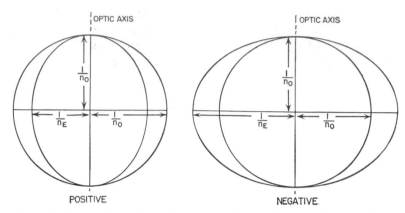

Fig. 7. Principal sections of positive and negative ray-velocity surfaces.

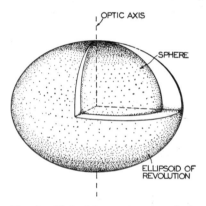

Fig. 8. Uniaxial negative ray-velocity surface sectioned to show sphere within an ellipsoid of revolution.

is represented in cross section by an ellipse and in three dimensions by an ellipsoid of revolution.

Figure 7 shows principal sections of ray-velocity surfaces of positive and negative crystals. Sections drawn normal to the optic axis consist of two concentric circles.

To assist in the visualization of the ray-velocity surfaces in three dimensions, Fig. 8 is useful. The drawing depicts the ray-velocity surface for a negative crystal sectioned so as to show the spherical surface for the ordinary rays enclosed by an oblate ellipsoid of revolution representing the velocities of light waves traveling along extraordinary rays.

Positive ray-velocity surfaces in three dimensions consist of a prolate spheroid of revolution enclosed by a sphere.

The equation for the ellipsoid in the two-shelled ray-velocity surface in three dimensions is

$$\frac{x^2 + z^2}{(1/n_E)^2} + \frac{y^2}{(1/n_O)^2} = 1$$

and for the ellipse in the principal section

$$\frac{x^2}{(1/n_E)^2} + \frac{y^2}{(1/n_O)^2} = 1$$

The ellipsoid and the elliptical section of the ray-velocity surface have the same form as the indicatrix and the elliptical principal section from which they are derived but have shorter semimajor and semiminor axes, a statement that can be verified by constructions based on arbitrarily assigned values for n_O and n_E. Therefore, wave fronts obtained from constructions employing ray-velocity surfaces must be parallel to wave fronts similarly obtained from indicatrices.

Huygenian Constructions

Ray-velocity surfaces serve one of their most useful functions in the geometric study of the passage of light through crystals. By using Huygenian constructions it is possible to trace the paths of refracted polarized light waves and wave fronts through a crystal for light of any angle of incidence. Huygenian constructions are usually drawn in planes of optical symmetry, because in these planes the paths followed by the light may be represented graphically in two dimensions. Huygenian constructions not in a plane of symmetry require difficultly constructed three-dimensional drawings.

Figure 9 indicates the use of Huygenian constructions in two examples. As a basis for construction it is assumed that the ray-velocity surfaces are derived from a uniaxial positive indicatrix in which $n_O = 1.5$ and $n_E = 2.0$. The drawings are made in a principal section, and the optic axis is parallel to the surface of a crystal plate on which the light is incident. In Fig. 9A normally incident nonpolarized light upon entering the crystal is resolved into two components vibrating in mutually perpendicular planes. One component, the E component, contains waves vibrating in the principal section that pass through the crystal with a velocity proportional to $1/n_E = 1/2.0$. The other component, the O component, contains waves vibrating in a plane perpendicular to the plane of the drawing and having a velocity proportional to $1/n_O = 1/1.5$. The rays and the wave normals coincide, and the ray velocities are the same as the wave-normal velocities.

Figure 9B shows monochromatic light falling with inclined incidence on the surface of the crystal plate and indicates the constructions necessary for the calculation of the angles of refraction of the waves traveling along the O and E rays and the angle of refraction of the wave normal for the E component. For simplicity in calculation and in order to describe a specific example the angle of incidence is assumed to be 45 degrees. Unit velocity in air is assumed to be proportional to the distance AO', and the ray-velocity surfaces about O are constructed with proportional dimensions. To obtain the wave fronts for the O and E components tangents are drawn from O' to the

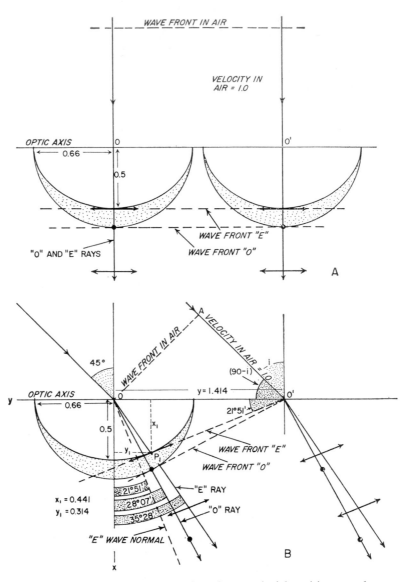

Fig. 9. Huygenian constructions for a uniaxial positive crystal.

A. Light falling with normal incidence on a crystal plate.
B. Light falling with inclined incidence on a crystal plate.

circle and the ellipse. The O ray is located by drawing a line from the point of incidence, O, through the point of tangency of the appropriate wave front with the circle. The E ray is constructed by drawing a line through the point of tangency of the wave front for the E component with the ellipse. The point of tangency in Fig. 9B is P_1. The light waves for the E component vibrate in the principal section and parallel to the wave front for the E component. The wave normal for the E component is drawn perpendicular to the E wave front and indicates the direction that the E wave front travels through the crystal.

The angles of refraction of the rays and the wave normal can be calculated from the given data. The angle of refraction for the O ray, which coincides with the O wave normal, is obtained by substitution in the equation for Snell's law,

$$n_O = \frac{\sin i}{\sin r}$$

and is calculated to be $28°\ 07'$. Determination of the angle between the surface of incidence and the E wave front requires use of the equation for the tangent to an ellipse, which is

$$\frac{x_1 x}{(1/n_E)^2} + \frac{y_1 y}{(1/n_O)^2} = 1$$

where x_1 and y_1 are the coordinates for the point P_1. For $x = 0$ the above equation reduces to

$$\frac{y_1 y}{(1/n_O)^2} = 1$$

The value of y when $x = 0$ can be obtained from the triangle OAO', and, in this instance, is 1.414. Substitution yields a value of 0.314 for y_1. By using the equation for the elliptical section of the ray-velocity surfaces

$$\frac{(x_1)^2}{(1/n_E)^2} + \frac{(y_1)^2}{(1/n_O)^2} = 1$$

x_1 is determined to be 0.441.

Using the values for x_1, y_1, and y, the angle between the surface of incidence and the E wave front is determined to be $21°\ 51'$, an angle equal to the angle of refraction of the wave normal for the E component. By substituting the values for x_1 and y_1 the angle of refraction of the E ray is calculated to be $35°\ 28'$. The angle between the surface of incidence and the E wave front can be used in the equation of the principal section of the indicatrix as it is expressed in polar coordinates and indicates the refractive index of the crystal for light in the E component for a particular angle of incidence. In the example calculated the index for the E waves is 1.903.

Similar calculations may be used for any angle of incidence and for the ray-velocity surfaces derived from any uniaxial indicatrix of

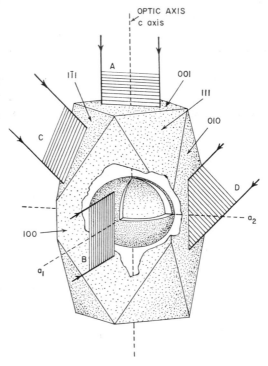

Fig. 10. Tetragonal crystal showing ray-velocity surfaces. Hatched planes indicate sections for Huygenian constructions in Fig. 11.

arbitrarily assigned dimensions. Not shown in Fig. 9 is the light as it leaves the crystal plate. However, if the lower and upper surfaces of the plate are parallel, the waves are refracted upon leaving so as to travel in a direction parallel to that of the incident light. Depending on the angle of incidence, the thickness of the crystal plate, and the dimensions of the indicatrix (and the ray-velocity surfaces), a certain path difference is produced between the waves emerging from the crystal. This path difference can be calculated as will be shown in a later section of the book.

Figure 10 illustrates a uniaxial negative crystal in which the ray-velocity surfaces are derived from an indicatrix with $n_o = 2.0$ and

$n_E = 1.5$. The ray-velocity surfaces are sectioned to show a sphere contained by an ellipsoid of revolution. Light is assumed to be incident on several faces of the crystal in planes which include the principal sections of the ray-velocity surfaces. Figure 11 shows Huygenian constructions for the light incident on the several crystal faces indicated in Fig. 10.

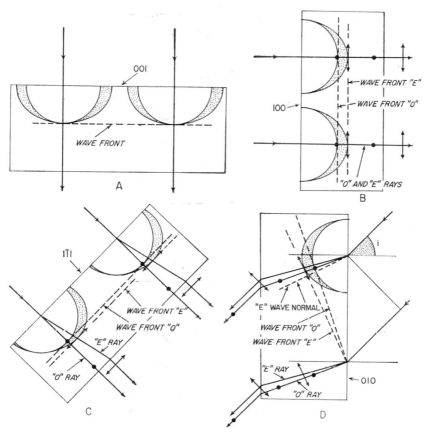

Fig. 11. Huygenian constructions for crystal shown in Fig. 10.

The Calcite Experiment

Experimental proof of double refraction is easily demonstrated with a clear calcite cleavage rhomb. If a calcite rhomb is placed over a dot on a piece of paper or a pinhole source of light, two dots are seen through the calcite, one at a shallower depth than the other. When the rhomb is rotated, one dot revolves about the other, as is shown in Fig. 12*A*. Figure 12*B* shows in cross section the apparent depth of each dot. Light waves moving along the rays for the stationary dot (1) pass through the calcite as if it were ordinary glass, but light waves following the rays for the other dot (2) act in an extraordinary manner.

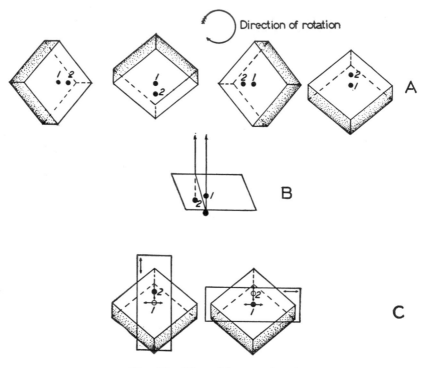

Fig. 12. The calcite experiment.

It can be demonstrated that the light waves traveling the two paths shown in Fig. 12*B* vibrate in mutually perpendicular planes by superimposing a polaroid plate, a Nicol prism, or a tourmaline plate over the rhomb. These devices permit light waves that vibrate in one plane only to pass through. If the plane of vibration of the superimposed plate parallels a principal optical section of the calcite the revolving dot will be seen, but the other dot is extinguished. From this experiment it is known that the refracted waves are the extraordinary waves. If the plane of vibration of the superimposed plate is perpendicular to the principal section of the calcite, only the stationary dot is seen. These experiments are indicated diagrammatically in Fig. 12*C*.

The behavior of light passing through calcite is explained with the aid of Fig. 13, which shows the indicatrix for sodium light and the derived ray-velocity surfaces drawn to scale in a principal section of a calcite cleavage rhomb. The angle between the c crystallographic axis and a cleavage surface on which the rhomb rests is 45° 24′, and the optic axis has been drawn so as to be parallel to the c axis. Non-

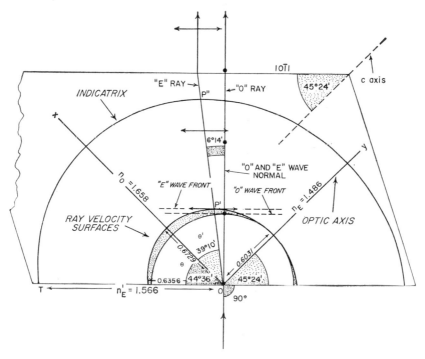

Fig. 13. Passage of light through calcite in a principal section.

polarized light from a dot on a piece of paper or from a pinhole opening at O is normally incident on the lower surface of the rhomb and, upon entering the rhomb, is resolved into two components the waves in which vibrate in mutually perpendicular planes. The light waves in the O component travel through the rhomb without being refracted and with a velocity proportional to $1/n_0$ and, for the O component, the directions of the rays and wave normal coincide. The velocity of the waves in the O component is indicated by the spacing of the solid circles in the wave train along the O ray.

The E component, in which the waves vibrate in the principal section, is refracted. The light waves travel along the E ray, and, upon emergence, are again refracted so as to be parallel to the incident light, and an observer looking directly down on the cleavage rhomb sees the image of the dot for the E component displaced relative to the image produced by the O component. The light waves traveling along the E ray do not vibrate at right angles to the ray but parallel to the E wave front and normal to the wave normal for the E component. The angle of refraction of the waves following the E ray can be calculated by considering the angular relationships and the dimensions of either the indicatrix or the ray-velocity surfaces, but only the calculations based on the indicatrix will be shown here. In Fig. 13 OT and OP'' are conjugate radii of the elliptical section of the indicatrix. The angle between the x axis of the indicatrix and OT, parallel to the surface of the cleavage, is θ, in this instance 44° 36′. The angle between the x axis and OP'', the radius conjugate to OT, is θ' and can be obtained by substitution in the formula

$$\tan \theta' = -\frac{(n_E)^2}{(n_O)^2} \cot \theta$$

and turns out to be 39° 10′. The angle between the E ray and the normal to the surface of the rhomb is $90 - (\theta + \theta') = 6° 14′$. If the thickness of the calcite cleavage rhomb through which a dot is observed from directly above is measured, it can be shown that the dot for the E component is displaced with respect to the dot for the O component by an amount depending on this angle. The horizontal displacement, h, equals $d \cdot \tan 6° 14′$, where d is the measured thickness.

Substitution of the values for θ, n_O, and n_E in the formula

$$(OT)^2 = (n_E')^2 = \frac{(n_O)^2 (n_E)^2}{(n_O)^2 \sin^2 \theta + (n_E)^2 \cos^2 \theta}$$

yields a value of 1.566 for n_E', the refractive index of the crystal for light vertically incident on the cleavage rhomb and vibrating in the principal section.

The apparent difference in the depths of the images of the dots as viewed from directly above the rhomb can be explained by analogy with optically isotropic substances. If two plates of glass of identical thickness but with different refractive indices are placed over separate dots on a piece of paper and viewed from above, the image of the dot in the plate with the higher index appears at a shallower depth than the image of the dot in the plate with the lower index. In calcite the refractive index of the crystal for the O component is 1.658. For light normally incident on a cleavage face and vibrating in a principal section the calcite has a refractive index of 1.566, and, as would be expected, the image of the dot for the *O* component appears to be at a shallower depth than the image for the *E* component.

Wave-Normal-Velocity Surfaces

Consideration of the passage of light through uniaxial crystals in terms of the indicatrix and the ray-velocity surfaces is entirely adequate for the solution of most problems of crystal optics. The litera-

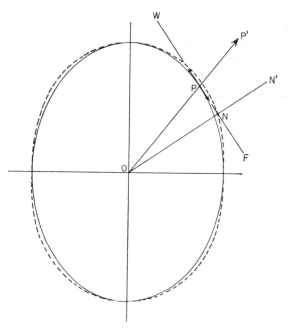

Fig. 14. Relationship of wave-normal velocity (wave-front-normal velocity) to ray-velocity surface.

ture on optical crystallography contains many references to "wave surfaces," and in many instances the "wave surfaces" are defined in the same manner that "ray-velocity surfaces" are defined in this book. A difficult concept to grasp is the fact that, in most directions in uniaxial (and biaxial) crystals, the direction of propagation of light waves along an extraordinary ray does not coincide with the direction of the associated wave normal. In Fig. 14 a principal section of a ray-velocity surface (solid line) for the extraordinary component of light transmitted by a uniaxial crystal is shown. *OP'* is a ray, and the light energy transmitted along the ray vibrates in the principal section and parallel to the wave front, *WF*. The wave front corresponding to the particular direction of ray *OP′* moves in the direction of the normal to the wave front, *ON′*, and while a light wave moves along *OP′* from *O* to *P* the wave front advances from *O* to *N*. The distance *ON* measures the *wave-normal velocity* (wave-front-normal velocity). Determination of wave front velocities in the directions of the wave normals for all possible rays yields an ovaloid (dashed line) outside of the ray-velocity ellipse and, in three dimensions, an ovaloid of revolution whose axis coincides with the optic axis. For the ordinary waves similar constructions yield, in three dimensions, a sphere which coincides with the spherical ray-velocity surface for the ordinary waves. The ovaloid of revolution and the sphere showing the wave-front velocities in all directions in three dimensions are designated either as *wave-normal-velocity surfaces* or, more precisely, *wave-front-normal-velocity surfaces.*

CHAPTER 7 POLARIZED LIGHT

Ordinary light waves in isotropic media, according to the electromagnetic theory, can be considered as vibrating in all directions at right angles to the direction of propagation. If only the electric (light) vector is considered, the oscillations at any particular instant lie in a plane normal to the direction of propagation, that is, in the wave front. If ordinary light is constrained to vibrate systematically in the wave front, the light is said to be polarized. Light vibrating in a line in a plane at right angles to the direction of propagation is said to be *plane polarized* or *linearly polarized*. If the motion of the electric vector describes a circle as projected into a plane at right angles to the direction of propagation, the light is described as *circularly polarized*. Finally, an elliptical motion characterizes *elliptically polarized light*.

There are several methods for producing plane-polarized light. Polarizing microscopes generally utilize devices that produce plane-polarized light by double refraction or by differential absorption. Plane-polarized light also is produced by reflection from smooth surfaces and by scattering of light by extremely small particles.

There is much confusion regarding the correct definition of the expression *plane of polarization* as applied to plane-polarized light. Various definitions that may be encountered in the older and newer literature indicate (1) that the plane of polarization is the plane in which, at any instant, both the electric and magnetic vectors vibrate, (2) that the plane of polarization is the plane in which the magnetic vector vibrates and is perpendicular to the plane including the electric vector, and (3) that the plane of polarization is the plane including the electric vector and the direction of propagation. In all these definitions there is one point of agreement: plane-polarized light, in one respect or another, vibrates in a plane. To avoid confusion it seems necessary to avoid the expression *plane of polarization* and to refer, instead, to the *plane of vibration*. The *plane of vibration* is the plane including the direction of propagation (the ray) and the direction of oscillation or vibration of the electric vector, the electric vector being specified because it is the vector that apparently produces observable optical effects.

Plane-Polarized Light from Doubly Refracting Crystals

Nonpolarized light entering an optically inactive anisotropic crystal so as to pass through the crystal in any direction except that of an

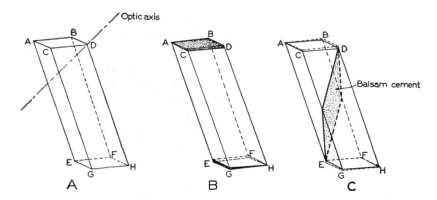

Fig. 1. Steps in construction of simple Nicol prism.

A. Calcite cleavage rhomb.
B. Cleavage rhomb showing portion ground away (stippled).
C. Cut and recemented rhomb, completed prism.

optic axis is resolved into two components, each plane polarized. The planes of vibration of the two components are mutually perpendicular, but the direction of vibration may or may not be perpendicular to the direction of transmission of the light waves along the rays.

Strong double refraction of light by calcite has led to its use in the construction of polarizing prisms. The construction of the *Nicol prism,* the first type to be used in petrographic microscopes, is indicated in Fig. 1. A flawless piece of clear calcite, "Iceland spar," is split to produce an elongated cleavage rhomb about three times as long as it is broad (Fig. 1*A*). The end faces, which naturally meet the edges *AE* and *DH* at angles of 70° 53′, are ground so that the angles become 68 degrees (Fig. 1*B*). The calcite is then sawed diagonally, as in Fig. 1*C*, at right angles to the ground and polished end faces. The halves are cemented together with balsam and the sides of the prism are covered with an opaque, light-absorbing coating.

The passage of light through a Nicol prism, or "Nicol," is indicated diagrammatically in Fig. 2, a cross section. Light moving along the ray, *MN*, in air upon striking the lower surface of the prism is doubly refracted into two components which vibrate in mutually perpendicular planes. Inasmuch as the index of refraction of calcite for the ordinary component is 1.658 and the index of the balsam film is about 1.54, the ordinary component *NOP* is totally reflected at the contact of the calcite with the balsam film and passes into the walls of the prism, where the light is absorbed. The index, n_E, of calcite is 1.486. It so happens that for the extraordinary waves, traveling

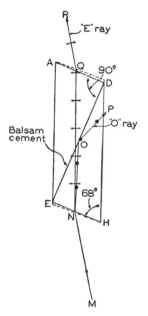

Fig. 2. Cross section of Nicol prism, showing paths of transmitted light.

parallel or nearly parallel to the long direction of the prism, the crystal has a refractive index in the neighborhood of 1.54, the index of balsam. Therefore, the component containing the extraordinary waves travels directly through the balsam film and emerges from the upper surface of the prism as plane-polarized light vibrating in a principal section.

Since the Nicol prism was invented, many other types of polarizing calcite prisms have been constructed. In some of the more modern calcite prisms the effective angle between the extreme rays of the transmitted light is considerably greater than in the Nicol prism, and more light passes through the microscope than when a Nicol prism is used.

Plane-Polarized Light by Differential Absorption

Some anisotropic substances, such as tourmaline, absorb certain transmitted light waves vibrating in one direction much more strongly than the light waves vibrating in another direction. Nonpolarized light incident on tourmaline in a direction normal to the optic axis is resolved into two components, one in which the waves vibrate in the principal section (the E component) and the other in which the waves vibrate in a plane perpendicular to the principal section (the O component). Waves for certain colors in the O component are strongly absorbed, and the emergent waves for these colors have only very small amplitudes compared to the incident waves. Waves in the E component are absorbed somewhat, but much less than for the O component, and, as a result, most of the transmitted light consists of plane-polarized light waves of relatively large amplitude that vibrate in a plane which includes the c crystallographic axis of the tourmaline.

The absorption of light energy transmitted by a substance is expressed by either of the following equations:

$$I_x = q^x I_0$$

or

$$I_x = I_0 e^{-\alpha x}$$

where I_x is the intensity of the light energy at a distance x from the point of incidence, q is the fraction of light energy transmitted through some arbitrarily measured thickness and is the *transmission coefficient,* and I_0 is the intensity of light energy entering a substance. The constant α (alpha) in the second equation is the *absorption coefficient* and is the intensity decrease per unit thickness when the thickness is very small. In Fig. 3A the first equation was used and q values of 0.9 and 0.5 were selected arbitrarily to obtain the curves. In both curves the intensities are plotted against distance, and the intensity, I_0, of the incident light energy entering the substance is assumed to be unity. A q value of 0.9 might be assumed to correspond to the transmission coefficient for the E component of tourmaline, and a q of 0.5 might define the transmission coefficient for the O component.

The amplitude of light varies directly as the square root of the intensity, or, stated another way, the intensity varies as the square of the amplitude. The square roots of the intensities determined for Fig. 3A were computed to obtain the amplitudes of the waves in Fig. 3B. Note that the amplitude for the wave corresponding to a q of 0.5

decreases much more rapidly as a function of distance than the ampli tude for the wave with a q value of 0.9.

The drawings in Fig. 3 are for monochromatic light. The absorption of white light is a very complex process and cannot be shown

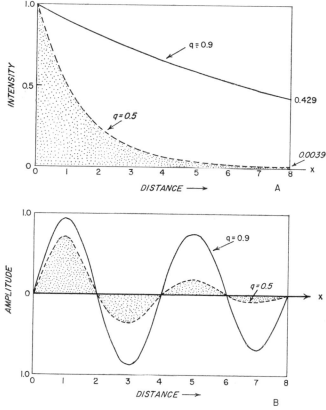

Fig. 3. Change in (A) intensity and (B) wave amplitude for transmitted light as a function of different transmission coefficients.

by a simple diagram. In tourmaline practically all colors for the O component are strongly absorbed, and most of the colors for the E component are transmitted, but with reduced intensity. Selective absorption of colors for certain portions of the spectrum for white light yields colored transmitted light, and many substances that are strongly absorbing are also strongly colored.

Polaroid, a manufactured substance widely used in sun glasses and optical instruments, owes its ability to produce essentially plane-polarized light to strong differential absorption of transmitted light.

Plane-Polarized Light by Reflection

Light is partly polarized by reflection; the amount of polarization is a function of the angle of incidence of the light, the index of refraction of the reflecting substance, and the quality of the reflecting surface. In Fig. 4, suppose that light is incident at an angle of i on

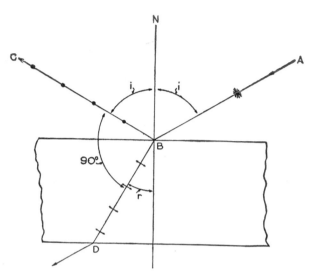

Fig. 4. Polarization of light by reflection and refraction. Brewster's law.

the reflecting surface of a plate of a substance. Part of the light is reflected through an angle equal to i, and part is refracted through an angle r. It has been proved experimentally that the reflected light is plane polarized most efficiently when the angle between the reflected and refracted light is 90 degrees (Brewster's law).

When this condition obtains,

$$n = \frac{\sin i}{\sin r} = \frac{\sin i}{\sin (90 - i)} = \tan i$$

where n is the index of refraction of the reflecting substance.

In Fig. 4 the polarized reflected light waves in ray BC vibrate parallel to the reflecting surface. The refracted light waves in ray BD vibrate in a plane including the ray for the incident light and the normal to the surface at the point of incidence. It should be emphasized that the reflected and refracted light is not completely plane polarized. However, repeated reflection results in light with a high degree of plane polarization.

The reflected and refracted light actually is elliptically polarized, but with repeated reflection the major axis of the elliptical motion as projected into a plane normal to the ray becomes longer and longer as the minor axis becomes shorter and shorter, and finally approaches zero length. When the length of the minor axis reaches zero, the reflected light is plane polarized in the strict sense.

Polarization by Scattering

This phenomenon is of slight importance in optical crystallography and is given only brief notice here. Light waves cause small particles in suspension in a liquid or gas, or even the molecules of the medium themselves, to serve as sources of secondary "scattered" radiation which spreads out from the particles in all directions. The "scattered" light is "partly" plane polarized, in that it has transverse vibrations of greater amplitude in one direction than in other directions. Almost all the light reaching the earth from the sky is the result of scattering by the upper atmosphere and is partly plane polarized, a fact that can be tested by observing sky light directly above the observer through a polarizing prism. Inasmuch as the short wave lengths of white light are scattered more than the long ones, the sky appears blue. Tiny inclusions in clear crystals sometimes cause a bluish opalescence resulting from scattering of white light.

Vector Analysis of Light Waves

A *vector* is a directed magnitude. Passage of light through crystals is analyzed conveniently in terms of the composition and resolution of light vectors. Light waves traveling the same path in isotropic media interfere and the nature of the resultant motion can be predicted if the velocities of the waves, their amplitudes, and directions of vibration of the light vectors are known. Light entering anisotropic crystals in general is resolved into two components, and the amplitudes and vibration characteristics of each component can be determined by vector analysis, if the direction and nature of the incident light relative to crystallographic directions is known.

Composition and Resolution of Waves in a Plane

Light waves vibrating in a plane and moving in the same direction along the same path interfere. Figure 5 shows the results of superimposition of one wave train on another containing waves of like phase, wave length, and amplitude. The resultant wave train (dashed line) contains waves with twice the amplitude of the original waves

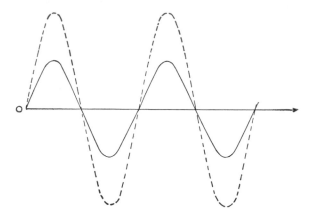

Fig. 5. Constructive interference of light waves of the same phase, wave length, and amplitude. Resultant is the dashed line.

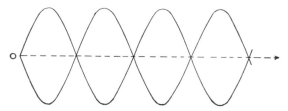

Fig. 6. Destructive interference of light waves with the same wave length and amplitude, but with 180 degrees phasal difference.

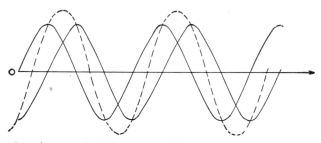

Fig. 7. Interference of similar waves with a phasal difference of 90 degrees.

but with the same wave length. This illustrates *constructive interference.* Figure 6 shows the interference of trains of waves of the same wave length and amplitude but with a phasal difference of 180 degrees (π radians), corresponding to a path difference of one-half wave length. The resultant (dashed line) is zero and shows *destructive interference*. Figure 7 portrays the interference of two similar waves having a phasal difference of 90 degrees ($\pi/2$ radians), corresponding to a path difference of one-quarter wave length. A general case is illustrated in Fig. 8. Here two unlike waves in wave trains

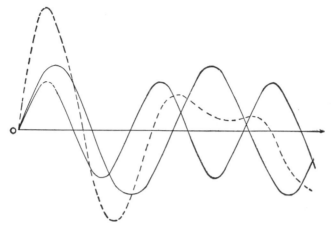

Fig. 8. Interference of unlike waves.

interfere and produce a train of waves of irregular amplitude and wave length.

The resultant of the interference of two or more waves vibrating in the same plane and traveling in the same direction is constructed by adding the light vectors at right angles to the direction of transmission at all points along the line of transmission.

Composition and Resolution of Plane-Polarized, Circularly Polarized, and Elliptically Polarized Wave Motions

Light passing through anisotropic crystals in most directions is resolved into two components for which the electric vectors vibrate in mutually perpendicular planes. For monochromatic light vibrating in mutually perpendicular planes in a crystal the variables are velocity, wave length, and amplitude, but the period of vibration remains constant. Upon emergence into air or any optically isotropic medium the waves interfere to produce plane-polarized, circularly polarized, or elliptically polarized wave motions, depending on the amplitudes of the waves and the phasal difference (path difference) produced between the waves by the crystal. The resultants of the emerging interfering waves can be obtained by vector addition of the simple-harmonic oscillations in each of the waves, and in the general case where the emergent waves have unequal amplitudes and are not in phase the resultant is an elliptically polarized wave train.

In Fig. 9 two simple-harmonic motions emerging from a crystal oscillate in AA' and PP', the traces of mutually perpendicular planes

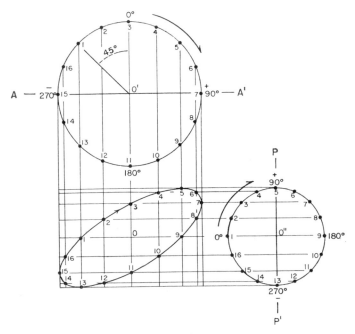

Fig. 9. Construction of an ellipse from projected circular motions.

of vibration in an anisotropic substance. The oscillations have different amplitudes but the same period and wave length and are represented as the motion of the projection on the diameter of a circle of a point moving with constant velocity around the circle. The amplitude of each oscillation is the radius of the circle containing it. The phasal difference between the oscillations can be stated as the difference in degrees or radians between corresponding points on the circles. In Fig. 9 the motion around the circles arbitrarily is made right handed, and the positive end of the oscillation in AA' is indicated as the right end of the oscillation. Similarly, the positive end of the oscillation in PP' is indicated at the upper end of the oscillation. In conformance with the assignment of positive and negative ends to the oscillations the movement of the points around the circles is indicated in degrees of rotation from zero to 360 degrees in the appropriate direction.

In Fig. 9 it is assumed that the two oscillations have a phasal difference of 45 degrees ($\pi/4$ radians). The oscillation in the circle with center O' is 45 degrees behind (or 315 degrees ahead of) the oscillation

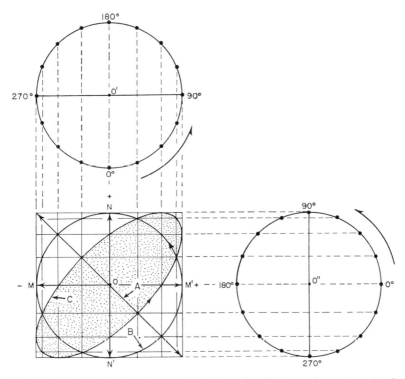

Fig. 10. Resultants of various combinations of oscillations of equal amplitude.

in the circle with center O''. To obtain the radius vectors corresponding to the various combinations of the two oscillations lines are drawn parallel to AA' and PP' to intersection, as indicated. As the radius vectors are determined for a complete 360-degree rotation about each circle an ellipse with right-handed motion is generated.

Figure 10 shows the resultants of various combinations of oscillations of equal amplitude in MM' and NN'. The uniform motion of points about the circles with centers O' and O'' is projected into MM' and NN' to indicate the simple-harmonic nature of the oscillations. In contrast with the motions about the circles in Fig. 9, the motions about the circles in Fig. 10 are assumed to be left handed (counterclockwise). After arbitrarily assigning positive and negative ends to the oscillations and locating the zero points on the circles, various phasal differences between the two oscillations may be indicated by reference to the motions about the circles. If the phasal difference between the oscillations in MM' and NN' is 180 degrees (π radians), the resultant is plane-polarized light (A) vibrating in a diagonal of the grid. For interfering vibrations with no phasal difference the resultant lies in the other diagonal. For an assumed phasal difference between the oscillations of 90 degrees ($\pi/2$ radians) and corresponding to a path difference of one-fourth wave length between the waves the resultant is a left-handed circular motion and the light wave is said to be *circularly polarized*. For a phasal difference of 45 degrees ($\pi/4$ radians) and corresponding to a path difference of one-eighth wave length between the interfering waves the resultant motion is elliptical, and the wave motion is described as *elliptically polarized*. Any combination of oscillations for which the phasal difference is not zero, 90 degrees, or 180 degrees will result in an elliptical motion.

The three-dimensional diagrams in Fig. 11 assist in the visualization of the relationships indicated in Fig. 10. In Fig. 11 the direction of transmission is from right to left. Two identical sinusoidal wave trains emerging from a crystal and traveling along the same path interfere yielding a single wave train, the characteristics of which depend on the phasal difference of the interfering waves. In Fig. 11A the waves have a phasal difference of 180 degrees (path difference of a half wave length), and the resultant is plane-polarized light vibrating in a diagonal plane. For zero phasal difference the resultant wave would vibrate in the other diagonal plane. In Fig. 11B the phasal difference between the interfering waves is 90 degrees (one-fourth wave length path difference) and the resultant is a circularly polarized wave train. The elliptically polarized wave train in Fig. 11C has formed from the interference of waves vibrating in mutually perpendicular planes and having a phasal difference of 45 degrees (one-eighth wave length path difference).

Depending on the manner in which the waves in the mutually perpendicular planes combine into circularly or elliptically polarized waves the resultants at successive equally spaced points along the line of direction of propagation will be radius vectors which sweep in a clockwise or counterclockwise direction. The radius vector sweeps across equal areas of the circle or ellipse in equal time intervals as the circle or ellipse is viewed in projection in a plane perpendicular to the direction of propagation.

If the light waves in Fig. 11 travel from left to right so as to enter the crystal, the complex single wave train is resolved into two wave trains vibrating in mutually perpendicular planes and consisting of waves of different wave lengths and velocities. This phenomenon is observed in light entering anisotropic crystals.

Interference of waves of unequal amplitude emerging from a crystal

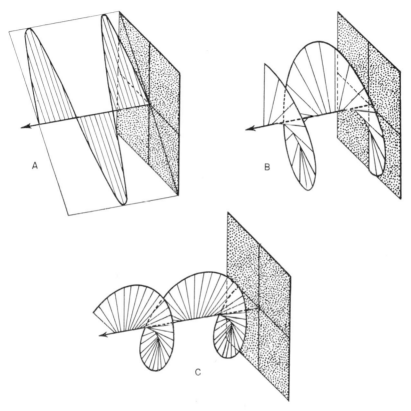

Fig. 11. Resultants of various combinations of mutually perpendicular oscillations.

       A. Path difference one-half wave length.
       B. Path difference one-fourth wave length.
       C. Path difference one-eighth wave length.

and vibrating in mutually perpendicular planes yields only plane-polarized or elliptically polarized waves as indicated in Fig. 12. Right-handed motion about the circles is arbitrarily assumed. A diagonal oscillation (*A*) results when there is no phasal difference. A symmetrical elliptical motion (*B*) is produced for a phasal difference of 90 degrees, and a diagonal elliptical motion results from interference of waves 45 degrees out of phase.

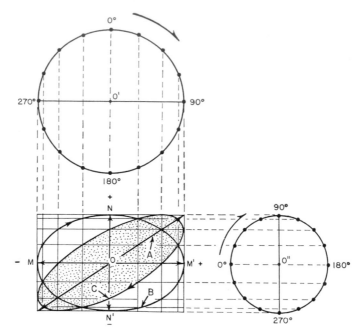

Fig. 12. Resultants of interference of oscillations of unequal amplitude.

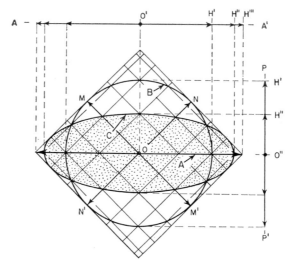

Fig. 13. Method for obtaining amplitudes of the oscillations in mutually perpendicular directions resulting from resolution of various kinds of wave motions.

Plane-polarized, circularly polarized, or elliptically polarized waves incident on crystals in most directions are resolved into plane-polarized waves vibrating in mutually perpendicular planes in the crystals. In polarizing devices in microscopes plane-polarized light is transmitted that vibrates in a single direction only. Determination of the ampli-

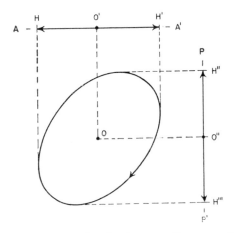

Fig. 14. Method of finding amplitudes in mutually perpendicular directions of oscillations resulting from resolution of an oblique elliptical motion.

tudes of the waves transmitted by crystals or polarizing devices is a relatively simple procedure if the nature of the incident light is known and if it is assumed that none of the light is reflected from or absorbed by the crystal.

Figure 13 shows various kinds of wave motions that have formed from interference of plane-polarized waves vibrating in MM' and NN' and indicates the procedure for obtaining the amplitudes of the plane-polarized waves resulting from the resolution of the various kinds of wave motions into AA' and PP' as might happen when light enters a crystal. In AA' the amplitude of the wave derived from the plane-polarized oscillation in the grid (A) is $O'H'''$, and in PP' the amplitude is zero. The amplitudes in AA' and PP' for the oscillations formed by resolution of the circular motion (B) are $O'H'$ and $O''H'$ and are equal. Resolution of the elliptical motion (C) yields a wave of amplitude $O'H''$ in AA' and a wave of smaller amplitude $O''H''$ in PP'.

Figure 14 indicates the method of finding the amplitudes of waves vibrating in AA' and PP' and resulting from the resolution of an oblique elliptical motion. Normals are erected from AA' and PP' that are tangent to the ellipse. $O'H'$ is the amplitude of the component vibrating in AA', and $O''H''$ is the amplitude of the oscillation in PP'.

Path Difference and Phasal Difference for Waves Vibrating in Mutually Perpendicular Planes

The index of refraction has been defined as the ratio of the velocity of light in vacuum (or air) to the velocity in a particular medium, and in Chapter 3 this relationship has been used as the basis for

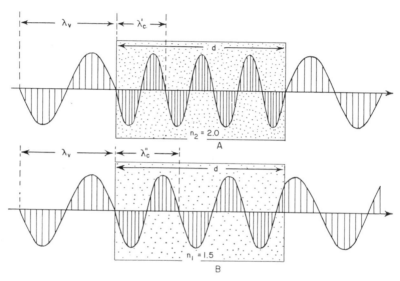

Fig. 15. Diagram illustrating phasal difference and path difference.

deriving Snell's law. In Fig. 15 it is assumed that light waves enter and are transmitted by two media with different refractive indices. It is also assumed that all the incident light energy enters and is transmitted by the media, so that the amplitudes of the waves in the media are the same as in vacuum. In Fig. 15A the medium has an arbitrarily assigned refractive index of 2.0, and the velocity of the waves in the medium is just half of that in vacuum. Also, the wave length in the medium is half the wave length in vacuum. In Fig. 15B the velocity and the wave length in a medium of arbitrarily assigned refractive index of 1.5 is 0.666 of the velocity and wave length in vacuum.

Instead of defining refractive indices in terms of relative velocities it is possible to define refractive indices in terms of traveled distances or wave lengths. The refractive index of a medium may be defined as the ratio of the distance that a light wave travels in vacuum to the distance that the wave travels in the medium in the same time interval, or the index may be defined as the ratio of the wave length in vacuum to the wave length in the medium. In Fig. 15A, for example, the refractive index of the medium is equal to λ_v/λ_c'. In considering the passage of light energy through a medium it is convenient to use the expression *optical path,* which, for a particular medium, is obtained by multiplying the refractive index of the medium by the distance, d, that the light travels through the medium. In Fig. 15A the optical path is $n_2 \cdot d = 2.0 \cdot d$, and in Fig. 15B $n_1 \cdot d = 1.5 \cdot d$.

Now assume that the light waves in the two media in Fig. 15 are following the same path in a single, optically anisotropic medium and that within the medium the waves are vibrating in mutually perpendicular planes. *Upon emergence* there will be an *optical path difference* between the waves, or, more simply, a *path difference.* If the path difference is designated as Δ, then

$$\Delta = n_2 d - n_1 d = d(n_2 - n_1)$$

If it is desired to express the path difference in wave lengths in vacuum, the above expression can be equated as follows:

$$\Delta = p\lambda = d(n_2 - n_1)$$

where p is a whole or fractional number. For the emergent waves in Fig. 15 the path difference is $3.5\lambda - 2.6\lambda = 0.9\lambda$. If it is assumed that the waves are those of monochromatic sodium light with a wave length in vacuum of 589 mμ, calculation indicates that the anisotropic medium must have a thickness, d, of 1060 mμ to produce the path difference indicated above.

The corresponding phase difference is

$$\delta = \frac{2\pi}{\lambda} d(n_2 - n_1)$$

Substitution of the appropriate values in this equation gives a value for δ of 1.8π radians phasal difference between the emergent waves in Fig. 15.

Calculations similar to those above may be made for any crystal for which appropriate data are given.

CHAPTER **8** UNIAXIAL CRYSTALS IN PLANE-POLARIZED LIGHT

The presence of polarizing plates or prisms (polars) in a petrographic or chemical microscope distinguishes it from an ordinary biological microscope and makes it an ideal instrument for the study of the manner of passage of light waves through crystal plates or fragments. In a petrographic microscope the waves passing through the lower polar and entering a crystal are vibrating in one direction only; moreover, if the upper polar is inserted, the waves leaving the crystal, before they reach the eye, are again constrained to vibrate in a single direction. Ordinarily the planes of vibration of the upper and lower polars are in a fixed position 90 degrees apart.

Interference Colors

Anisotropic nonopaque crystal fragments or plates between crossed polars are characterized by interference colors, the nature and intensity of which depend on (1) the orientation of the fragment, (2) the thickness, (3) the birefringence (the difference between the maximum and minimum refractive indices), and (4) the amount and kind of selective absorption of light waves for various colors by the fragment. The last-named factor is of no importance in uncolored substances.

The particular interference color that is formed by a crystal plate or fragment is a function of the path difference between two sets of waves that emerge from the crystal and that, within the crystal, vibrate in mutually perpendicular planes.

If a colorless anisotropic crystal plate of uniform thickness is rotated on the microscope stage between crossed polars, it shows a particular interference color which changes in intensity from a maximum to a minimum four times during a 360-degree rotation. The positions occupied by the plate at minimum illumination (usually complete darkness) are described as the *extinction positions*. The intensity of the light energy reaching the eye is directly proportional to the squares of the amplitudes of the light waves transmitted by the analyzer.

Vector Analysis of Passage of Light Waves through Microscope

In many types of microscopes the plane of vibration of the waves transmitted by the polarizer is north-south to the observer as he looks down the barrel of the microscope.[1] The waves from the polarizer pass through the substage condensing lens and, for a condensing lens of low numerical aperture, are caused to converge slightly. For the purposes of the present discussion it can be assumed that for all practical purposes the waves leaving the condenser fall with normal or nearly normal incidence on a crystal plate or fragment on the stage of the microscope. The crystal plate or fragment in general resolves the incident waves into two sets of waves which travel through the crystal with different velocities and, upon emergence, interfere to produce plane-polarized, circularly polarized, or elliptically polarized waves. The waves above the crystal enter the upper polar, the analyzer, and are resolved again into two sets of waves, only one of which is transmitted. The plane of vibration of the analyzer is east-west (assuming that the plane of vibration of the polarizer is north-south), and, if there is nothing on the stage or somewhere else in the optical system to produce double refraction, no waves pass through the analyzer when the polars are crossed.

A uniaxial crystal plate cut perpendicular to the optic axis (*c* axis) remains dark between crossed polars during a complete rotation of the microscope stage. Light waves for all colors falling with normal incidence on the plate pass through the plate without double refraction, and no path difference is produced upon emergence for any of

---

[1] For microscopes constructed so that the plane of vibration of the polarizer is east-west the vector diagrams in this chapter should be rotated 90 degrees to indicate the passage of light through the microscope.

the waves. The plane of vibration of the waves emergent from the crystal is parallel to the plane of vibration of the incident waves and perpendicular to the plane of vibration of the analyzer. An exception to this statement is provided by *optically active* crystals, which are described in a later section of this chapter.

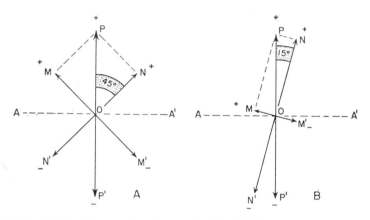

Fig. 1. Resolution diagram showing amplitudes of light waves transmitted by an anisotropic crystal in two positions of rotation.

The interaction of the microscope and an anisotropic crystal plate is analyzed graphically by use of vector diagrams of the type described in the preceding chapter. Figure 1 is a resolution diagram which shows the traces of the planes of vibration of waves in the crystal and in the polars. In Fig. 1*A* the planes of vibration in the crystal, *MM'* and *NN'*, are 45 degrees from the planes of vibration of the polarizer, *PP'*, and the analyzer, *AA'*. The amplitude of monochromatic-light waves leaving the polarizer is *OP* (or *OP'*), and the waves are resolved into two sets of waves of equal amplitude, *OM* and *ON,* in the vibration planes of the crystal. In Fig. 1*B* the planes of vibration of the crystal are 15 degrees from the planes of vibration of the polars, and the amplitude, *ON,* of the waves in one set in the crystal is greater than the amplitude, *OM,* of the waves in the other set. A path difference is produced between the two sets of waves emerging from the crystal because the waves in one set travel with a greater velocity in the crystal than the waves in the other set. Upon emergence the two sets of waves interfere in a manner depending on the magnitude of the path difference and the orientation of the vibration planes of the crystal relative to the vibration planes of the polars. If the top end of the vibration in *PP'* is assumed to be the positive end, the positive ends of the vibrations in MM' and NN' are as indicated in Fig. 1, a convention that has been adopted in the subsequent discussions in this chapter.

Figure 2 shows the passage of light waves of a particular color through the microscope when the crystal produces a path difference of $p\lambda$, where p is a whole number. In Fig. 2A and Fig. 2B the vibration planes of the crystal are 45 degrees from the planes of the polars. Two sets of waves of equal amplitude combine on emergence to produce waves vibrating in the same plane as that of the incident waves and having the same amplitude (except for reflection and absorption) as the incident waves. Because the vibration plane for the analyzer is 90 degrees to the plane of the waves leaving the crystal, no light can pass through the analyzer, and the result is darkness. Figure 2C and Fig. 2D show crystal vibration planes 15 degrees from the planes of the polars. Again no light is transmitted by the analyzer. Figure 2A and Fig. 2C are vector diagrams in which MM' and NN' are the traces of the planes of vibration of the crystal and AA' and PP' are the traces of the planes of vibration of the polars. OM, ON, and OP are the amplitudes of the waves vibrating in the appropriate planes.

In Fig. 3 it is supposed that the crystal plate produces a path difference of $(p/2)\lambda$, where p is a whole odd number. Combination of the waves leaving the crystal produces plane-polarized waves, but, in contrast to the manner of combination in Fig. 2, the plane of vibration of the waves is 90 degrees from the plane of the incident light waves and is parallel to the plane of vibration of the analyzer. Except for reduction of the amplitude by reflection and absorption, the waves passing through the analyzer when the crystal is in the 45-degree position have the same amplitude as the waves incident on the crystal. Rotation of the crystal from the 45-degree position decreases the amplitude of the waves passing through the analyzer as indicated by the different magnitudes of the vector $O'H$ in Fig. 3A and Fig. 3C. When the planes of vibration of the crystal are parallel to the planes of the polars, no light is transmitted by the analyzer, no matter what path difference has been produced by the crystal, and the crystal is at extinction. Also, because the intensity of the light energy transmitted varies as the square of the amplitude of the waves, as the planes of vibration of the crystal and polars approach each other, the intensity of the energy transmitted by the analyzer may become so small that no sensation of light is felt by the observer. Accordingly, the crystal may be rotated through a few to several degrees about the extinction position before the observer is aware that the analyzer is transmitting any light.

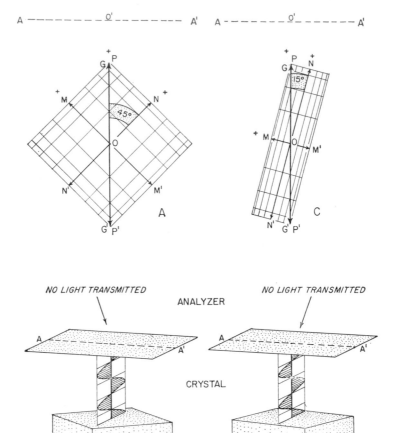

Fig. 2. Passage of light through an anisotropic crystal when crystal produces a path difference of $p\lambda$, where p is a whole number.

        A. Vector diagram for crystal in 45-degree position.
        B. Block diagram for 45-degree position.
        C. Vector diagram for 15-degree position.
        D. Block diagram for 15-degree position.

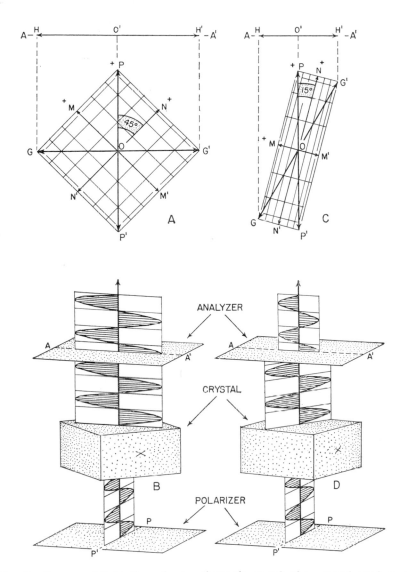

Fig. 3. Passage of light through an anisotropic crystal when crystal produces a path difference of $(p/2)\lambda$, where p is a whole odd number.

    A. Vector diagram for crystal in 45-degree position.
    B. Block diagram for 45-degree position.
    C. Vector diagram for 15-degree position.
    D. Block diagram for 15-degree position.

Figure 4 indicates the interaction of the microscope and a crystal plate when the crystal plate produces a path difference of $(p/4)\lambda$ for monochromatic light, where p is an odd number. Interference of waves leaving the crystal produces circularly polarized waves when the crystal is in the 45-degree position and elliptically polarized waves when the crystal is in the 15-degree position. Rotation to parallelism with the vibration planes of the polars causes the ellipse to disintegrate into a line in the plane of the projection, and no light is transmitted by the analyzer. Note that the amplitude of the waves transmitted by the microscope for the crystal in the 45-degree position is greater than for the 15-degree position but less than that for the 45-degree position when the plate produces a path difference of $(p/2)\lambda$, p odd.

Figure 5 indicates the passage of light waves through the microscope and an anisotropic crystal when the path difference produced by the crystal is $(p/8)\lambda$, where p is an odd number. Similar constructions might be drawn for any path difference except those indicated for Figs. 2, 3, and 4, and the combination of the waves from the crystal in any position except the parallel position will yield elliptically polarized waves. As in the other diagrams $O'H$ is the amplitude of the waves passing through the analyzer.

The diagrams in Figs. 1 through 5 indicate that, if a path difference is produced by a crystal plate between light waves for a particular color, the following observations may be made: (1) For a path difference of a whole number of wave lengths, no light is transmitted by the analyzer. (2) Light waves of maximum amplitude are transmitted by the analyzer if the path difference produced by the crystal is $(p/2)\lambda$, p odd, and the vibration planes of the crystal are 45 degrees from the vibration planes of the polars. (3) For any manner of combination of waves leaving the crystal the maximum possible amplitudes of waves transmitted by the analyzer are obtained when the crystal is in the 45-degree position. (4) Rotation from the 45-degree position in either direction causes the amplitudes of the transmitted waves to diminish. (5) Rotation of the planes of the crystal to parallelism with the planes of the polars produces extinction.

Another method for determining the amplitudes of the waves transmitted by the analyzer is indicated in Figs. 6 and 7. This method does not consider the state of polarization of the waves as they leave the crystal and creates a possible misimpression of the manner of interaction of the crystal and the polars. Nevertheless, the method provides an easy graphical solution for the amplitudes of the waves transmitted by the analyzer and yields amplitudes identical with those determined by the more complicated methods of vector analysis. In

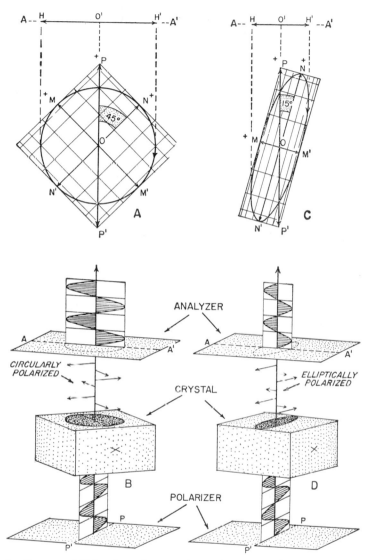

Fig. 4. Passage of light through an anisotropic crystal when crystal produces a path difference of $(p/4)\lambda$, where p is a whole odd number.

A. Vector diagram for crystal in 45-degree position.
B. Block diagram for 45-degree position.
C. Vector diagram for 15-degree position.
D. Block diagram for 15-degree position.

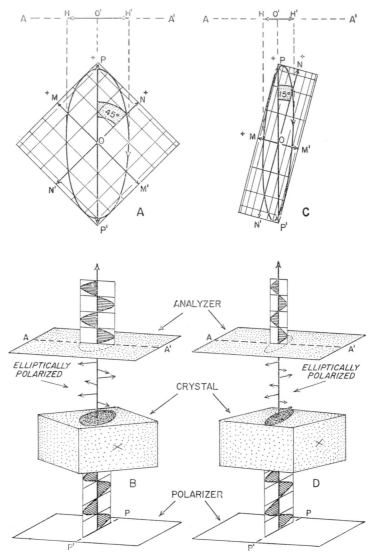

Fig. 5. Passage of light through an anisotropic crystal when crystal produces a path difference of $(p/8)\lambda$, where p is a whole odd number.

      A. Vector diagram for crystal in 45-degree position.
      B. Block diagram for 45-degree position.
      C. Vector diagram for 15-degree position.
      D. Block diagram for 15-degree position.

Fig. 6*A* the traces of the vibration planes for the crystal, *XX′* and *YY′*, are 45 degrees from the vibration planes for the polars, *PP′* and *AA′*. *OB* is the amplitude of the waves leaving the polarizer. The waves are resolved by the crystal into two sets of waves with amplitudes *OC*

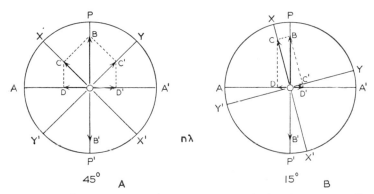

Fig. 6. Action of petrographic microscope on crystal plate in a vector diagram. Plan view. Path difference *p*λ, *p* a whole number.

A. 45-degree position.
B. 15-degree position.

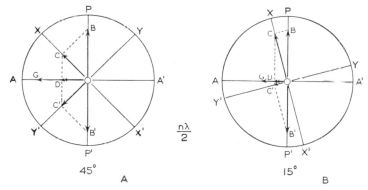

Fig. 7. Action of petrographic microscope on crystal plate in a vector diagram. Plan view. Path difference (*p*/2)λ, where *p* is an odd number.

A. 45-degree position.
B. 15-degree position.

and *OC′* as determined by normals dropped from *B* to *XX′* and *YY′* to conform to the assumption that the path difference between the two sets of waves emerging from the crystal is *p*λ, *p* a whole number. The waves upon emergence interfere to produce a more or less complex motion, which is not indicated on the diagrams. Instead of showing the resultant wave motion above the crystal, the waves in the two sets emerging from the crystal are not combined, and it is assumed that the waves in each set are separately resolved by the analyzer. It is seen that the waves transmitted by the analyzer have equal and opposed vectors, and destructive interference results in waves of zero amplitude. Figure 6B shows the same relationships as Fig. 6A except that the crystal has been rotated to a position 15 degrees from the planes of the polars. Again equal and opposite vectors in the plane of the analyzer result in waves of zero amplitude.

In Fig. 7A and Fig. 7B it is assumed that the crystal has produced a path difference of $(p/2)\lambda$, p a whole odd number. The amplitudes of the waves transmitted by the analyzer are equal to OD, and, because the vectors are equal and in the same direction, waves of amplitude OG, twice OD, are generated by constructive interference in the analyzer. The amplitude of the waves transmitted by the analyzer decreases to zero as the crystal is rotated from the 45-degree position to parallelism with the polars.

Similar diagrams may be constructed for any assumed path difference, and it will be seen that waves of maximum amplitude are transmitted by the analyzer when, for any particular path difference, the crystal plate is in the 45-degree position.

The Quartz Wedge

Two crystal plates differing only in thickness have different interference colors because they produce unlike path differences. The thicker plate shows a higher color than the thinner plate. The principle operating here is illustrated by the quartz wedge—an elongate wedge cut from clear quartz and usually oriented so that its shorter dimension is parallel to the optic axis and the longer dimension is parallel to a normal to the optic axis.

Quartz is optically positive, so that the crystal has a higher index, n_E, for the waves vibrating at right angles to the long dimension and a lower index, n_O, for the waves vibrating parallel to the long dimension. For light waves normally incident on the quartz wedge the path difference for the emergent light is

$$\Delta = p\lambda = d(n_E - n_O)$$

For monochromatic sodium light of wave length 589 mμ the principal refractive indices are $n_O = 1.544$ and $n_E = 1.553$, giving a birefringence of 0.009. Substitution of the birefringence $(n_E - n_O)$, various thicknesses, *d,* and the wave length in the above equation permits easy calculation of the path differences produced for various portions of the wedge.

If a monochromatic-light source is used and the wedge is inserted into the microscope, thin edge first, color bands are seen where fractional path differences are produced by the wedge. Maximum intensity of color in the center of each band corresponds to a path

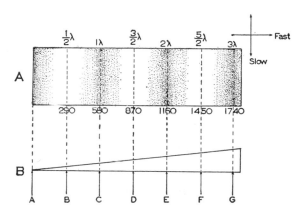

Fig. 8. Quartz wedge in monochromatic yellow (580 mμ) light between crossed polars. Stippled areas dark.

A. Plan.

B. Cross section.

difference of $(p/2)\lambda$, where $p = 1, 3, 5$, etc. The intensity of the light decreases in both directions from the center of a band and finally becomes zero where the path difference produced by the wedge is zero or $p\lambda$, and p is a whole number. The wave length of average yellow light is about 580 mμ (1 mμ = one millionth of a millimeter). Where the path difference produced by the wedge, in millimicrons, is 580/2, $3 \cdot 580/2$, etc., maximum intensity in yellow bands is seen; maximum darkness appears where the path difference, in millimicrons, is 580, $2 \cdot 580$, $3 \cdot 580$, etc., as indicated in Fig. 8. If monochromatic sodium light is used for illumination, maximum intensity in the yellow color bands is seen where the path difference, in millimicrons, is $589 \cdot p/2$ and p is a whole odd number.

With a white-light source, insertion of the quartz wedge into the microscope between crossed polars produces the succession of colors indicated in Fig. 9. These colors are called *Newton's colors* because of their similarity to the colors produced by reflection of white light from a convex glass surface in contact with a plane surface and by thin films such as soap films and oil slicks on water described by Newton. The colors seen under the microscope are produced by interference of doubly refracted light waves and in this respect differ from Newton's colors as originally described. The succession of colors produced by the quartz wedge is divided into *orders,* and a particular color in the sequence is assigned to an order depending on its position in the sequence.

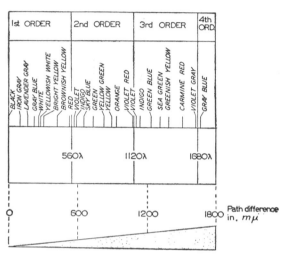

Fig. 9. Distribution of Newton's colors in quartz wedge between crossed polars.

Figure 10 helps to explain the succession of colors observed in the quartz wedge as it is viewed in transmitted white light. The distribution of the colored and dark bands for the average wave lengths in vacuum of various colors of white light is shown as a function of path difference. For a particular thickness of the quartz wedge a greater path difference is produced for the shorter wave lengths than for the longer wave lengths. For the short wave lengths of violet the wedge produces alternating dark and colored bands spaced considerably closer together than for the long wave lengths of red. Where the path difference produced by the wedge is $p\lambda$ (p is a whole number), interference produces waves that cannot pass through the analyzer, and the color for these waves is in effect subtracted from the white light. Where the path difference is $(p/2)\lambda$ (p is an odd number) for a particular color, the analyzer transmits light waves with maximum amplitude. For fractional path differences more or less energy for each of the wave lengths is transmitted. The total effect for any part of the wedge, then, is a function of partial to complete elimination of certain bands of wave lengths of white light and moderate to maximum transmission of others by the analyzer.

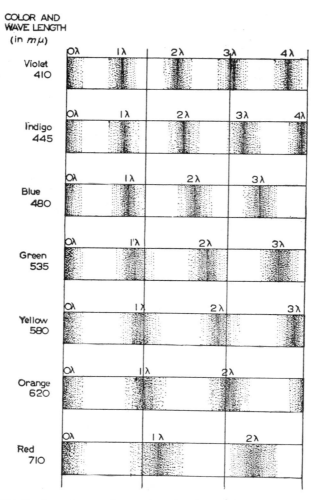

COLOR AND
WAVE LENGTH
(in *m μ*)

Violet
410

Indigo
445

Blue
480

Green
535

Yellow
580

Orange
620

Red
710

Fig. 10. Distribution of monochromatic color bands in quartz wedge between crossed polars. Stippled areas dark; clear areas light.

The succession of first-order colors produced by the quartz wedge is black, gray, white, yellowish white, yellow, brownish yellow, and red. The white is the result of mixing of colors. The yellow and the red result from partial to complete subtraction of certain colors and mixing of others. Experiments have demonstrated that the *visual in-*

tensities or *luminosities* of light, as measured by the ability of the eye to perceive the various colors of white light, differ considerably as a function of the wave length. The final effect in the quartz wedge for any thickness depends not only on the path difference produced by the wedge but also on the manner of mixing and subtraction of colors of different luminosities. In general, the eye is more sensitive to colors in the middle of the visible spectrum and less sensitive to colors near the ends of the spectrum. Discussion of the exact effects of color subtraction and addition is beyond the scope of this book, and mere description of the effects will be made to suffice. For a path difference of approximately 560 mμ, subtraction of colors of high luminosity from the middle of the spectrum by interference and transmission of large fractions of colors of low luminosities from near the ends of the visible spectrum produce a delicately balanced mixture of colors in which a slight change in path difference causes a change from red to violet, or the reverse. Because of this phenomenon, path differences near 560 mμ or whole number multiples of 560 mμ have been used as the division points between the color orders in Newton's scale of colors. The violet at the bottom of the second-order series of colors, just above the red at the top of the first-order colors, has been called the *sensitive tint* because of its pronounced change with a slight change in path difference.

In the second-order series of colors violet is followed, in sequence, by indigo, blue, green, yellow, orange, and red. The colors of the third order occur in the same sequence, but color separation is less pronounced. The fourth, fifth, and higher orders show a peculiar tinted white color resulting from the irregular mixing of colors of various wave lengths, path differences, and luminosities. This white is called *white of the higher order.*

Analysis of the white of the higher order with a spectrometer with a slit opening indicates that, unlike ordinary white light, the spectrum is "banded" or "channeled." That is, within the span of colors from the shortest to the longest wave lengths color bands with gradational borders alternate with irregularly spaced bands of darkness as the spectrum is viewed from one end to the other. The spectrum is not "continuous," as it is for white light of the ordinary kind. The dark bands correspond to portions of the spectrum of ordinary white light for which the path difference produced by the crystal plate between waves of a certain color is exactly or nearly a whole number of wave lengths. The color bands correspond to path differences intermediate between those that result in darkness.

The Function of the Analyzer

Interference colors are not seen when the upper polar, the analyzer, is not inserted into the optical system of the microscope. Instead, the undifferentiated color of the light source, as more or less modified by absorption, reaches the eye. This is true in spite of the fact that the light waves for any particular wave length and for any particular path through the crystal are polarized in some manner upon leaving the crystal. From the discussion in the preceding paragraphs it is evident that the kind of interference that is necessary for the formation of visible interference color occurs only in the analyzer. The analyzer, in effect, receives colors of many wave lengths and in many states of polarization and produces effects that result in the generation of transmitted waves that stimulate color sensations.

The Fresnel-Arago laws specify the nature of the interference in the analyzer. Two of the laws that are particularly pertinent state that: (1) Two rays polarized at right angles do not interfere. (2) Two rays polarized at right angles will interfere in the same manner as ordinary light only when brought into the same plane.

Each wave that is incident on the analyzer, whatever its state of polarization or whatever its amplitude, is resolved into two components, only one of which is transmitted. The transmitted components, traveling in the same direction and vibrating in the same plane in the analyzer interfere constructively or destructively. The net result upon emergence is a plane-polarized wave or set of waves of definite characteristics capable of producing a particular color sensation.

Birefringence

The *birefringence* of a crystal is the numerical difference between the maximum and minimum indices of refraction. The interference color of a crystal fragment or plate between crossed polars depends in part on the birefringence, as is shown by the fact that two crystal plates having identical thicknesses and orientations but different birefringences give different interference colors. The plate with higher birefringence yields the higher color. The velocities of the ordinary and extraordinary waves within the crystal vary as the reciprocals of the refractive indices. Consequently, as the birefringence of crystal plates of constant thickness and orientation increases, the path differences produced by the plates increase.

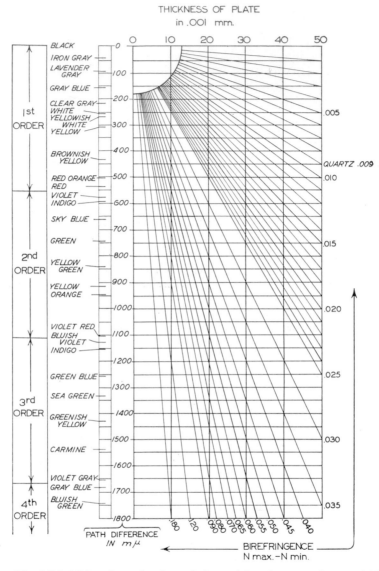

Fig. 11. Michel-Lévy chart showing relations of interference colors to thickness and birefringence in crystal plates.

The interrelationships of thickness, birefringence, and interference colors may be seen in the Michel-Lévy chart in Fig. 11. This chart shows interference colors and the path differences in millimicrons necessary to produce them, thickness in thousandths of a millimeter, and birefringence (diagonal lines).

Quartz, which has a birefringence of 0.009, serves to illustrate the use of the diagram. Suppose that a plate of quartz shows a maximum interference color of yellowish white, and it is desired to determine the thickness of the plate. The diagonal line for birefringence 0.009 is followed with the eye until it intersects the horizontal line for a path difference corresponding to yellowish white. The point of intersection projected upward on a vertical line gives the thickness of the plate (in this case 0.030 mm).

Suppose that it is desired to determine the birefringence of a crystal fragment of known thickness and displaying a maximum interference color. Assume that the thickness is 0.040 mm, and the interference color is blue of the second order. The vertical line for thickness 0.040 mm is followed downward until it intersects a horizontal line corresponding to a path difference necessary to produce second-order blue. The diagonal line passing through the point of intersection gives the birefringence, which turns out to be 0.016.

Determination of the Order of an Interference Color by Use of Color Bands

It may be necessary at times to determine the order of an interference color. This is easily accomplished if a crystal fragment has a wedge edge which shows the colors of Newton's scale in sequence from the edge toward the center of the fragment. Red bands are conspicuous and mark the upper limit of each order. Suppose that the color of a crystal fragment is predominantly blue and two red bands are seen in the wedge edge of the fragment. The lower red band marks the upper limit of the first-order colors, and the higher red band the upper limit of the second-order colors. Accordingly, the blue must be a third-order color.

Determination of the Order of an Interference Color with a Quartz Wedge

The quartz wedge is one of many types of compensators that may be used to determine the order of an interference color. In addition, most compensators, including the quartz wedge, can be used to measure or estimate other optical characteristics of crystals. The wedge is particularly useful with crystal plates of uniform thickness. Some quartz wedges are plain wedges in an appropriate mount. Others are calibrated and give by means of an etched scale the path differences for sodium light for the various thicknesses of the wedge. The use of a simple wedge will be described to indicate its particular use, and, also, to indicate the principles behind the use of all kinds of compensators.

The path difference produced by an anisotropic crystal for monochromatic-light waves is a function of the thickness, the wave length of the incident light, and the difference between the refractive indices of the crystal for the transmitted waves, as described previously. The velocities of the waves in the crystal are inversely proportional to the refractive indices of the crystal for the waves. A conventional and widely used distinction may be made between waves comprising a *fast* (relatively faster) *component* and the waves comprising a *slow* (relatively slower) *component*. The fast component may be referred to as the *lower index component* and the slow component may be designated as the *higher index component*.

To determine the order of the interference color the crystal plate is turned to the extinction position, where the traces of the mutually perpendicular vibration planes in the crystal are parallel to the planes of vibration of the upper and lower polars. The crystal fragment then is rotated 45 degrees so that the trace of the plane of vibration of either the slow or fast component is parallel to the long direction of the quartz wedge as it is inserted in the microscope. Suppose that the quartz wedge is constructed so that the waves in the fast component vibrate in a plane parallel to the long direction of the wedge. If the direction of the trace of the plane of vibration of the waves in the fast component in the crystal is parallel to the direction of the trace of the plane of vibration of the waves in the fast component in the wedge, the interference color in the crystal fragment goes up as the wedge is pushed in, thin edge first. The wedge in effect adds to the thickness of the fragment and increases the total path difference.

If the trace of the vibration plane of the waves in the slow component in the crystal fragment is parallel to the trace of the vibration plane of the waves in the fast component in the wedge, the colors in the fragment go down in Newton's scale as the wedge is inserted. With slow and fast components parallel, darkness results when the path difference produced by the crystal fragment exactly equals the path difference produced by the wedge. When this occurs, the wedge is said to *compensate* the interference color of the fragment.

Suppose that a crystal fragment has a yellow interference color. The fragment is turned 45 degrees from extinction, and the quartz wedge is inserted, thin edge first. If the interference color changes to red, then violet, the traces of the vibration plane of the fast components in the fragment and the wedge are parallel, and the crystal fragment should be rotated 90 degrees. Now as the wedge is inserted, the

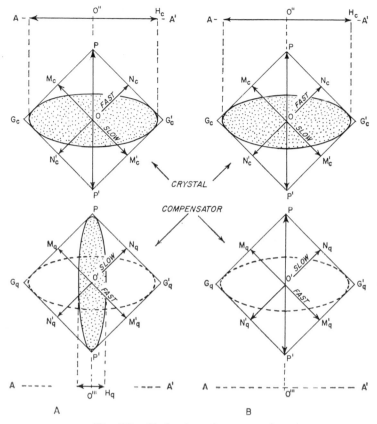

Fig. 12. Mechanism of compensation.

A. Partial compensation.
B. Complete compensation.

interference colors go down in Newton's scale. If the colors appear in the order yellow, green, blue, violet, red, orange, yellow, white, gray, and black, the yellow interference color of the fragment is a second-order color. If the crystal fragment is removed and the color is observed in the wedge alone, the colors listed above will appear in the same order as the wedge is pulled out.

The general mechanics of compensation are indicated in Fig. 12. In Fig. 12*A* monochromatic waves of amplitude *OP* from the lower polar are vibrating in *PP'* and are resolved into waves of amplitude OM_c and ON_c by a crystal plate on the stage of the microscope. Suppose that on emergence the path difference between the waves produces an elliptical motion in the resultant waves (the general case). If the waves above the crystal are unobstructed, they will enter the upper polar and after resolution will emerge with an amplitude of $O''H_c$. If a second crystal plate is inserted into the optical system of the microscope in the accessory slot above the objective and the fast and slow components of the crystal plate above the objective and on the microscope stage oppose each other, the result will be a reduction in the total path differences produced by the two plates. In Fig. 12A it is assumed that the crystal plate in the accessory slot reduces the total path difference so that the waves emergent from it combine to yield an elliptical motion different from that produced by the crystal plate on the stage. The amplitude of the light waves emerging from the upper polar now is $O'''H_q$, an amplitude much less than the amplitude of the waves passing through the upper polar before the crystal plate was inserted into the microscope above the objective lens. Figure 12A illustrates *partial compensation*.

In Fig. 12B a thicker crystal plate in the accessory slot produces resultant waves which vibrate in PP', and no light is transmitted by the upper polar. In this case the path difference produced by the crystal plate on the stage has been reduced exactly to zero by the opposing crystal plate in the accessory slot. This is an illustration of *complete compensation*, or, more simply, *compensation*.

The particular mechanism of compensation by a quartz wedge is indicated diagrammatically in Figs. 13 and 14. In Fig. 13 monochromatic light waves from the lower polar are incident on a crystal plate rotated 45 degrees from the extinction position and are resolved into waves vibrating in mutually perpendicular planes. For the sake of simplicity, it is assumed that the crystal plate produces a path difference of $1/2\lambda$ so that the waves emergent from the plate combine into resultant plane-polarized waves of the same amplitude as the incident waves but rotated 90 degrees. In general, the waves emerging from the crystal plate are circularly or elliptically polarized but are again resolved into plane-polarized waves upon entering the quartz wedge.

The waves entering the quartz wedge are resolved into waves which vibrate in the mutually perpendicular vibration planes of the wedge. If the trace of the vibration plane of the fast component in the quartz wedge is parallel to the trace of the vibration plane of the slow component in the crystal plate, the effect is a reduction of the path difference produced by the crystal plate, and the waves leaving the quartz wedge have a smaller path difference than the waves leaving the crystal plate. In Fig. 13A the quartz wedge has reduced the path difference only slightly; in Fig. 13B, more so; and in Fig. 13C the thickness of the wedge is such that it restores the waves to the condition that characterized them when they were incident on the crystal plate; that is, they vibrate in the plane of vibration of the lower polar. At this thickness the quartz wedge has *compensated* the color

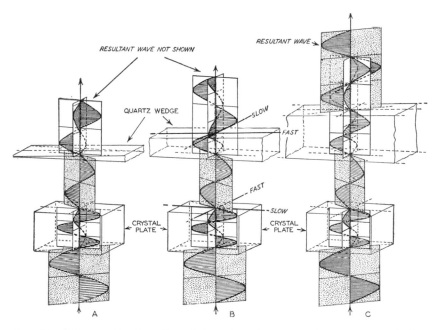

Fig. 13. Diagram showing effect of insertion of quartz wedge over a crystal plate which has produced a path difference of one-half wave length between the emergent waves. A monochromatic source of illumination is assumed. Direction of vibration of the waves for which the quartz wedge has a lower index (the fast direction) is parallel to the direction of vibration of the waves for which the crystal plate has a higher index (slow direction). Compensation has been effected in position *C*.

produced by the crystal plate, and between crossed polars the result is darkness.

The resultant wave for the waves emergent from the quartz wedge in Figs. 13*A* and 13*B* is not shown; both the emergent waves and their resultant are indicated in Fig. 13*C*.

Figure 14 is a two-dimensional drawing showing compensation by a quartz wedge. Monochromatic plane-polarized waves vibrating in a plane 45 degrees from the vibration planes for the crystal are incident on a crystal plate and are resolved into two sets of waves, one set vibrating in the plane of the drawing (solid line) and slower than

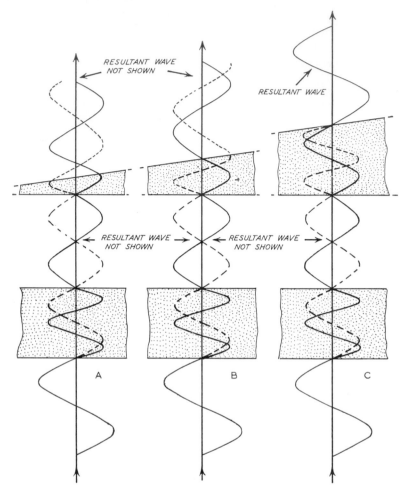

Fig. 14. Two-dimensional diagram showing compensation by a quartz wedge. Path difference (phasal difference) produced by crystal plate has been nullified by quartz wedge in position *C*.

the other set (dashed line) in which the waves vibrate normal to the plane of the drawing. The crystal plate has an orientation, thickness, and birefringence such that a path difference of one-half wave length is produced between the emergent waves. The waves resulting from the combination of the waves emerging from the crystal plate are not shown. If the trace of the vibration plane of the fast component (lower index component) of the wedge is parallel to the trace of the vibration plane of the slow component (higher index component) of the crystal plate, compensation results when the thickness of the wedge is such that the path difference produced by the crystal plate is nullified, as in Fig. 14C. As in the crystal plate the component vibrating in the quartz wedge in the plane of the drawing is indicated by a solid line and the component vibrating normal to the plane by a dashed line. The resultant wave in Fig. 14C vibrates in the same plane as the wave incident on the crystal plate and in a plane normal to the plane of vibration of the light waves transmitted by the upper polar.

Abnormal Interference Colors

Abnormal interference colors are produced by uniaxial crystals in two ways. If a crystal is isotropic for a particular color but not for the other colors of the spectrum, the color for which the crystal is isotropic is removed from white light passing through the crystal, and, in general, a complementary color appears. Melilite, for example, is sometimes isotropic or nearly so for yellow light and has a blue interference color even though the path difference produced by a plate of the mineral is only a fraction of one-half wave length for blue. This blue is called *abnormal blue.*

Minerals which are inherently colored, owing to the differential absorption of the colors of white light, give interference colors which depend not only on the path difference produced by a crystal fragment but also on the particular colors absorbed by the fragment.

Pleochroism (Dichroism)

Certain nonopaque crystals absorb light differently in different directions of vibration. If tourmaline, for example, is examined under the petrographic microscope with the upper polar removed, it will change color on rotation of the microscope stage (Fig. 15). When the optic axis of the tourmaline is parallel to the plane of vibration of the lower polar, the light is not as strongly absorbed as when the optic axis is at right angles to this plane. The absorption is expressed by the formula: E, weak; O, very strong, or $E < O$.

The variation in color resulting from differential absorption is called *pleochroism* (or *dichroism*) and is described by a *pleochroic formula.* Tourmaline might have the following formula: $O = $ buff, $E = $ neutral gray.

Advantage is taken of the differential absorption of light by tourmaline in the construction of tourmaline tongs (Fig. 16). These are constructed so that two plates of tourmaline cut parallel to the *c* crystallographic axis may be rotated into any position with respect to each other. If the plates are parallel, light is transmitted through both, but, if the plates are crossed, little or no light passes through.

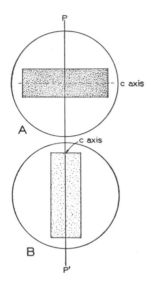

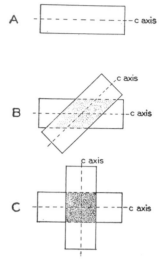

Fig. 15.   Tourmaline in plane-polarized light.

A. Optic axis is normal to plane of lower polar. Absorption strong.

B. Optic axis parallel to plane of vibration of lower polar. Absorption weak.

Fig. 16.   Tourmaline plates.

A. Two plates in parallel position. Light transmitted easily.

B. Two plates in 45-degree position. Intensity of transmitted light diminished.

C. Two plates at right angles. Transmitted light is practically zero.

Extinction Angles

Extinction angles are the angles between an extinction position and a plane, line, or edge in a crystal or crystal fragment.

If a crystal face is used to measure an extinction angle, care must be taken to identify the face, if the angle is to have any significance. For example, consider a quartz crystal lying on one of its prism faces. If the extinction angle is measured from the trace of a prism face, the angle will be zero, but, if a rhombohedron face is used, a much different result is obtained. If cleavage surfaces are used to measure extinction angles, the crystallographic directions of the cleavages should be known. Twin planes, inclusions, etc., may be used if their crystallographic orientations are known.

Index Determination in Uniaxial Crystals

Determination of n_O and n_E in uniaxial crystals is easily made by the immersion method. Matching of the refractive indices of the crystals with the refractive indices of immersion liquids can be accomplished by any of the methods outlined in Chapter 5.

The procedure for uniaxial substances is essentially as follows: crystals or powdered fragments are immersed in a suitable index medium on a glass slide. The relief is noted and the indices of the fragment relative to the immersion medium are determined by using central illumination, oblique illumination, or the Becke line. Next, several grains are placed in a medium which more nearly matches the indices of the substance being tested, and, if the match is close, the upper polar is inserted, and the grains are observed between crossed polars.

Every fragment of a uniaxial crystal permits measurement of n_O in one extinction position or the other. If a succession of fragments is rotated to extinction or, if necessary, 90 degrees from the first extinction position to the next extinction position, it will be noted by giving consideration to the relief that one of the refractive indices does not vary from fragment to fragment. The unvarying index is measured in successive immersions and is n_O. Fragments which between crossed polars remain dark gray or black during a complete rotation of the microscope stage, particularly for crystals of moderate to high birefringence, are oriented so that the optic axis is exactly or nearly parallel to the axis of the microscope. Fragments with this orientation permit a more or less accurate measurement of n_O in all positions of rotation of the stage. As will be indicated later, such fragments are particularly useful if they yield centered optic axis interference figures under the conoscope.

Now, when the n_O index is matched, insert the upper polar and search for a grain with a maximum interference color. Take into account the variation of the interference color with grain size. Grains showing the maximum interference color lie with the optic axis parallel to the microscope stage and, if rotated, extinguish when the n_O and n_E directions coincide with the planes of vibration of the polars. Such grains will give both n_O and n_E. The grain is rotated to extinction, and the upper polar is removed. If the index is still matched by the immersion medium, it is known that the vibration direction for n_O

parallels the plane of vibration of the lower polar, and the grain should be rotated 90 degrees, and it is ascertained whether n_E is greater or less than n_O. By successive immersions n_E is measured in fragments showing maximum colors. Because of variations in the thicknesses of fragments it may be difficult to identify fragments that actually show a maximum interference color. Fragments for which the optic axis does not parallel the microscope stage yield n_O in one extinction position and an index, n_E', in the other position. The index that varies from fragment to fragment will be larger or smaller than n_O, and to get an accurate value for n_E the fragments should be rolled and examined in multiple immersions until it is certain that a maximum or minimum value for the varying index has been measured.

If n_E is higher than n_O, the crystal is positive. If n_E is less than n_O, the crystal is negative.

Any fragment, no matter what its orientation may be, permits determination of n_O, but the full value of n_E is obtained only when the optic axis of a crystal is parallel to the stage of the microscope. Certain uniaxial crystals have conspicuous cleavages, and most of the fragments tend to lie on cleavage faces. In some substances it may be necessary to use a very viscous immersion medium or the problem may be solved by adding powdered cover glass to the immersion oil. This will serve to support the grains in any desired position. A single-axis rotation method for measurements of grains or crystals of unusual habit is described in Chapter 17.

In extreme examples, it may be necessary to resort to calculation to find the full value of n_E. As a matter of fact, in many crystals it is a simple matter to measure n_E', the index for the extraordinary wave, for a grain lying on a cleavage not parallel to the optic axis. In such crystals measurement of the angles between the cleavages and other appropriate crystal directions or planes by means of a contact or reflecting goniometer may permit the location of the indicatrix relative to the cleavage surface on which the crystal fragment is lying. Substitution of measured values of n_O and n_E' in the equation for the ellipse as expressed in polar coordinates permits calculation of the value for n_E.

The measurement of a value for n_E' that can be used with known or measured crystal angles for the calculation of n_E is at best generally unsatisfactory for precision work. Substances, even those with eminent cleavages, such as calcite, do not always roll over in the immersion liquid so as to lie on a surface exactly parallel to the cleavage. The reasons for this are suggested in Fig. 17. Figures 17A and

B show how grains of a substance such as calcite supported by the edges of interrupted cleavages yield different orientations of the *c* crystallographic axis in different grains. Similarly, in Figs. 17*C* and *D*

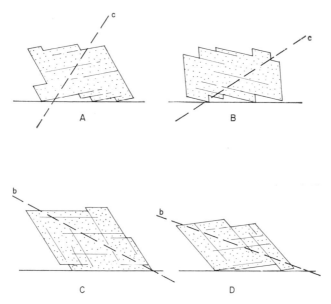

Fig. 17. Cleavage fragments showing how disposition of edges can give differing orientations for fragments lying on a glass slide on the microscope stage.

fragments of crystals in the orthorhombic or monoclinic systems possessing an excellent prismatic cleavage yield different orientations of the *b* crystallographic axis.

Stereographic Projections of Uniaxial Crystals

A study of the relationships of optical and crystallographic directions in uniaxial crystals is made conveniently with the aid of stereographic projections. Figure 18 shows stereographic projections of a calcite cleavage rhomb in two positions. In position *a* the optic axis and the *c* axis are polar, and under the microscope such a rhomb would permit measurement of n_0 for any position or rotation of the microscope stage. The angle between the normal to a cleavage and the optic axis for calcite is 44° 36′, so that to obtain the projection corresponding to a rhomb lying on one of its faces the projection for position *a* is rotated 44° 36′ with the aid of a stereonet (see p. 310).

This angle corresponds exactly to the angle θ used in calculating n_E' from n_E with the polar-coordinate equation (see p. 106). In position b

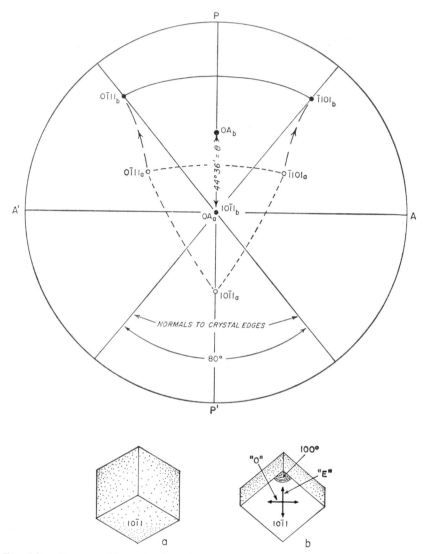

Fig. 18. Stereographic projections showing cleavages and optical directions in calcite in two different orientations. Projected from upper hemisphere of spherical projection.

the edges of the rhomb lie in the plane of projection, that is, parallel to the microscope stage. In position b the rhomb is at extinction between crossed polars, and n_E' can be measured when the upper polar is removed. The trace of the vibration plane of the E component is parallel to the trace of the plane of the lower polar, PP', and bisects the angle between the edges of the rhomb. The extinction angle measured from either edge to the direction of vibration of the E component is one-half of 100 degrees, that is, 50 degrees.

Rotation of Plane-Polarized Light

Crystals in several of the 32 crystal classes possess the ability to rotate the plane of vibration of transmitted light and are said to be *optically active*. The ability to rotate the plane of vibration is measured by the *rotatory power,* and the phenomenon is described as *rotatory polarization* or *rotary polarization*. The amount of rotation for 1-mm thickness is the *specific rotation, or specific rotatory power,* and is either right handed (dextrorotatory) or left handed (levorotatory) as viewed looking down on a crystal against the direction that light is advancing through the crystal. Crystals that display this effect are found in each of the six crystal systems; they have certain symmetry characteristics in common, notably the absence of a center of symmetry and few or no planes of symmetry. *Enantiomorphism* is evident, and left- and right-handed crystal forms may be present. Spiral arrangements of units of crystal structure in one or more directions may be noteworthy.

Unlike optically inactive uniaxial crystals, plates cut perpendicular to the optic axis produce a path difference for light waves normally incident on the plate and transmitted in the direction of the optic axis. Such plates are not completely dark as viewed between crossed polars under the microscope. In order to reduce the illumination of the plate to zero it is necessary to rotate either the upper or lower polar through an angle which is a function of the specific rotatory power and the thickness of the crystal plate.

Quartz, in the trigonal trapezohedral class, illustrates rotatory polarization. Quartz crystals are shown in Fig. 19 and are either left handed or right handed. If a section is cut at right angles to the c axis and plane-polarized light is passed through the crystal parallel to the c axis, the apparent result is something like that in Fig. 20, which shows a basal plate of left-handed quartz. It is not believed that the plane of vibration is actually rotated inside the crystal plate as shown in Fig. 20, but it is known that the amount of apparent rotation of the plane of vibration of the light leaving the plate with reference to the plane of vibration of incident light is a direct func-

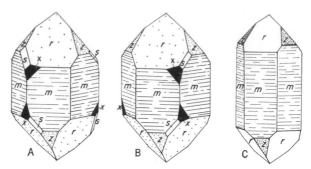

Fig. 19. Quartz crystals.
A. Left-handed quartz.
B. Right-handed quartz.
C. Typical elongate crystal.

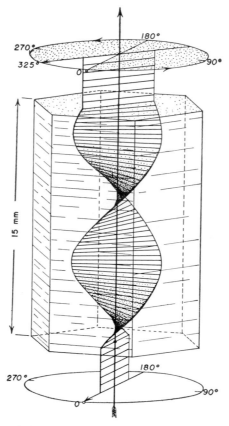

Fig. 20. Rotation of plane of vibration of monochromatic light by basal plate of left-handed quartz.

tion of the thickness of the plate. For the D wave length of the visible spectrum a basal plate of quartz 1-mm thick rotates the plane of polarization 21° 40′ at 20° C.

The amount of rotation depends not only on the thickness of a plate of an optically active crystal plate but also upon the wave length of the incident light. The amount of rotation is nearly proportional to the reciprocal of the square of the wave length. For quartz, violet light is rotated nearly three times as much as red light as indicated by a specific rotation of 48.9 degrees for a wave length of 404.6 mμ (violet) and a specific rotation of 16.5 degrees for a wave length of 680.7 mμ (red). Different rotations for the various colors of the spectrum are expressed as *rotatory dispersion* and have been used to separate white light into its component colors in optical instruments such as monochromators.

A common explanation of rotatory polarization, attributed to Fresnel, assumes that the crystal separates the incident plane-polarized light into two components, circularly polarized in opposite directions, and that these components travel through the crystal with different velocities. Upon emergence, one component will have rotated through a larger angle than the other. The resultant of the combination of the two components gives plane-polarized light, the vibration plane of which is rotated somewhat with respect to the vibration plane of the incident light.

Figure 21 indicates the mechanism suggested by Fresnel to account for the geometry of rotatory polarization. In Fig. 21A two circularly polarized motions oppose each other, and the motion of the radius vector starts from the same point for both the right-handed and the left-handed motions. A radius vector sweeps to the right at the same angular velocity that another radius vector sweeps to the left. Addition of the vectors at any instant, such as the addition of Ob and Ob' produces a resultant vector Ob''. The combination of both vectors as they sweep around the circle in opposite directions produces a simple-harmonic oscillation along $a''k$. The amplitude of this oscillation is Oa''. Plane-polarized light, in turn, may be resolved into opposed circular motions by reversing the mechanism. In an ordinary uniaxial substance, such as calcite, plane-polarized light normally incident on a basal plane may be considered as being resolved into two opposed circularly polarized components which travel in the direction of the optic axis with the same velocity. Upon emergence the resultant is a vibration in a plane parallel to the plane of the incident light.

In quartz and other optically active uniaxial crystals plane-polarized light normally incident on the basal plane, according to Fresnel's explanation, is resolved into two circularly polarized components that have opposite senses of rotation and move with different velocities in the direction of the optic axis. Upon emergence the rotation of the radius vector of one component will be ahead of (or behind) the other, and combination of the motions will produce a vibration ro-

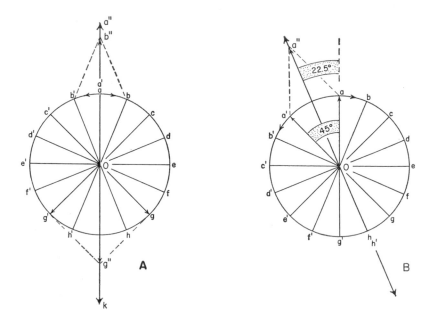

Fig. 21. Resultants of opposed circular motions of vectors.

A. Resultant is plane-polarized light vibrating in plane parallel to that of incident light.
B. Resultant rotated so that it vibrates at an angle to the plane of the incident light.

tated somewhat with respect to the vibration direction of the incident light. In Fig. 21B it is assumed that the left rotation is 45 degrees ahead of the right rotation. The linear vibration is rotated to the left (as in left-handed quartz) through an angle of 22.5 degrees with reference to the incident light.

For light traveling through uniaxial crystals at an angle to the optic axis the relationships become more complex. The manner of double refraction in the crystal depends not only on the angle of incidence but also upon the location of the plane of incidence. In general, the resultant of the emergent light can be explained geometrically by assuming that the light travels through the crystal as two opposed elliptically polarized components. Light falling with normal incidence on a plane parallel to the optic axis travels through the crystal as two plane-polarized components, the same as in crystals that are not optically active.

Rotatory polarization is of particular interest in thick-crystal optics. In most studies of crystals by the immersion technique or in thin sections the effects of rotatory polarization may be considered as negligible. Also, most crystalline substances belong to crystal classes which do not exhibit rotatory polarization. To indicate the effects of rotatory polarization in thin plates quartz may be used as an example. A plate of quartz in a standard thin section 0.03 mm thick rotates the plane of vibration of sodium light traveling along the optic axis only about 45 minutes of arc (0.75°).

CHAPTER 9 UNIAXIAL CRYSTALS IN CONVERGENT POLARIZED LIGHT

The petrographic microscope with the polars crossed is converted into a *conoscope* by inserting an accessory lens of short focal length just below the microscope stage and a Bertrand-Amici lens between the upper polar and the ocular. This arrangement of lenses, when used with a high-power objective of large numerical aperture, permits the observation of interference figures and other interference phenomena. The condensing lens produces strongly converging light which comes to a focus in the plane of an object on the stage of the microscope. This light may be thought of as forming a solid cone of illumination just above the accessory condensing lens.

If the ocular and the Bertrand-Amici lens are removed, interference figures are seen just as clearly as when these lenses are used but at reduced magnification. The optical system of the conoscope brings the magnifying lens system above the objective lens system to a focus on the upper (back) focal plane of the objective instead of on the object on the stage of the microscope and, in effect, converts the orthoscope into a wide-angle telescope for looking *through* the object rather than *at* the object. The interference effects, as in the case of interference colors, result from interference of the light waves transmitted by the analyzer.

The student may wish to review the description of the construction and manner of passage of light through the conoscope as it is presented in Chapter 4 before attempting to follow the discussion in the subsequent portions of this chapter.

Figure 1 diagrammatically indicates the paths of light waves from the substage condensing lens falling with a particular angle of incidence on an anisotropic crystal plate and passing through the crystal plate. After emergence from the crystal, waves vibrating in mutually perpendicular planes in the crystal interfere so as to produce plane-polarized, circularly polarized, or elliptically polarized wave trains, the nature of the interference depending on the path difference (or phasal difference) produced by the crystal plate. The interference picture as viewed through the analyzer forms in the curved back focal plane of the objective lens in what is sometimes referred to as the "interference sphere." The location of point P in Fig. 1 is a function of several variables, including the angle of incidence of the light from the stage of the substage condensing lens, the

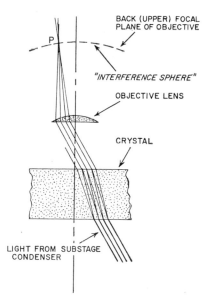

Fig. 1. Diagrammatic portrayal of passage of light of a particular angle of incidence through crystal plate and objective lens when microscope is used as a conoscope.

orientation, birefringence, and thickness of the crystal plate, and the angular apertures of the various lens combinations in the optical system.

Unlike light waves that are only slightly convergent or are falling with normal incidence on the crystal plate when the microscope is used for orthoscopic observation at low to medium magnifications, the light waves that are incident on the crystal plate from the strongly converging substage lens which is used in conoscopic observations are somewhat "rotated" with respect to the plane of vibration of the polarizer. The nature of the rotation has been described by Kamb[1] whose summary is the basis for the discussion in this section.

In Fig. 2A assume that nonpolarized light waves are incident on a hemispherical substage condensing lens. At a point of incidence for

[1] W. B. Kamb, "Isogyres in Interference Figures," *Am. Mineralogist*, Vol. 43, pp. 1029–1067, 1958.

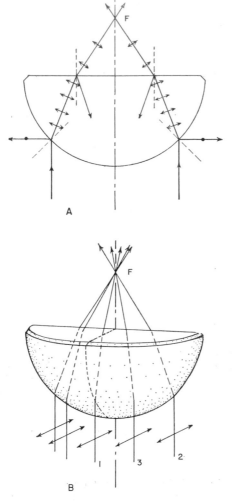

Fig. 2. Refraction and reflection of light waves passing through substage condensing lens of microscope.

A. Nonpolarized light waves incident on lens.

B. Plane-polarized light waves incident on lens. Reflected waves not shown.

light waves following a particular ray, part of the light energy is reflected, and part is refracted into the lens. The reflected and refracted waves are partly plane polarized into mutually perpendicular vibration planes. As the light waves leave the lens, they are again reflected and refracted, so that the waves leaving the lens are even more strongly plane polarized. However, in three dimensions, light waves following all possible rays through the lens converge above the lens and vibrate in all azimuths. Accordingly, the light transmitted by the lens essentially is not different from the incident light except for a reduction in intensity caused by subtraction of the reflected light.

In Fig. 2B plane-polarized light waves are incident on the lower surface of the condensing lens. At each point of incidence the waves are reflected and refracted (reflected waves not shown). Light waves of maximum amplitude are transmitted by the lens when the light vector for the incident waves lies in the plane of incidence as for ray 1. Light waves of minimum amplitude are transmitted when the light vector of the incident light waves is normal to the plane of incidence, as for ray 2. A plane-polarized wave following ray 3, in which the light vector is in an intermediate position, upon entrance into the lens will be subjected to a greater diminution of the component of the vector of the incident wave perpendicular to the incident plane than of the component of the vector parallel to the incident plane. Upon emergence from the lens the resultant wave will be rotated somewhat with respect to the vector for the incident wave. Kamb[2] presents the details of the mathematical treatment that enables calculation of the magnitudes of the vectors transmitted by the refracting medium.

The rotation of the light vectors is indicated diagrammatically in Fig. 3A and B. Figure 3A is a stereographic projection in which N_i is the pole of the wave normal for the wave front of the incident light waves, D_i is the pole of the light vector of an incident wave, and v_i is the spherical angle that D_i makes with the trace of a vertical north-south plane. N_t and D_t are the corresponding poles, and v_t is the corresponding angle after refraction has made N_t polar. Kamb offers proof that D_i and D_t lie on a great circle through N_i. From the projection it can be determined that $v_t < v_i$, so that a measure of the rotation of the vector is given by the difference between v_i and v_t.

In Fig. 3B P is a point in the interference figure as viewed by looking down the tube of the microscope. The projection that is used is orthographic because, although the interference picture forms in the spherical back plane of the objective lens, the view from above is essentially orthographic. A vector at P is rotated by reflection and refraction toward the radial line OP (extended) from the position, PD_o, that it would occupy if there had been no rotation by the lenses above and below the microscope stage. Before the light reaches the eye it travels in the general direction of the axis of the microscope and passes through a succession of lenses, both above and below the microscope stage, and reflection and refraction occur at the surfaces of all the lenses. Thus the calculation of the exact amount of net rotation of the light waves that reach the eye with respect to the direction of vibration of the light leaving the polarizer and the determination of the amplitudes of the rotated vectors becomes a very complicated procedure. However, the pattern of the vectors in the interference field above the objective lens is of the kind indicated in Fig. 3B. In Fig. 3B no scale is indicated, and the lengths of the vectors as shown have no particular significance. For the usual lens combinations in the microscope the rotation is about 6 to 7 degrees, and it can be demonstrated that the rotation by the substage lens is partly compensated for by rotation in the opposite direction as the light waves pass through the upper lenses of the microscope.

The pattern of vectors in Fig. 3B indicates the origin of the "isotropic cross," a diffuse black cross seen under the conoscope when the polars are crossed and when there is no birefringent substance on

[2] Kamb, *loc. cit.*, p. 1036.

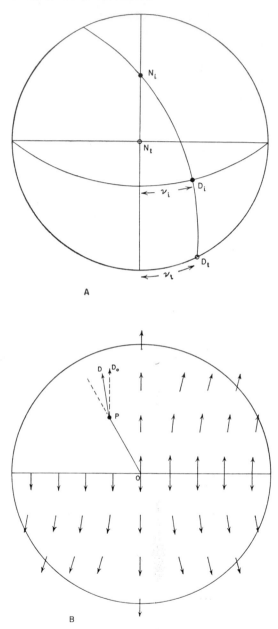

Fig. 3. Rotation of light vectors by microscope lenses. (After W. B. Kamb, *Am. Mineralogist*, Vol. 43, p. 1037, 1958.)

A. Stereographic projection showing poles of wave normals and light vectors.
B. Orthographic projection showing rotation of light vectors in interference field.

the stage of the microscope. The cross forms where the vectors are normal or nearly normal to the plane of vibration of the analyzer. Other kinds of crosses are seen when the microscope tube is raised above the position where the objective lens is at focus on an object on the stage of the microscope and probably are the result of repeated reflection of light by the lenses in various portions of the optical system.

Interference Figures

Optically anisotropic crystals under the conoscope yield interference figures consisting of *isogyres* and *isochromatic curves*. The isogyres are black or gray areas which may or may not change position as the microscope stage is rotated. The isochromatic curves are color bands or areas which are systematically distributed with respect to the isogyres.

Interference figures are useful in evaluation of optic sign and assist in the determination of the optical orientation of a crystal. Moreover, interference figures permit estimation of birefringence and thickness of crystal plates or fragments.

If light in parallel or subparallel beams passes through a crystal plate of uniform thickness between crossed polars, a uniform interference color results which, as indicated in Chapter 8, depends on the thickness, orientation, and birefringence of the plate. If the orientation is changed and the other factors remain constant, the interference color changes. In the conoscope the orientation of the crystal plate is in effect different for the extraordinary light waves transmitted in each direction within a particular azimuth. The interference effects depend on thickness and birefringence as above but vary in response to a variation in the angles of incidence of the light waves entering the crystal plate from the substage condensing lens.

Isochromatic Curves in Uniaxial Interference Figures

An understanding of the shapes and distribution of the color curves in uniaxial interference figures is reached by consideration of the geometry of double refraction of light waves falling with different angles of incidence on a crystal plate of a particular crystallographic orientation. In order to simplify the discussion the effects of rotation of the light vectors of waves emerging from the polarizer by passage through the substage condensing lens are not considered. In Fig. 4 a plate of a uniaxial negative crystal of thickness d is cut at right angles to the optic axis. The indicatrix is shown in a principal section and arbitrarily has been assigned dimensions of 2.0 for n_O and 1.5 for n_E. A beam of light containing both O and E waves is assumed to be moving through the crystal in the direction, ON, of a wave normal common to both sets of waves and making an angle of θ with the optic axis. The exact path followed by each wave as it passes through the crystal is of little concern because interference figures

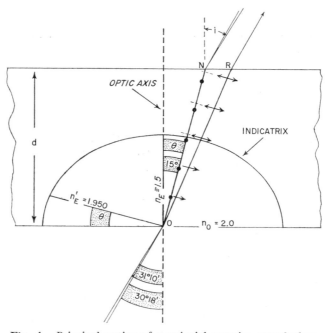

Fig. 4. Principal section of a uniaxial negative crystal plate.

are dependent only on the directions and azimuths of transmission of families of waves refracted by the crystal and not on the location in the crystal of any particular ray. Consideration of wave fronts and wave normals is more pertinent than consideration of the paths followed by individual waves or wave trains. OR is the direction of the ray associated with the normal to the wave front for the E waves, but, as just explained, it is regarded as of little importance in the present discussion. In order to obtain wave fronts for which the normals coincide for both the O and E waves, slightly different angles of incidence for incident light waves are required, but, for crystals in which the birefringence is not high and for which the angles of incidence are small, it can be assumed that for a particular angle of refraction of the wave normals in the crystal the angles of incidence of the incident light waves are approximately equal.

In the direction of the wave normal the wave fronts advance with velocities that are proportional to $1/n_O$ for the wave front for the ordinary waves and $1/n_E'$ for the wave front for the extraordinary waves, and a path difference is produced in the emergent light waves. The path difference can be regarded as proportional to $(n_O - n_E')$. If *only the emergent light waves* are considered, the path difference in wave lengths can be expressed in terms of the thickness of the plate as

$$\Delta = p\lambda = d \sec \theta (n_O - n_E')$$

Substitution of the value for n_E' from the equation of the ellipse in polar coordinates yields the equation

$$\Delta = p\lambda = d \tan^2 \theta (n_O - n_E) \sec \theta$$

which includes an expression for the birefringence $(n_O - n_E)$.

For small angles of θ and for crystals of low to moderate birefringence $\sec \theta$ approaches unity and $\tan^2 \theta$ is nearly equal to $\sin^2 \theta$, so that the equation may be written in the form that is sometimes seen, as follows

$$\Delta = p\lambda \doteqdot d \sin^2 \theta (n_O - n_E)$$

Now, consider a succession of plates of different thicknesses for some uniaxial substance. For a particular angle θ, the path difference for the emergent light waves increases as the thickness increases. For plates of the same thickness the path difference for the emergent waves increases as the angle θ increases. If particular values for the path difference are assumed and various values for θ and d are substituted in one or the other of the above equations, curves such as those in Fig. 5 may be plotted. The curves in Fig. 5 were calculated for the indicatrix shown in Fig. 4 for path differences of 1λ, 2λ, 3λ, and 4λ and are *curves of equal path difference,* or, as sometimes designated, *curves of equal retardation.* A line drawn from the center, O, to intersection with any one of the curves indicates by the distance from O to the point of intersection how far the wave fronts for light waves vibrating in mutually perpendicular planes must move through the crystal in the direction of a particular wave normal to produce a particular path difference upon emergence from the crystal. Similar curves may be calculated for any specified succession of path differences.

We are primarily concerned in constructions similar to Fig. 5 with the path difference (or phasal difference) between the two components upon *emergence*. The wave length upon emergence is the same as that of the incident light waves and is different from the wave lengths for the two sets of waves in the crystal. Within the crystal the wave lengths vary inversely as the refractive indices of the crystal for the light waves that form wave fronts moving in the directions

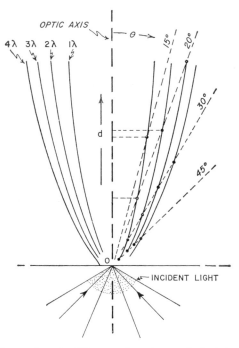

Fig. 5. Curves of equal path difference (equal retardation) in principal section of a uniaxial crystal.

of the various wave normals. Thus, the wave lengths of the extraordinary waves within the crystal are different for the different directions of propagation of light through the crystal, whereas the wave lengths for the ordinary waves are the same for all directions of transmission.

If it is desired to emphasize the phasal difference between the emergent waves, each wave length of path difference corresponds to a phasal difference of 2π radians. Thus in Fig. 5 the path differences of 1λ, 2λ, 3λ, and 4λ correspond to phasal differences of 2π, 4π, 6π, and 8π.

In three dimensions and for an imaginary point source of light in a crystal the curves of equal path difference generate surfaces such as those shown in Fig. 6 and called *Bertin's surfaces.* These surfaces are formed by revolution about the optic axis of curves of the type shown in Fig. 5. Isochromatic curves in uniaxial interference figures may be considered as cross sections of Bertin's surfaces formed by the intersection of the surface of the crystal with the Bertin's surfaces. In monochromatic light, curves of darkness in the interference figure correspond to sections of Bertin's surfaces for path differences of $p\lambda$, where p is a whole number. Curves of maximum illumination correspond to cross sections of Bertin's surfaces for path differences of $(p/2)\lambda$, where p is a whole odd number, and so on. In white light, the color curves may be regarded as sections across an infinite number of nested Bertin's surfaces for which the path difference increases with increasing distance from the optic axis as expressed by a steady increase in the value of angle θ.

For a crystal plate cut perpendicular to the optic axis the color curves are circles. For plates cut in other directions the shapes of the curves are a function of the manner in which the section of the crystal intersects the Bertin's surfaces. For thin plates of substances of low birefringence the color curves appear to be spaced farther apart than for thick plates of the same substance or for thin plates of substances of high birefringence. In interference figures for plates normal to the optic axis, the spacing of the

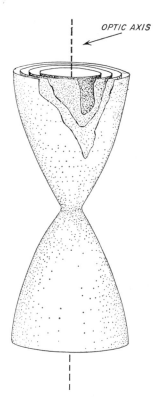

Fig. 6. Nested Bertin's surface for a uniaxial crystal.

color curves decreases in all directions away from the point of emergence of the optic axis. The light waves leaving the crystal are refracted away from the optic axis, and the angle of refraction outside of the crystal plate increases in the same manner and in the same amount as the angle of incidence of the corresponding light waves entering the crystal. Bending of the paths of light waves leaving the crystal tends to spread the outer curves but is insufficient to overcome the spacing dependent on double refraction within the crystal. The angle of refraction for extraordinary light waves leaving the crystal is related to the angle θ by the equation

$$\sin i = n_E' \sin \theta$$

where i is the angle of refraction upon emergence and, for a plate of uniform thickness, is equal to the angle of incidence of the light waves entering the crystal plate.

Isogyres in Uniaxial Interference Figures

The color curves in uniaxial interference figures can be regarded as sections of Bertin's surfaces for systematically varying path differences. The *isogyres* are black or gray areas which seem to be superimposed on the color curves and have been called *curves of equal vibration direction*. The intensity of illumination in any color curve decreases from some point of maximum illumination to minimum (zero) illumination in the direction of some portion of the isogyre. In a crystal plate cut perpendicular to the optic axis a particular circular color curve shows maximum illumination 45 degrees from the center lines of bars of an isogyre that forms a black cross. The color curve shows minimum illumination where it fades into the isogyre. The shape of the color curves is explained by reference to Bertin's surfaces, but the decrease in the intensity of illumination around the circles requires consideration of the vibration directions of doubly refracted light waves within the crystal and as they leave the crystal.

Location of the Isogyre

Isogyres are regions in the interference figure where the intensity of the light transmitted by the analyzer is zero or at a minimum. Kamb[3] has discussed the factors that contribute to the formation of isogyres, and a brief summary of a portion of his discussion is presented here. For a detailed analysis the interested student is urged to refer to Kamb's work.

In Fig. 7*A* let *P* be a point in the interference field in orthographic projection. If *P* corresponds to a point for which light waves of minimum amplitude are transmitted by the analyzer (that is, it lies on an isogyre), the problem becomes one of locating the vectors for light waves in the crystal that will yield waves of minimum amplitude upon passing through the analyzer. Kamb analyzes the passage of light through the crystal by means of the stereographic projection in Fig. 7*B*. The plane-polarized light waves that enter the crystal are

[3] Kamb, *loc. cit.*

indicated by the vector D that has been rotated through the angle δ_1, on passing through the substage condensing lens. The waves, upon entrance into the crystal, are resolved into two waves with vectors D_1 and D_2 whose orientations are defined by the angle ξ, an angle of not more than 1 degree, and a phasal difference (path difference) is pro-

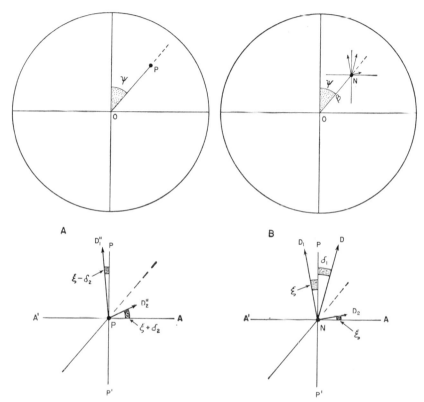

Fig. 7. Diagrams to illustrate the factors that determine isogyre position. (After W. B. Kamb, *Am. Mineralogist,* Vol. 43, p. 1042, 1958.)

      A. Orthographic projection and enlargement around point *P.*
      B. Stereographic projection and enlargement around point *N.*

duced between the emergent waves. The vectors of the refracted waves emergent from the crystal are designated as D_1' and D_2' and combine to form a more or less complex motion. D_1' and D_2' are rotated by the amount δ_2 toward the incident plane, ON. D_1' and D_2' are not shown in Fig. 7. The vectors of the waves that arrive at the analyzer are D_1'' and D_2'' and are shown in the enlarged portion of Fig. 7A. Note that D_1'' and D_2'' are *not* mutually perpendicular. D_1'' is rotated from PP', the direction of vibration of light waves from the polarizer, by an amount equal to the angle $(\xi - \delta_2)$. D_2'' is rotated from AA', the direction of vibration of light waves transmitted by the analyzer, by an amount equal to the angle $(\xi + \delta_2)$. The amplitude of the waves transmitted by the analyzer is

$$D_A = -D'' \sin (\xi - \delta_2) + D_2'' \cos (\xi + \delta_2)$$

The intensity of the light, I, for the light corresponding to point P that reaches the eye through the analyzer is

$$\frac{I}{C_2 I_0}$$

where I_0 is the intensity of the light entering the crystal plate and C is a constant factor. The intensity expression can be equated to a very complex function involving ξ, δ_1, δ_2, and ψ; ξ, δ_1, and δ_2 are all less than 5 degrees, and, by assuming that I is zero or a very small value and by making other simplifying assumptions, the following equation that specifies that P is in an isogyre may be derived:

$$[2\xi + (\delta_1 - \delta_2)](1 - \cos \phi) = 0$$

where ϕ is the phase shift (phasal difference) produced by the crystal plate for a specified wave length of incident light. When $\cos \phi = 1$, a condition that locates dark fringes in monochromatic light and corresponds to a path difference of p wave lengths, where p is a whole odd number, the above equation reduces to

$$2\xi = (\delta_1 - \delta_2)$$

or

$$\xi = \frac{(\delta_1 - \delta_2)}{2}$$

an equation that indicates, because ξ is a small angle, that the effects of rotation by the substage condenser and the objective lens tend to cancel each other. Although the rotation by the condenser may be as much as 10 to 15 degrees, the rotation in the opposite direction by the objective lens tends to reduce the total rotation in the interference figure to a small value. For the above equation to specify the location of a point on the isogyre, assumptions are made that the birefringence of the crystal plate is small and that the variation of C with position in the interference field is not large enough to be significant.

The Uniaxial Skiodrome

The skiodrome concept was proposed by Becke[4] and later was developed and elaborated by Johannsen.[5] The concept has been the subject of considerable debate, and Kamb[6] has strongly urged abandonment of the use of the skiodrome in optical crystallographic treatments on the grounds that it is based on faulty theory and, in some instances, gives an incorrect picture of the distribution of isogyres in interference figures. Nevertheless, the skiodrome provides an easily visualized interpretation of isogyres and in spite of its shortcomings has certain advantages, especially ease of construction, over the more difficult but theoretically more sound constructions proposed by Kamb. In the skiodrome, vibration directions on a reference sphere are projected orthographically into a plane to permit interpretation of the optical picture of the isogyres, and in all instances it is assumed that the vibration directions on the reference sphere and in the critical portion of the skiodrome are mutually perpendicular or nearly so.

Light energy passing in any direction through a uniaxial crystal, except in the direction of the optic axis, consists of two sets of waves vibrating in mutually perpendicular planes. The O waves vibrate in a plane perpendicular to a plane including the direction of the rays and the optic axis, that is, perpendicular to the principal section of the crystal. The E waves vibrate in a principal section.

If, as in Fig. 8A, wave normals for the wave fronts for the E waves in a principal section are located for various angles of θ with the optic axis, it is possible to calculate a series of wave-normal velocities for an indicatrix of specified dimensions. In three dimensions the wave normals for a particular wave-normal velocity form a cone about the optic axis. If a reference sphere having the same center as the indicatrix is assumed to envelop the indicatrix, it can be seen that, as in Fig. 8B, the cones intersect the sphere in circles. The vibration direction for a particular set of E waves is in the principal section and at right angles to any point on a circle on the sphere. For this same point on the circle the O waves are vibrating parallel to a tangent to the circle. The circles on the sphere may be called *curves of equal wave-normal velocity*, or *isotaques*.

[4] F. Becke, "Die Skiodromen," *Tsch. Min. Pet. Mitt.*, Vol. 24, pp. 1–34, 1905. Also, same publication, Vol. 28, pp. 290–293, 1909.

[5] A. Johannsen, *Manual of Petrographic Methods*, McGraw-Hill Book Co., New York, 1918.

[6] Kamb, *loc. cit.*

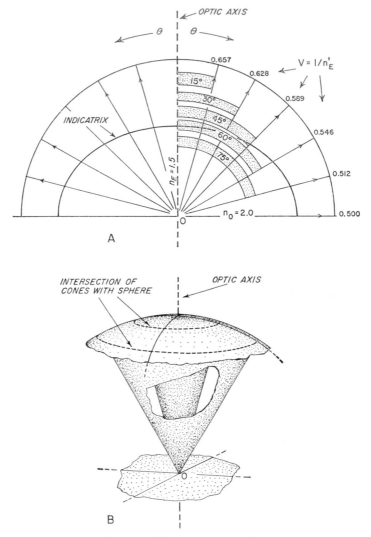

Fig. 8. Wave-normal velocities.

A. Wave-normal directions and velocities for the *E* component for several angles of *θ* in a uniaxial negative crystal. Drawing is in a principal section.

B. Intersection of cones containing directions of equal wave-normal velocities for *E* component with a spherical reference surface.

The uniaxial interference figure is an optic picture which appears to lie in a plane in spite of the fact that it is formed by light waves refracted through a great many angles and traveling through the crystal in all azimuths from 0 to 360 degrees. Accordingly, the optic picture is in some respects similar to an orthographic projection of refractive effects that are geometrically related to a hemisphere. In Fig. 9 circles on a sphere obtained as in Fig. 8*B* are projected orthographically into a plane normal to the optic axis to obtain a *skiodrome*. The circles are projected isotaques for equal wave-normal

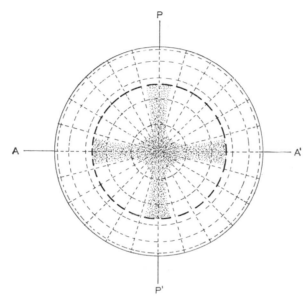

Fig. 9. Skiodrome of a uniaxial crystal. Plane of projection normal to optic axis. Heavy dashed circle indicates approximate area covered by field of microscope. Stippled area indicates location of isogyre.

velocities for the *E* wave fronts, and the radial lines are projected isotaques for the wave-normal velocities for *O* wave fronts. The circle outlined by the heavy dashed line indicates the approximate area of the field of a microscope containing the interference figure. The traces of the planes of vibration of the *E* and *O* waves at the intersection of a radial line and a circle are, respectively, parallel and at right angles to the radius at the point of intersection. A path difference can be calculated between the two sets of waves emergent from the crystal, if a birefringence and thickness are specified, but in this discussion we are concerned only with the use of the skiodrome for obtaining vibration directions, or, more precisely, the directions of the traces of the planes of vibration.

Figure 9 indicates by the extent of the stippled area within the dashed circle the points on the skiodrome for which the emergent light waves are vibrating in directions parallel or nearly parallel to the directions of vibration of light transmitted by the polars, *PP'* and *AA'*. Light waves for which the vibration directions are approximately or exactly parallel to the vibration directions of the polars is transmitted by the analyzer with very small or zero amplitude, so that the stippled area in Fig. 9 also indicates the shape and dimensions of the isogyre. Vibration directions taken from the skiodrome in greater detail than in Fig. 9 were used to construct the isogyre shown in Fig. 10.

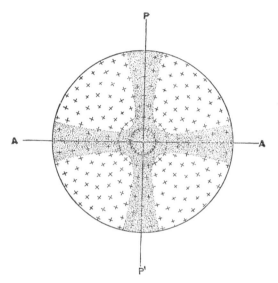

Fig. 10. Isogyre constructed from the skiodrome.

The light waves emerging from the crystal at any point interfere to produce plane-polarized, circularly polarized, or elliptically polarized waves, depending on the path difference produced by the crystal and the azimuth of the paths followed by the light waves relative to the planes of vibration of the polars. The light waves emerging from the crystal can be studied by means of vectors in the same manner as light that interferes to produce interference colors. Instead of considering the state of polarization of the light waves after emergence from the crystal in order to determine the amplitudes of the light waves that will pass through the analyzer, a more direct, approximate method of vector analysis will be used. This method assumes components of monochromatic light acting to reinforce or oppose each other in the analyzer, but, nevertheless, it gives approximately the same amplitudes as a more rigorous method of vector analysis.

In Fig. 11*A* suppose that we are considering monochromatic light waves at some point on a circle in the skiodrome. Light waves from the polarizer vibrating in *PP′* and with an amplitude of *Ob* are resolved by the crystal into two sets of waves of amplitudes *Oc* and *Oc′*.

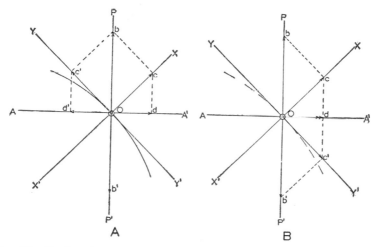

Fig. 11. Explanation of isogyre and color rings in uniaxial optic-axis figure.

A. Path difference *p*λ, where *p* is a whole number.

B. Path difference (*p*/2)λ, where *p* is a whole odd number.

If the path difference between the *E* and *O* waves upon emergence from the crystal is *p*λ, where *p* is a whole number, the waves upon entering the analyzer, *AA′*, will be resolved so as to cancel each other and yield light waves of zero amplitude. In Fig. 11*B* it is assumed that the crystal produces a path difference of (*p*/2)λ, where *p* is a whole odd number, so that light waves of measurable amplitude are transmitted by the analyzer. The amplitude of the transmitted light waves is the sum of the individual vectors in the plane of vibration of the analyzer.

The effects of azimuth are indicated in Figs. 12 and 13. In Fig. 12 vector diagrams are located on a circle for a path difference of *p*λ, *p* a whole number. The circle is a circle of darkness (zero illumination) for all azimuths. In Fig. 13 light with a path difference of (*p*/2)λ, *p* odd, results in transmission of light waves with maximum amplitude by the analyzer for an azimuth 45 degrees from the vibration planes of the polars and transmission of light waves of decreasing amplitude

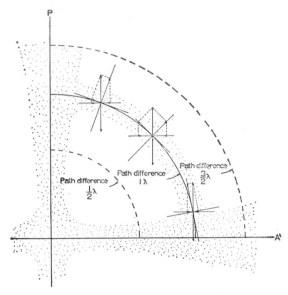

Fig. 12. Vector analysis of effect of conoscope on uniaxial crystal plate. Optic-axis figure. Path difference 1λ.

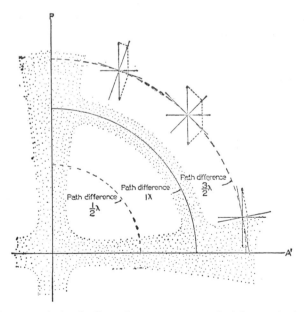

Fig. 13. Vector analysis of effect of conoscope on uniaxial crystal plate. Optic-axis figure. Path difference 3⁄2λ.

as the azimuths approach coincidence with the planes of vibration of the polars.

For a crystal plate cut perpendicular to the optic axis and illuminated by monochromatic light the result under the conoscope is an optic picture which consists of alternating dark circles and illuminated circles which grade around the circles in both directions from the 45-degree azimuths into a more or less diffuse black cross.

The Optic-Axis Figure

A centered optic-axis figure is formed in the conoscope by uniaxial crystal plates cut exactly perpendicular to the optic axis. Rotation of the microscope stage does not cause any movement of the color circles or the isogyre. The number of color circles and the sharpness of the gradation of the color curves into the isogyre is a function of the thickness and birefringence of the crystal plate and the optical system of the microscope. Thick plates of substances of low birefringence or thin plates of high birefringence yield closely packed color circles and sharply defined isogyres. Thin plates of substances of low to moderate birefringence show wide color circles grading into a more or less diffuse isogyre.

The optic-axis figure observed in one microscope may differ from the figure seen in another microscope in the number of visible color circles. The number of circles that may be counted for a crystal plate of a certain thickness and birefringence depends on the numerical apertures of the condensing lens and the objective lens. The number of circles increases as the numerical apertures increase. A typical condensing lens for conoscopic observations might have a numerical aperture near 0.9. The numerical aperture, N.A., equals $n \sin u$, where n is the lowest index of refraction in the path of the light, usually the index of air, and u is half the angular aperture. An objective lens used for conoscopic observation might have a numerical aperture of 0.65. The angle between the extreme light beams that can enter the objective lens to produce conoscopic effects is about 80 degrees for this objective lens. The same angle for an objective lens with a numerical aperture of 0.50 is only about 60 degrees. These considerations indicate that, in the explanation of the optic picture in an interference figure by use of the skiodrome and Bertin's surfaces, only the central portion of the skiodrome and only the Bertin's surfaces for the angles of emergence that can be accommodated by the objective lens should be considered.

In monochromatic light a centered optic-axis figure consists of a black cross superimposed on alternating circles of light and darkness. If a white-light source is used, the uniaxial optic-axis figure in general consists of a black cross and a series of concentric color circles. From the center outward, the colors rise in order through Newton's color scale as the path difference produced by the crystal increases. Gray near the center of the figure grades outward into yellow, then red, violet, blue, green, yellow, etc. If the birefringence of the crystal plate is low or the plate is very thin, only the gray and white circles are seen, and the edges of the isogyre are very diffuse. As the plate increases in thickness or birefringence, or both, the color bands become more numerous and more closely spaced, and the isogyre becomes more sharply defined.

Under the orthoscope, crystal plates cut exactly normal to the optic axis remain black on rotation between crossed polars. Accordingly, in the search for a fragment or grain which will give an optic-axis interference figure, the observer should look for a grain which has a black or dark-gray interference color during a complete rotation of the microscope stage.

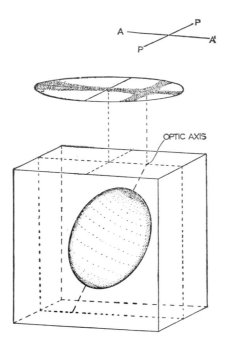

Fig. 14. Off-center optic-axis figure. Point of emergence of optic axis in field of microscope.

Off-Center Optic-Axis Figures

Perfectly centered optic-axis figures are rarely observed, and it becomes necessary to work with more or less off-center figures. Such interference figures can be as informative as the more symmetrical ones. Off-center figures result when the optic axis is not parallel to the axis of the microscope. Two possibilities are considered to illustrate cause and effect in such interference figures.

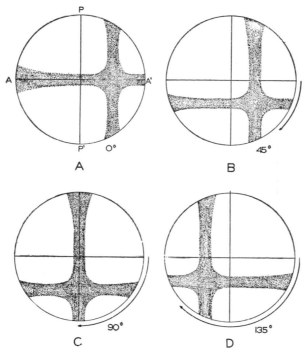

Fig. 15. Clockwise rotation on an off-center optic-axis figure. Point of emergence of optic axis in field of microscope.

Figure 14 shows a positive uniaxial crystal plate in which the indicatrix is slightly inclined with respect to the surface of a crystal plate. The drawing shows the plate in a position such that the plane of vibration of the analyzer is a plane of symmetry of the interference figure.

As the crystal plate is rotated, the optic axis describes a cone; and the point of emergence of the optic axis, a circle. Figure 15 shows in plan the effects of rotating the crystal plate. The arms of the isogyres move across the field essentially as straight bars, paralleling the traces of the planes of vibration of the upper and lower polars.

Figure 16 illustrates an example in which the point of emergence of the optic axis lies outside the field of the microscope. The crystal plate is uniaxial negative, as indicated by the outlines of the indicatrix, and has a higher birefringence than the example described above.

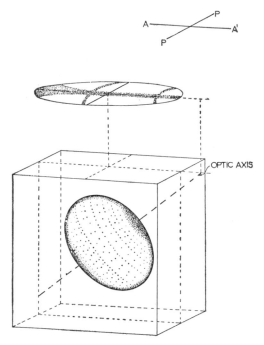

Fig. 16. Off-center optic-axis figure. Point of emergence of optic axis outside the field of the microscope.

As the crystal plate is rotated on the microscope stage, the point of emergence of the optic axis describes a circle which lies outside the field of view. The effects of rotation are indicated in Fig. 17, which shows that the brushes of the isogyre move as nearly straight bars across the field of the microscope as the stage is rotated. A study of the motion of the bars permits location of the approximate position of emergence of the optic axis. For example, the isochromatic curves and brushes in Fig. 17C suggest that the point of emergence of the optic axis lies in the lower right-hand quadrant.

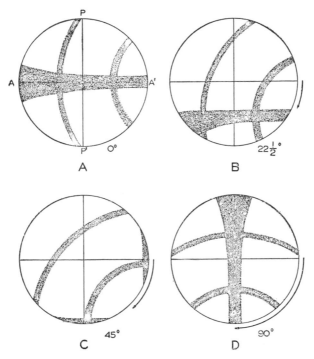

Fig. 17. Clockwise rotations on optic-axis figure. Point of emergence of optic axis outside the field of the microscope.

Flash Figures

Uniaxial crystal plates lying so that the optic axis is parallel to the microscope stage give *flash figures* under the conoscope. In the parallel position (that is, when the optic axis parallels the plane of vibration of either the upper or lower polar) the flash figure is a poorly defined black cross. The cross separates into two diffuse segments, which quickly leave the field upon slight rotation of the microscope stage from the parallel position. The segments leave the field of the microscope in the quadrants into which the optic axis has been rotated and, in this respect, are useful in determination of optic orientation.

Because flash figures are formed by crystal plates cut parallel to the optic axis, such plates as viewed under the orthoscope have maximum interference colors. If the flash figure is centered and the direction of the optic axis is located by noting the motion of the isogyres as the stage of the microscope is rotated, it is possible accurately to measure n_E for the crystal when the optic axis is north-south (in most microscopes) and n_O when the optic axis is east-west.

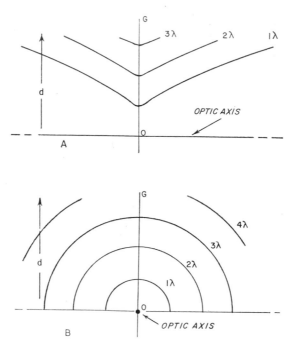

Fig. 18. Sections of Bertin's surfaces for path difference of $p\lambda$, where p is a whole number. Crystal plate has been cut parallel to optic axis.

A. Vertical section in a principal section.
B. Vertical section normal to optic axis.

The color curves that are observed in flash figures can be regarded as related to sections of Bertin's surfaces of equal path difference (equal retardation) in somewhat the same manner as the color circles in optic axis figures. The isogyre in the parallel position is explained by reference to a skiodrome, the plane of projection of which is parallel to the optic axis.

Figure 18*A* shows Bertin's surfaces in a principal section, and Fig. 18*B* shows the Bertin's surfaces in a section perpendicular to the optic axis. The sections indicate the distance that light incident at *O* must travel through the crystal in any direction within the section to produce a specified path difference in the emergent light waves. The curves in Fig. 18*A* and the circles in Fig. 18*B* were calculated for path differences of $p\lambda$, where p is a whole number, for a particular wave length of light, but similar curves could be calculated for any designated succession of path differences. The curves in Fig. 18 correspond to curves of darkness in an interference figure observed in monochromatic light. Bertin's surfaces for $(p/2)\lambda$ path difference,

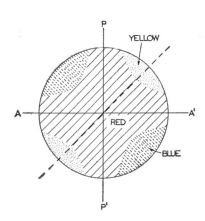

Fig. 19. Nested uniaxial Bertin's surfaces. Outer surfaces sectioned parallel to the optic axis in a principal plane.

Fig. 20. Distribution of colors in flash figure in 45-degree position for crystal plate producing a path difference of 560 mμ ±.

where p is odd, would locate curves of maximum intensity of illumination. Figure 19 indicates the shapes of sections of Bertin's surfaces in three dimensions where the plane of the section is parallel to the optic axis.

In white light the color for light passing through the crystal without refraction is the same as the interference color produced under the orthoscope and occupies the central portion of the interference figure. In a direction at right angles to the optic axis the color in the center of the figure grades into a succession of colors higher in Newton's scale. In the direction of the optic axis the color goes down as the crystal surface intersects Bertin's surfaces for increasingly lower path differences.

Figure 20 shows the distribution of the color curves for a crystal of moderate birefringence in the 45-degree position and illuminated by white light. A red color in the center grades into blue (a higher color) in a direction normal to the optic axis and into yellow (a lower color) in the direction of the optic axis. Figure 21 illustrates the distribution of color curves for a thick plate of a highly birefringent crystal plate in the 45-degree position as observed in monochromatic light.

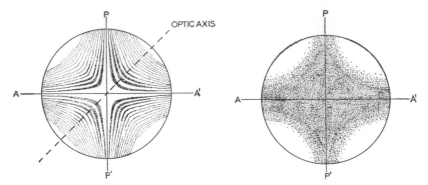

Fig. 21. Interference figure of highly birefringent crystal plate cut parallel to optic axis. Monochromatic light.

Fig. 22. Flash figure in parallel position.

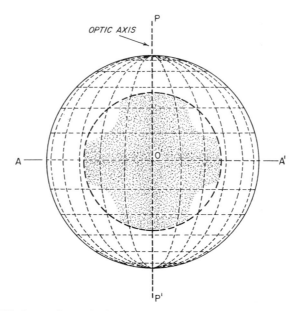

Fig. 23. Skiodrome for uniaxial crystal showing location of isogyre (stippled). Plane of projection parallel to optic axis. Parallel position with respect to polars. Heavy dashed circle indicates approximate field of microscope.

In the parallel position most of the field of the microscope is covered by a diffuse black cross as indicated in Fig. 22. Figure 23 shows a skiodrome in which the plane of projection of curves of equal wave-normal velocity is parallel to the optic axis. The area within the circle outlined by the heavy dashed line indicates the approximate portion of the skiodrome covered by the field of the microscope. The trace of the vibration plane at any point on a curve is normal to the

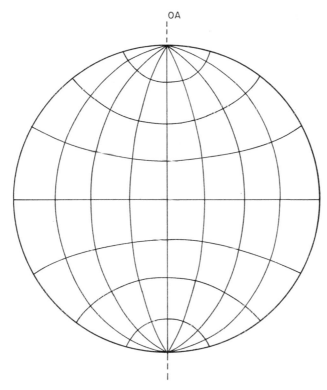

OA

Fig. 24. "Extinction direction net" for uniaxial flash figure. (After W. B. Kamb, *Am. Mineralogist,* Vol. 43, p. 1066, 1958.)

curve at the point. At any point of intersection of two curves two sets of waves emerging from the crystal vibrate in mutually perpendicular planes. Inspection of Fig. 23 indicates that in the parallel position with reference to the planes of the polars, *PP'* and *AA'*, most of the light waves emergent within the field of the microscope vibrate parallel to the vibration plane of one or the other of the polars and are transmitted by the analyzer with zero or minimum amplitude. Figure 23 also shows the resulting isogyre.

Figure 24 is the "extinction direction net" calculated by Kamb[7] from theoretically sounder assumptions than those used for calcula-

[7] Kamb, *loc. cit.*

tion and construction of the skiodrome in Fig. 23. Vibration directions in the interference picture are tangent to all points on the lines on the net.

Rotation of the crystal from the parallel position through only a few degrees places the crystal in a position such that none of the vibration planes for the crystal are parallel to the planes of the polars, and, except where the crystal has produced a path difference of a whole number of wave lengths for some particular wave length, light waves of measurable amplitude will be transmitted by the analyzer. The rapid breakup and disappearance of the isogyre from the field of the microscope as the stage is rotated slightly is characteristic of flash figures and accounts for the name.

CHAPTER 10 OPTICAL ACCESSORIES

Optical accessories have an important and varied use in optical crystallography. Many special types of accessories have been designed to assist in observation and measurement, but relatively few of these are needed for routine work. Three accessories—the quartz wedge, the gypsum plate, and the mica plate—are standard equipment and suffice for all but the most exacting investigations. Present-day manufacturers of microscopes generally have standardized the construction of the accessories, but it should be kept in mind that some microscopes are accompanied by accessories of diverse and sometimes unusual construction.

Certain expressions referring to the passage of light through optical accessories are in common use. Light waves incident on the birefringent crystal plates employed in the construction of optical accessories in general are resolved into two sets of waves vibrating in mutually perpendicular planes. Inasmuch as waves in one set travel through the plate with greater velocity than waves in the other set, a distinction may be made between the *fast* and *slow components* where a component is a set of waves vibrating in a particular direction or in a particular plane of vibration. In this terminology emphasis is placed on the *relative velocities* of the two sets of waves transmitted by the crystal plate rather than on the *relative refractive indices* of the crystal plate for the transmitted waves. Some investigators refer to the *fast component* as the *lower index component* and to the *slow component* as the *higher index component,* a practice that is not generally followed in this book. The *fast direction* of an optical accessory (or a crystal) is the direction of the trace of the plane of

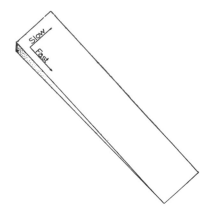

Fig. 1. Quartz wedge.

vibration of the component for which the crystal plate in the accessory has a relatively *lower* refractive index. Similarly, the *slow direction* is the direction of the trace of the plane of vibration of the component for which the crystal plate in the accessory has a relatively *higher* refractive index. The *trace of a vibration plane* is the intersection of the plane with a surface such as a crystal face or a cut surface.

The Quartz Wedge

The quartz wedge is used to determine the directions of the traces of the vibration planes of fast and slow components in crystal plates, to determine the order of interference colors, and to make optical sign determinations with or without interference figures.

Quartz wedges usually are cut so that the long direction of the wedge is parallel to the fast direction of the quartz, that is, parallel to the direction of the trace of the plane of vibration of the ordinary component. The slow component (extraordinary component) vibrates in a plane normal to the long direction of the wedge.

Some wedges are cut so that the slow component vibrates in a plane the trace of which is parallel to the long dimension of the wedge. In any event, the wedge should be tested with a crystal of known optical characteristics. The theory of the quartz wedge has been described in Chapter 8 and will not be repeated here. Figure 1 is a drawing of a typical quartz wedge.

The Gypsum Plate

The gypsum plate is made of clear gypsum or selenite ground or cleaved to such a thickness that it gives a first-order red interference color. Actually, the color is closer to magenta than to red. The plate is usually mounted in a metal holder so that the trace of the vibration plane of the fast component parallels the longer direction of the holder and the trace of the vibration plane of the slow component is normal to the longer direction.

The gypsum plate sometimes is called the *sensitive tint* or *red of first-order plate*. In use slight changes in the interference color of the plate are very apparent to the observer.

The gypsum plate is used for sign determination with crystals or interference figures, for determination of the locations of the traces of vibration planes in crystal plates, and for exact determination of extinction positions. It is most advantageously used with crystals of low birefringence or slight thickness, or both.

The gypsum plate like the quartz wedge usually is inserted into the microscope in the 45-degree position. If, for example, it is desired to determine the direction of the traces of the planes of vibration of the slow and fast components in a crystal plate with a first-order gray interference color, the crystal is turned to extinction and then to the 45-degree position. If the fast component in the crystal plate coincides with the fast component in the gypsum plate, the original magenta color of the plate goes up in the color scale, say to blue. If the slow component of the crystal is parallel to the fast component of the gypsum plate, the order of the color will go down, perhaps to yellow. It is important to observe that the effect is that of the crystal on the color of the gypsum plate and not the reverse.

The gypsum plate assists in the determination of exact extinction position. A crystal, as it is rotated, approaches extinction gradually, and it is sometimes difficult to ascertain when complete extinction is reached. If the gypsum plate is inserted when the crystal plate is exactly at extinction, the interference color that is seen is that of the gypsum plate. If the crystal plate is rotated slightly in either direction, a change in the interference color of the gypsum plate will be immediately apparent. If the crystal does not fill the entire field of view, it may be rotated until the color over the crystal exactly matches the color of the gypsum plate alone. The crystal is then at extinction.

Figure 2 shows a sketch of a common type of gypsum plate.

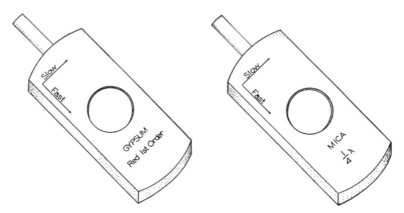

Fig. 2. Gypsum plate.   **Fig. 3.** Mica plate.

The Mica Plate

The mica plate, also called the *quarter undulation plate* or $\frac{1}{4}\lambda$ *plate,* is made of a sheet of muscovite mica cleaved so that its interference color in white light is pale neutral gray. A plate of proper thickness produces a path difference of one-fourth wave length for sodium light. Monochromatic sodium light emergent from the mica plate is circularly polarized. Light for other wave lengths is plane polarized or elliptically polarized.

The mica plate is used to determine optical sign from interference figures and may be used to ascertain the directions of fast and slow components in crystal plates or fragments. The mica plate, when superimposed over a crystal in the 45-degree position in effect increases or reduces the path difference produced in the crystal by the equivalent of one-fourth wave length for sodium light.

The mica plate is usually mounted in a metal holder and, like the gypsum plate, is ordinarily oriented so that the trace of the plane of vibration of its fast component is parallel to the long direction of the holder. It is most useful if used with crystals showing interference colors above white of the first order. Suppose, for example, that the mica plate is superimposed over a crystal plate with a second-order green interference color. If the fast components in crystal and mica plate are parallel, the total path difference is increased, and the color goes up the scale, perhaps to yellow. If the fast and slow components are parallel, the interference color goes down, say to blue.

Figure 3 shows a sketch of a mica plate as commonly constructed.

Accessories for Measurement of Extinction Angles

For accurate measurement of extinction angles, two accessories have proved very useful. They are the *Bertrand ocular* and *Wright's biquartz* wedge. Both require a cap analyzer that is placed above the accessories and rotated to the proper position.

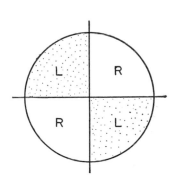

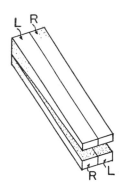

Fig. 4. Bertrand ocular.   **Fig. 5.** Wright's biquartz wedge.

The *Bertrand ocular* consists of four plates of quartz of the same thickness cut normal to the optic axis. Two plates are cut from right-handed quartz and two from left-handed quartz. Pairs of plates are mounted in alternate quadrants so that their rectangular edges correspond to the cross hairs (Fig. 4). The plane of vibration of light from the polarizer is rotated to the same extent by the left and right segments but in opposite directions. When the plane of vibration of the cap analyzer is exactly at right angles to that of the polarizer, the plates all yield a uniform pale bluish-green color.

A birefringent substance on the microscope stage, if not at extinction, causes the quadrants containing right-handed quartz to assume one color, the other quadrants a different color. Exactly at extinction all quadrants have the same color.

The biquartz wedge devised by Wright requires not only a cap analyzer but also a special ocular cut to allow for the insertion of the wedge at the level of an image in the optical system of the microscope. The wedge is constructed of two plates, over which are placed two wedges. The pieces are all cut at right angles to the optic axis, two from right-handed quartz and two from left-handed quartz, and are arranged as shown in Fig. 5. Zero rotation of the plane of vibration of light is produced where each half wedge has the same thickness as the underlying plate. A black band extending across the wedge marks the position of zero rotation.

When the wedge is placed over a birefringent substance not at extinction, the illumination of the two halves of the wedge is unequal. At exact extinction the half-wedges are equally illuminated.

Accessories for Measurement of Path Difference

Path difference (or phasal difference) produced by a birefringent crystal plate may be accurately measured by several devices. Three are widely used: the graduated quartz compensator, the Berek compensator, and the Babinet compensator. The graduated quartz com-

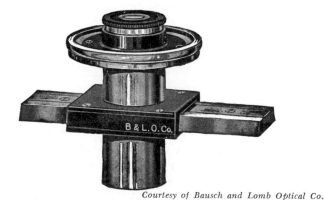

Courtesy of Bausch and Lomb Optical Co.

Fig. 6. Holder and eyepiece with graduated quartz compensator.

pensator requires a special ocular (Fig. 6) and a cap analyzer. Compensation produces a dark line across the wedge. The position of this line on a graduated scale etched on the surface of the wedge gives the path difference directly in millionths of a millimeter ($m\mu$).

The Berek compensator (Fig. 7) is used in the tube slot above the objective and, therefore, does not require a cap analyzer and a special ocular. A plate of calcite 0.1 mm thick is cut normal to the optic axis and mounted on a rotating axis in a metal holder. A calibrated drum controlling the rotation permits measurement of the angular position of the calcite plate.

To determine path difference the crystal plate is rotated on the microscope stage so that the trace of the vibration plane of its fast

component is parallel to the trace of the vibration plane of the slow
component in the inclined calcite plate in the compensator. The
angle through which the calcite plate is rotated to obtain compensation measures the path difference produced by the crystal plate.

The Berek compensator assists in the determination of optic sign.
Also, it may be used effectively to determine the directions of vibration of the fast and slow components in crystals.

Courtesy E. Leitz and Co.

Fig. 7. Berek compensator.

The Babinet compensator consists of two thin wedges of quartz
arranged so that one wedge can be moved over the other. The wedge
edges oppose each other so that the upper and lower surfaces of the
compensator remain parallel for all adjustments. One wedge is cut
with its long dimension parallel to the optic axis of the quartz, and
the other wedge is cut so that the optic axis is transverse. With this
arrangement the slow and fast components of one wedge oppose the
fast and slow components of the other wedge, and where light passes
through the same thickness in both wedges no path difference is
produced for the emergent light. For other portions of the compensator a path difference is produced which is a measure of the differential thickness of the wedges in the compensator. The wedges can
be adjusted so as to produce a desired path difference for any wave
length of light for any part of the compensator within the limits of the
design.

The Universal Stage

The universal stage, when attached to the microscope stage, converts the microscope into an instrument of diversified uses. A brief
summary of the theory and application of the universal stage is given
in Chapter 17.

11

By definition uniaxial crystals are positive if the index of refraction for the extraordinary waves, n_E, is greater than the index for the ordinary waves, n_O. If the reverse relationship holds, the crystal is negative. In positive crystals the velocity of the ordinary waves is greater than that of the extraordinary waves; the reverse is true in negative crystals.

Most methods of determining optic sign depend on measurement of the indices of refraction or on the determination of the relative velocities of the ordinary and extraordinary waves. Three methods are outstanding: (1) direct measurement of the indices of refraction; (2) determination of the directions of the traces of vibration planes of fast (lower index) and slow (higher index) components in crystals or cleavage fragments in which the orientation of the c crystallographic axis is known; and (3) examination of interference figures, including optic axis and flash figures.

Sign Determination with Indices of Refraction

This method is useful when index determinations are being made in immersion media. The index for the ordinary waves may be measured in all uniaxial crystal fragments. A crystal fragment lying so that its optic axis is parallel to the axis of the microscope produces no path difference in the emergent light waves and remains black or gray between crossed polars during a complete rotation of the microscope stage. A fragment in this position yields n_O only.

A fragment lying so that its optic axis is parallel to the stage of the microscope produces a maximum path difference between the emergent waves for the two components of transmitted light and, accordingly, shows a maximum interference color. A fragment in this orientation permits measurement of both n_O and n_E. A grain in an intermediate orientation gives the ordinary index n_O but will not yield the full value for the index of the crystal for the extraordinary waves. That is, for grains in random positions n_O remains constant, but the index of the crystal for the waves in the extraordinary component varies with the orientation of the grain.

If it is ascertained that the varying index is consistently higher than the index of the crystal for the ordinary waves, it is known that the crystal is positive. Conversely, if the varying index is less than n_O, the crystal is negative.

Sign Determination with Crystals or Cleavage Fragments

Uniaxial crystals and cleavage fragments permit determination of optical sign if they are sufficiently well formed and symmetrical to permit recognition of the direction of the c crystallographic axis. Waves in the extraordinary component vibrate in the principal section, which includes the optic axis and the c crystal axis, and waves in the ordinary component vibrate normal thereto.

Suppose that, as in Fig. 1, two hexagonal crystals lie 45 degrees from extinction and show second-order green interference colors between crossed polars. Crystal A is oriented so that its optic axis parallels the fast direction (lower index component) of an accessory plate. Crystal B, at right angles to crystal A, is oriented with its optic axis perpendicular to the fast direction of the accessory plate. If a mica plate is inserted, and the interference color in A goes up in the color scale to second-order yellow and the color in B goes down to second-order blue, the crystals are negative. The color goes up in A because the fast direction of the plate parallels the fast component (the extraordinary component) of the crystal. In crystal B fast and slow components are parallel.

If a quartz wedge is used, the interference colors go up in Newton's scale in crystal A and down in crystal B as the wedge is inserted. When the path difference of the wedge equals the path difference produced in the emergent waves by crystal *B*, the compensation point will have been reached, and the crystal will have a gray or black interference color.

With positive crystals the effects on crystals *A* and *B* are the reverse of those described above.

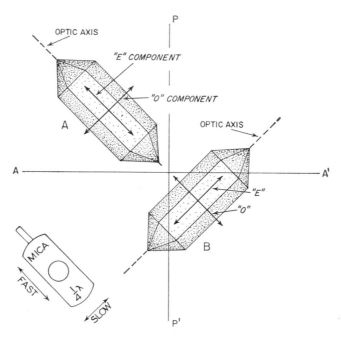

Fig. 1. Sign determination in uniaxial crystals with mica plate.

In Fig. 2 two tetragonal crystals lie in the 45-degree position. Suppose that the interference color is first-order gray. The crystals bring about interference color changes in a gypsum plate, and, if the crystals are positive, crystal *A* causes the first-order red of the plate to fall in order, perhaps to yellow. Crystal *B* might change the color in the accessory plate to blue. Both color changes are expressions of the fact that in uniaxial positive crystals the waves in the extraordinary component are slower than the waves in the ordinary component.

Negative crystals under the gypsum plate give effects which are opposite to those described above.

Cleavage fragments may be characteristic enough in certain substances to permit determinations of optical sign. In practice, the trace of the vibration plane of the extraordinary component is turned to coincide with the fast direction of the accessory plate to ascertain whether waves in the extraordinary component are faster or slower than waves in the ordinary component. It should be remembered that waves in the extraordinary component vibrate in the principal section, which includes both the optic axis and the *c* crystal axis.

In general, in sign determination with crystals, the gypsum plate should be used for crystals with gray or first-order white interference colors, although it may be used effectively with grains showing higher

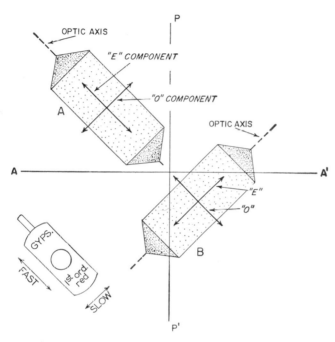

Fig. 2. Sign determination in uniaxial crystals with gypsum plate.

order colors. The mica plate and quartz wedge serve well for grains with colors above first-order yellow.

In thick or highly birefringent crystal fragments the interference colors may be whites of a higher order. A quartz wedge should be used, and particular attention should be paid to the motion of the conspicuous red color bands in wedge edges of the fragments. If the fast direction of the quartz wedge parallels the trace of the vibration plane of the slow component of the crystal, the color bands move in toward the center of the crystal as the quartz wedge is inserted. If the fast directions are parallel, the color bands move toward the edge of the crystal.

Sign Determination with Optic-Axis Figures

Uniaxial crystals or fragments lying so that their optic axes are parallel to the axis of the microscope are black or dark gray between crossed polars during a complete rotation of the microscope stage and yield optic-axis figures under the conoscope.

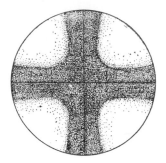 

Fig. 3. Diffuse uniaxial optic-axis figure without isochromatic curves.

Fig. 4. Uniaxial optic-axis figure showing isochromatic curves.

Two types of optic-axis interference figures are shown in Figs. 3 and 4. Figure 3 illustrates the diffuse black cross seen in interference figures of a crystal plate having low birefringence or slight thickness, or both. Only first-order gray or white color curves are present. The gypsum plate is the best accessory for sign determination with this type of figure.

Figure 4 is an interference figure of a more highly birefringent or thicker crystal fragment. Concentric color curves are conspicuous, and the arms of the isogyre are narrow and sharply defined. Most suitable accessories for determination of sign with this figure are the mica plate and quartz wedge; however, a gypsum plate may be used effectively at times.

The theory underlying the determination of sign in uniaxial optic-axis figures is easily grasped if one keeps in mind the manner of double refraction of the light waves entering and passing through the crystal plate. Light waves in each beam emerging from the crystal plate vibrate in the principal section and at right angles to the principal section. In Fig. 5 light emerging at any point on the dashed circle consists of two components: the extraordinary component E', containing waves in a plane the trace of which is a radial line; and the ordinary component O, containing waves vibrating in a plane the trace of which is tangent to the circle. Note that in the 45-degree position the traces of the vibration planes of the extraordinary components in quadrants 2 and 4 are parallel to the vibration direction of the ordinary components in quadrants 1 and 3. Likewise the ordinary components in quadrants 2 and 4 vibrate parallel to the extraordinary components in quadrants 1 and 3.

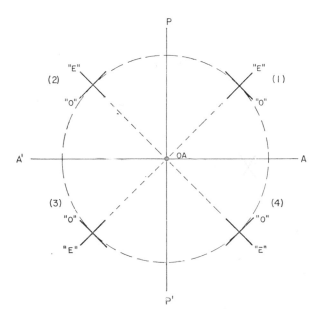

Fig. 5. Traces of the planes of vibration of the ordinary and extraordinary components in uniaxial optic-axis interference figures.

Ordinarily, an accessory plate is inserted into the microscope so that its fast direction lies in quadrants 2 and 4, parallel to the traces of the planes of vibration of the extraordinary components. In quadrants 1 and 3 the fast direction of the plate parallels the traces of the vibration planes of the ordinary components. Also, the slow direction of the accessory plate parallels the traces of the vibration planes of the ordinary components in quadrants 2 and 4 and the traces of the vibration planes of the extraordinary components in quadrants 1 and 3.

In positive crystals waves in the extraordinary component are slower than waves in the ordinary component. In Fig. 6 the effects of the introduction of a gypsum plate on a diffuse optic-axis figure of a positive crystal are shown. The source of illumination is white light. In quadrants 2 and 4 the trace of the vibration plane of the extraordinary component is parallel to the fast direction of the plate, and the red of the gypsum plate goes down in order to yellow. In the opposite quadrants fast components in both the accessory plate and the crystal are parallel, and the color of the plate is elevated to blue. In white

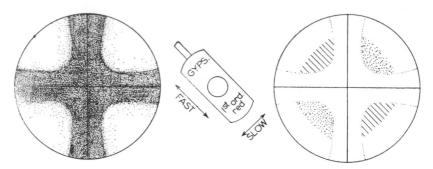

Fig. 6. Determination of sign with gypsum plate. Positive uniaxial optic-axis figure. Stippled area blue; hatched area, yellow. The student may wish to color the appropriate areas to emphasize the effects.

light the area occupied by the isogyre assumes the interference color of the gypsum plate alone. In negative crystals the effects of insertion of the gypsum plate are the opposite of those obtained with positive crystals.

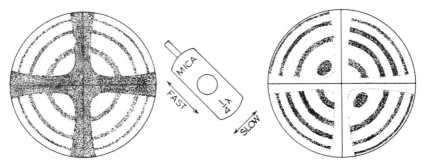

Fig. 7. Determination of sign with mica plate. Positive uniaxial optic-axis figure.

If a gypsum plate is used on interference figures with isochromatic curves, the color changes are seen in the plate very close to the isogyre. Moreover, black curves appear where the plate compensates the first-order red curves.

Figure 7 illustrates the action of a mica plate on a positive crystal giving an optic-axis figure showing color curves. Black spots form close to the isogyre in quadrants in which the fast direction of the plate parallels the traces of the vibration planes of the slow components of the crystal, and the path difference of the light traveling through the crystal is compensated for by the $\frac{1}{4}\lambda$ path difference for yellow light produced by the mica plate. In the quadrants containing the black spots (actually compensated isochromatic curves), the isochromatic curves are displaced outward because in these quadrants the mica plate in effect decreases the path difference produced by the crystal. In the opposite quadrants, where the fast directions of plate and crystal are parallel, the color curves move in because of the $\frac{1}{4}\lambda$ increase of the path difference of all components emerging in these quadrants. With white-light illumination the area occupied by the isogyre assumes the first-order gray interference color of the mica plate alone.

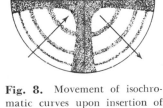

Fig. 8. Movement of isochromatic curves upon insertion of quartz wedge. Uniaxial positive interference figure.

Figure 8 shows the direction of movement of the isochromatic curves in an interference figure when a quartz wedge is pushed into the microscope. Black spots or black curves appear where compensation occurs, but the positions of these spots or curves change as the wedge is inserted.

In the quadrants where compensation is observed the wedge compensates for the path difference for color circles obtained in white light at increasingly greater distances from the center of the figure as the wedge is inserted. Thus, if the path difference produced by the wedge alone is the same as the path difference that has produced a circle of second-order blue in Newton's color scale, the position of the blue circle will be occupied by a dark circle and the next rings beyond will show a succession of colors beginning with first-order gray and increasing systematically in the color scale. Behind the compensated color curve the wedge overcompensates, and the total effect is that of outward movement of all the color curves away from the center of the figure. The color of the isogyre changes to correspond to the path difference produced by the wedge alone. In the quadrants where the fast directions of the wedge and crystal plate are parallel, insertion of the wedge causes a steadily increasing path difference, and the color curves move toward the isogyre.

Perfectly centered optic-axis figures are not seen as frequently as off-center figures. However, off-center figures may be used as effectively as the centered ones. Sign is easily determined if the point of emergence of the optic axis lies in the field of view. If, however, the point of emergence of the optic axis lies outside the field of view, its position must be determined by observing the distribution of the

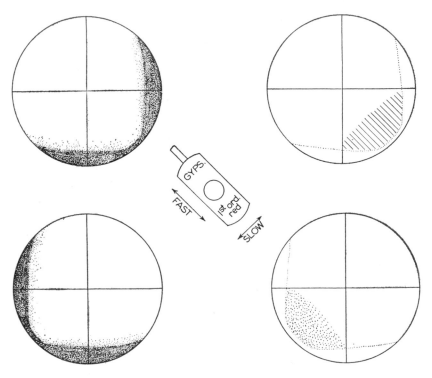

Fig. 9. Positive off-center uniaxial interference figure. Effect of insertion of gypsum plate. Stippled area, blue; hatched area, yellow. The student may wish to color the appropriate areas to emphasize the effects.

isochromatic curves and the motion of the arms of the isogyre during rotation of the stage of the microscope. Figures 9 and 10 show the changes that take place upon insertion of accessory plates over off-center optic-axis figures in which the point of emergence of the optic axis lies outside the field of the microscope.

Sign Determination with Flash Figures

Uniaxial flash figures may be used to determine sign. Upon rotating the microscope stage, the diffuse black cross in flash figures

Fig. 10. Positive off-center uniaxial interference figure.   Effect of insertion of mica plate.

splits into two segments which leave the field of the microscope in the quadrants containing the optic axis (*c* crystallographic axis).   When the optic axis is located, the crystal is rotated to the 45-degree position; the Bertrand-Amici lens and the auxiliary substage condenser are removed, and it is determined by means of accessory plates whether the waves in the component parallel to the optic axis are faster or slower than the waves in the component perpendicular to it.

Sign of Elongation

Hexagonal and tetragonal crystals commonly display a prismatic habit and are elongate parallel to the *c* crystallographic axis.   If it is determined in such crystals that waves in the fast component vibrate in a plane the trace of which is parallel or nearly parallel to the long direction of the crystal, the *sign of elongation* is said to be *negative,* and the crystal is said to be "length fast."   Conversely, if the trace of the vibration plane of the waves in the slow component is parallel to the length, the elongation is described as *positive,* and the *crystal* is said to be "length slow."

However, some crystals are flattened normal to the c axis and in section may give elongate plates. Again, as above, if the waves in the fast component vibrate parallel or nearly parallel to the long direction, the sign of elongation is negative; it is positive if wave vibrations in the slow component parallel the longer dimension.

Because of the differences of crystal habit, then, the sign of elongation of a crystal may or may not be the same as the optic sign. In the same substance one section may give a positive sign of elongation, and another negative elongation. However, because most of the crystals of a given substance commonly assume the same habit, determination of sign of elongation may be useful despite its limitations.

CHAPTER **12** BIAXIAL CRYSTALS—

THE BIAXIAL INDICATRIX

Crystals in the orthorhombic, monoclinic, and triclinic crystal systems are *biaxial* and are characterized by three principal refractive indices. Biaxial crystals receive their name from the fact that they possess *two* directions along which the wave-normal velocity (wave-front-normal velocity) for monochromatic light is constant regardless of the directions of vibration of the waves perpendicular to the wave normal. In *uniaxial* crystals there is only *one* such direction.

Biaxial Indicatrix

The relations among the indices of refraction in biaxial crystals are best seen in a *biaxial indicatrix* (Figs. 1 and 2), a triaxial ellipsoid for a particular color of light which has three planes of symmetry and is so constructed that the three principal indices of refraction of a crystal for light waves in their *directions of vibration* (*not* directions of transmission) are equal to its three mutually perpendicular semi-axes. A clear understanding of the function and construction of the ellipsoid is necessary for the development of optical theory for biaxial crystals.

The three principal indices of refraction of a crystal for light waves in their direction of vibration in biaxial crystals are designated as

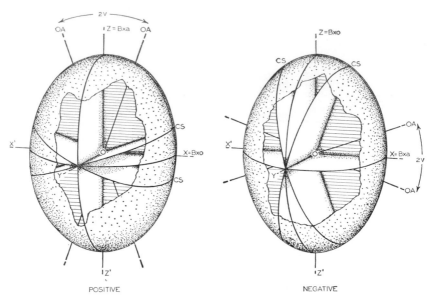

Fig. 1. Biaxial indicatrices. *OA,* optic axis; *CS,* circular section; *Bxa,* acute bisectrix; *Bxo,* obtuse bisectrix.

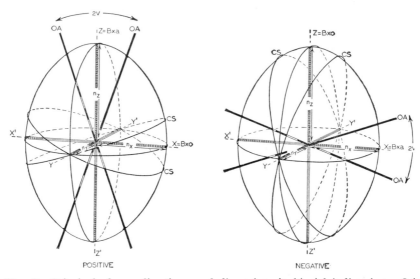

Fig. 2. Principal planes, directions, and dimensions in biaxial indicatrices. *OA,* optic axis; *CS,* circular section; *Bxa,* acute bisectrix; *Bxo,* obtuse bisectrix; n_X, n_Y, and n_Z, principal refractive indices.

n_X, n_Y, and n_Z and are equal, respectively, to the OX, OY, and OZ semiaxes of the ellipsoid; n_X is the smallest index, n_Y the intermediate index, and n_Z the largest. In a given crystal, the indices of refraction are specified for a particular wave length of the incident light. Hence the accompanying diagrams are exactly representative of conditions that exist only when strictly monochromatic light is used. The practical and theoretical implications that arise when white light is used are discussed in Chapter 15.

In positive biaxial crystals as n_Y approaches n_X, the indicatrix approaches the form of a prolate ellipsoid of revolution—the form of a uniaxial positive indicatrix. In negative biaxial crystals as n_Y approaches n_Z, the indicatrix assumes the form of a negative uniaxial indicatrix lying on its side—in a position such that its optic axis is horizontal.

Various designations for the three principal refractive indices of biaxial crystals are given in the accompanying table.[1]

Equivalent Designations of the Principal Refractive Indices of Biaxial Crystals

n_X	α	N_X	n_α	N_α	X	N_p
n_Y	β	N_Y	n_β	N_β	Y	N_m
n_Z	γ	N_Z	n_γ	N_γ	Z	N_g

The *circular sections* of the biaxial indicatrix pass through the Y axis of the indicatrix. All radii of the circular sections are equal to n_Y; thus it is seen that the particular position occupied by a circular section is a function of the value of n_Y as it is related to n_X and n_Z.

The *primary optic axes* are perpendicular to the circular sections. The *optic angle, 2V,* is the smaller (acute) angle between the optic axes and lies in the XZ plane, the *optic plane*. In positive crystals the optic angle is bisected by the Z axis of the indicatrix, and Z is described as the *acute bisectrix*. In negative crystals X is the acute bisectrix. The axis bisecting the larger (obtuse) angle between the optic axes is designated as the *obtuse bisectrix*. In abbreviated notation the acute bisectrix is designated as *Bxa* and the obtuse bisectrix as *Bxo*.

The Y axis is perpendicular to the plane containing the optic axes (the optic plane), and, accordingly, is called the *optic normal*.

The numerical difference between the minimum and maximum

[1] Papers submitted for publication in the *American Mineralogist* should indicate the refractive indices as α, β, and γ.

refractive indices, n_X and n_Z, is the *birefringence* and is geometrically equivalent to the difference between the semimajor and semiminor axes in the XZ plane, the optic plane. The numerical differences between n_Z and n_Y, n_Y and n_X, or any other pair of refractive indices are *partial birefringences*.

The angle V_Z between the Z axis and an optic axis may be computed from the refractive indices. The following equation is useful; for positive crystals it gives an angle less than 45 degrees and for negative crystals, an angle greater than 45 degrees. For negative crystals the computed angle is subtracted from 90 degrees to obtain one-half the optic angle.

$$\tan^2 V_Z = \frac{\dfrac{1}{(n_X)^2} - \dfrac{1}{(n_Y)^2}}{\dfrac{1}{(n_Y)^2} - \dfrac{1}{(n_Z)^2}}$$

The following equation gives the angle between an optic axis and the X axis of the indicatrix. In positive crystals the computed angle is greater than 45 degrees.

$$\cos^2 V_X = \frac{(n_Z)^2[(n_Y)^2 - (n_X)^2]}{(n_Y)^2[(n_Z)^2 - (n_X)^2]}$$

When approximations suffice, the following equations are useful:

$$\cos^2 V'_X = \frac{n_Y - n_X}{n_Z - n_X}$$

or

$$\tan^2 V'_X = \frac{n_Z - n_Y}{n_Y - n_X}$$

Wright[2] derived several equations for rapid computation of the axial angle. He states that, within the limits of 1.400 to 2.000 for n_X the equations yield values for the optic angle accurate to one minute of arc for birefringences of 0 to 0.050 and to three minutes of arc for birefringences of 0.050 to 0.100. One of his equations, slightly modified, is

$$\cos 2V_Z = \frac{\epsilon - \delta}{\epsilon + \delta} - \frac{6\epsilon\delta}{(\epsilon + \delta)(n_Z + n_X)}$$

[2] F. E. Wright, "Computation of the Optic Axial Angle from the Three Principal Refractive Indices," *Am. Mineralogist,* Vol. 36, pp. 543–556, 1951.

where

$$\epsilon = n_Z - n_Y$$

$$\delta = n_Y - n_X$$

Many nomograms and other types of plots have been devised for graphical determination of the optic angle when the principal refractive indices are known. Wright[3] discusses several of the graphical

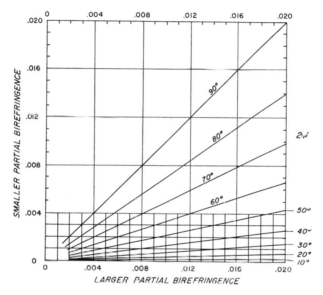

Fig. 3. Chart for estimating approximate $2V$ angle from partial birefringences.

devices for optic angle determination and lists bibliographic references that will enable the interested student to pursue the subject farther.

Figure 3 is a diagram that will permit estimation of the approximate value for $2V$ from the refractive indices. The diagram is based on the approximate formula

$$\tan^2 V = \frac{n_Z - n_Y}{n_Y - n_X}$$

The appropriate partial birefringences are calculated and the $2V$ angle is obtained by comparing the smaller partial birefringence (ordinates) with the larger partial birefringence (abscissae) and locating the appropriate diagonal line for $2V$. The diagram is more useful for estimation of large $2V$ angles than for estimation of small angles.

[3] Wright, *ibid.*

Figure 4 is a nomogram of the type described by Mertie.[4] A straightedge, preferably a transparent one, is placed on the value for n_X to the left and on the value for n_Z on the right. The value for n_Y is projected on a horizontal line to intersection with the straight-

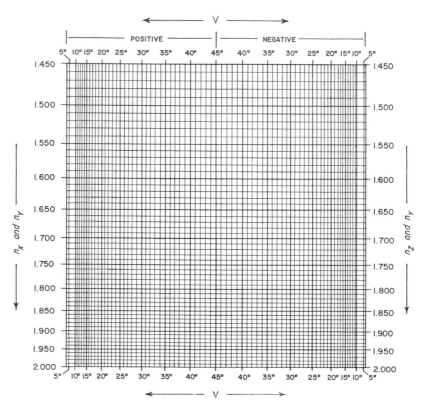

Fig. 4. Nomogram for determining V, half the optic angle, from measured values of n_X, n_Y, and n_Z. (After J. B. Mertie, Jr., *Am. Mineralogist,* Vol. 27, pp. 538–551, 1942.)

edge, and the value for V is indicated by a vertical line. Optic sign also is indicated. The nomogram is based on the $\sin^2 V_Z$ function, and, in common with most other types of nomograms, it does not give accurate estimations of V for crystals with small birefringences or with small optic angles.

Figures 5 and 6 show the important planes of biaxial positive and

---

[4] J. B. Mertie, Jr., "Nomograms of Optic Angle Formulae," *Am. Mineralogist,* Vol. 27, pp. 538–551, 1942.

negative indicatrices. In Fig. 5, $n_X = 1.5$, $n_Y = 1.6$, and $n_Z = 2.0$; in Fig. 6, $n_X = 1.5$, $n_Y = 1.9$, and $n_Z = 2.0$. Note that the relative posi-

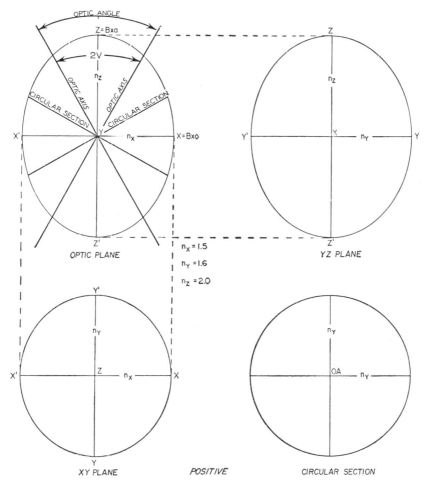

Fig. 5. Principal planes of a positive biaxial indicatrix in which $n_X = 1.5$, $n_Y = 1.6$, and $n_Z = 2.0$.

tions of the circular sections and the optic axes are determined by the value of n_Y relative to the values of n_X and n_Z.

Phemister[5] describes the mathematical relationships implied by the indicatrix as it is considered in terms of the electromagnetic theory

[5] T. C. Phemister, "Fletcher's Indicatrix and the Electromagnetic Theory of Light," *Am. Mineralogist*, Vol. 39, pp. 172–192, 1954.

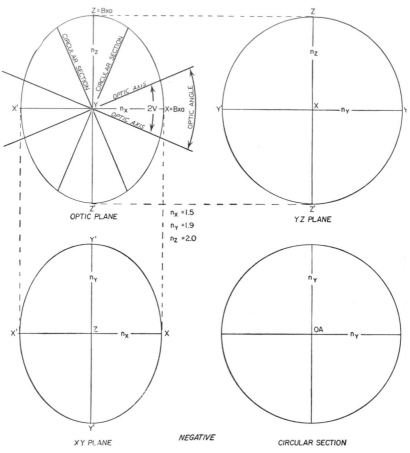

Fig. 6. Principal planes of a negative biaxial indicatrix in which $n_X = 1.5$, $n_Y = 1.9$, and $n_Z = 2.0$.

of light. The interested student, particularly if he is mathematically inclined, is urged to review Phemister's treatment.

Ray-Velocity Surfaces

The triaxial ellipsoid offers an easily visualized means of analyzing the passage of light through crystals. However, it is possible to construct other surfaces which, under many conditions, are more informative than the indicatrix. Among the most useful surfaces are the *ray-velocity surfaces,* which are mathematically and geometrically related to the indicatrix and are derivable therefrom.

The quantitative relationships between the indicatrix and the ray-velocity surfaces in the planes of symmetry of the indicatrix are of the same general kind as those described for the uniaxial indicatrix and its derived ray-velocity surfaces. To avoid repetition only the

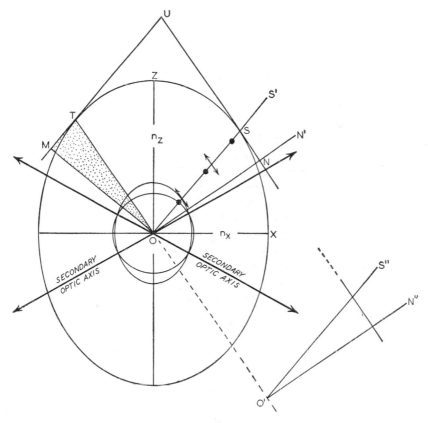

Fig. 7. Section in optic plane of a biaxial negative crystal showing relationships of wave normals and rays.

geometric aspects of the interrelationships of the surfaces are reviewed here. The student may wish to refer to the discussion on pages 92–99 before continuing with the following presentation.

In Fig. 7, O and O' are point sources of light waves of a certain frequency and are coincident with the centers of two identical indicatrices, only one of which is shown. The plane of the drawing is the optic plane. Now, let ON' be the direction of the wave normal for a wave front containing waves generated at O and O' vibrating in the optic plane parallel to the wave front. OT, the dimension of the indicatrix at right angles to the direction of the wave normal, is the index of refraction of the crystal for these waves in the direction of their vibration and is the refractive index that is measured experimentally. The velocity of advance of the wave front in the direction of the wave normal is proportional to $1/OT$.

To obtain the direction of movement of trains of individual light waves along the rays associated with the wave front, a line TU is drawn tangent to the indicatrix at T, and a line OS' is drawn through O parallel to TU and intersecting the indicatrix at S. OS' is the direction of the rays as determined in this manner. OM is determined by drawing a line from O to TU perpendicular to OS' and is the *ray index of refraction* of the crystal. The ray index has only a calculated value and is not obtained by direct physical measurement. The velocity of movement of the individual waves or pulses of energy in a train along OS' is proportional to $1/OM$ and is greater than the velocity of movement of the associated wave front in the direction of the wave normal.

OS and OT are *conjugate radii*. OT and OS and the tangents to the indicatrix TU and US outline a parallelogram $OTUS$. The area of the parallelogram is equal to the product of the base by the altitude and is $OS \cdot OM$. The area of all parallelograms enclosed by conjugate radii and the tangents to the ellipse at the ends of the radii is constant. In Fig. 7, OX and OZ represent a special case in which the conjugate radii are mutually perpendicular.

Accordingly,

$$OS \cdot OM = OX \cdot OZ = n_X \cdot n_Z$$

and

$$OM = \frac{n_X \cdot n_Z}{OS}$$

The velocity of the individual waves vibrating in the optic plane and constituting a train along OS' is, in the direction of OS', proportional to

$$\frac{1}{OM} = \frac{OS}{n_X \cdot n_Z}$$

and in Fig. 7 is indicated by the spacing of the arrows along OS'. Note that the arrows indicating the direction of vibration are drawn perpendicular to the wave normal, in keeping with an assumption of the electromagnetic theory of light. For waves vibrating in phase in the optic plane and moving along all possible rays outward from O, an ellipse is generated which has semimajor and semiminor axes which are proportional to $1/n_X$ and $1/n_Z$, respectively.   This ellipse is a section of a ray-velocity surface.   A second set of waves originating at O and vibrating normal to the optic plane move out in phase from O

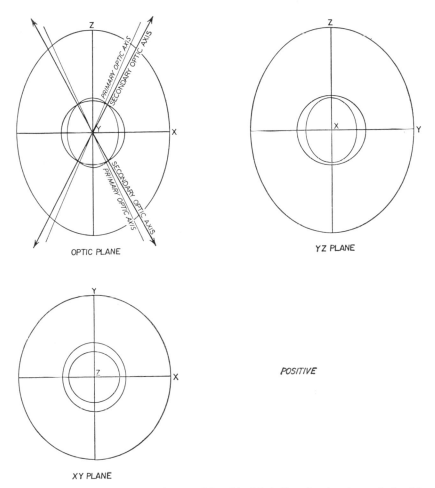

Fig. 8.   Symmetry planes of a positive biaxial indicatrix showing relationship between ray-velocity surfaces and indicatrix.

along all possible rays to generate a circle, which, again, is a section of a ray-velocity surface.   The radius of the circle is proportional to $1/n_Y$.

In two directions, OX and OZ, the rays and wave normals are parallel.   Accordingly, light traveling along OX consists of two com-

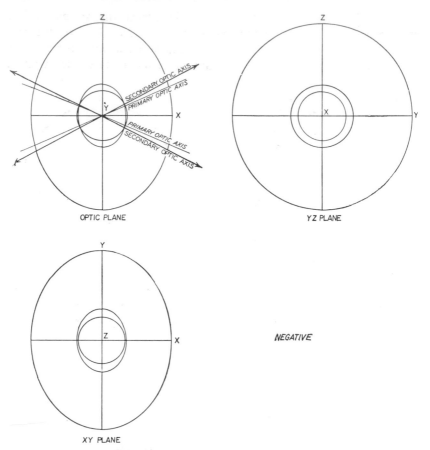

Fig. 9. Symmetry planes of a negative biaxial indicatrix showing relationship between ray-velocity surfaces and indicatrix.

ponents: one vibrating in the XZ plane and having equal wave-normal and ray velocities proportional to $1/n_Z$ and the other vibrating normal to the XZ plane and having equal wave-normal and ray velocities proportional to $1/n_Y$. The two components of the light moving in the OZ direction have equal wave-normal and ray velocities proportional to $1/n_X$ and $1/n_Y$, respectively.

The ray-velocity surfaces intersect at four points in the XZ plane, and lines drawn through these intersections give the directions of the *secondary optic axes.* The secondary optic axes are directions of *equal ray velocity,* as opposed to the *primary optic axes,* which are normal to the circular sections of the indicatrix and are directions of *equal wave-normal velocity.* The angle between the primary and secondary optic axes is commonly less than 2 degrees.

Sections of ray-velocity surfaces in the symmetry planes of positive and negative biaxial indicatrices are shown in Figs. 8 and 9.

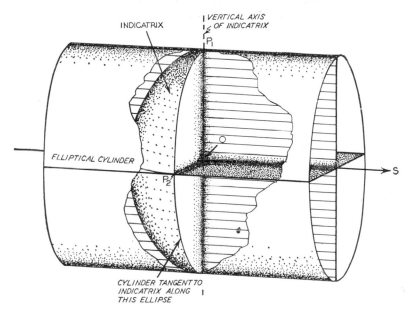

Fig. 10. Diagram to show relationship between rays and waves traveling in a direction normal to a symmetry plane of a biaxial indicatrix.

Generalized Interrelationships of Rays and Wave Normals (Wave-Front Normals)

The wave normal is perpendicular to the wave front and is the direction in which the wave front moves through a crystal. A ray is the path that the light energy in individual waves or wave trains follows in moving from one point to another in the crystal and, in general, does not coincide with the wave normal. The *plane of vibration* is a plane which includes both the ray and its associated wave normal.

In directions perpendicular to symmetry planes of the biaxial indicatrix rays coincide with their associated wave normals as indicated in Fig. 10. In Fig. 10 suppose that OS is a ray perpendicular to a symmetry plane of the indicatrix and is the direction of movement of two trains of waves vibrating in mutually perpendicular planes. An elliptical cylinder with its elements parallel to OS is drawn tangent to the indicatrix. The symmetry planes of the tangent cylinder coincide with the symmetry planes of the indicatrix, and OP_1 and OP_2 are at the same time the ray indices and the wave indices of refraction of the crystal. In the direction of *OS* the individual light waves vibrate in the wave front and at right angles to the rays and move in the same direction as the associated wave front.

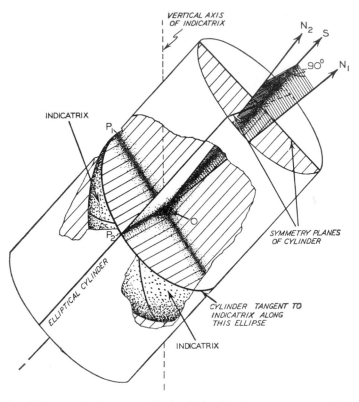

Fig. 11. Diagram showing generalized relationship between a ray and its associated wave normals.

Figure 11 portrays a more general example in which the ray does not coincide with its associated wave normals. Suppose that *OS* is the direction of propagation along a ray of wave trains vibrating in mutually perpendicular planes of vibration. The direction of vibration of the waves in each train is not normal to *OS* but is parallel to the associated wave fronts. To locate the associated wave fronts and wave normals a cylinder with its elements parallel to *OS* is drawn so as to be tangent to the indicatrix. This cylinder has an elliptical cross section even when the points of tangency with the indicatrix coincide with a circular section. The semimajor and semiminor axes of the cylinder measured at right angles to *OS* give the ray indices of refraction for the crystal, and the velocities of the wave trains moving along OS are inversely proportional to the ray indices of refraction.

The elliptical section of the indicatrix determined by the points of tangency of the cylinder with the indicatrix is *not* perpendicular to OS. OP_1 and OP_2 are dimensions of the indicatrix in the elliptical section that lie in the symmetry planes of the tangent cylinder and are the vibration directions of the waves in the trains along OS. ON_1 and ON_2, perpendicular to OP_1 and OP_2 and lying in the symmetry planes of the tangent cylinder (the planes of vibration), locate the wave normals associated with the two wave trains moving along OS. The refractive indices of the crystal for the waves in their direction of vibration are equal to OP_1 and OP_2. The velocities of movement of the wave fronts in the directions of the wave normals, ON_1 and ON_2, are proportional to $1/OP_1$ and $1/OP_2$, respectively.

Now, suppose that the direction of a wave normal for the parallel wave fronts for two sets of waves vibrating in mutually perpendicular planes is known, and it is desired to locate the directions of the rays corresponding to the two wave fronts. This is the situation that might exist when light is normally incident on a random section of a biaxial crystal, and it is wished to locate the paths taken by the light energy in traveling through the crystal. An analogous treatment for uniaxial crystals explains the two dots that are seen when a calcite cleavage rhomb is placed over a single dot. In biaxial crystals two dots are seen as in calcite, but, unlike calcite, neither dot is directly in line with the dot over which the crystal plate is placed. In Fig. 12, ON is the wave normal and is perpendicular to a random elliptical section of an indicatrix. The semimajor and semiminor axes of this section, OP_1 and OP_2, give the refractive indices of the crystal for the two sets of waves that comprise the wave fronts moving in the direction of ON. The velocities of propagation of the wave fronts are proportional to $1/OP_1$ and $1/OP_2$, respectively.

To obtain the ray indices of refraction normals to the indicatrix surface are erected at P_1 and P_2. OS_1 and OS_2, drawn perpendicular to these normals in mutually perpendicular planes including OP_1 and OP_2 and the direction of the wave normal, ON, are the directions of the rays. P_1Q_1 and P_2Q_2 are the ray indices of refraction of the crystal for the light waves following the two rays. The velocities of the individual waves (or energy pulses) following the rays are $1/P_1Q_1$ and $1/P_2Q_2$, respectively.

When the velocity for light waves (not wave fronts) moving along all rays in a crystal has been determined, it becomes possible to construct three-dimensional ray-velocity surfaces such as those shown in Fig. 13. The ray-velocity surfaces intersect at four points—at the bottoms of four "dimples" in the surface of the outer shell. The directions obtained by drawing lines through the bottoms of the

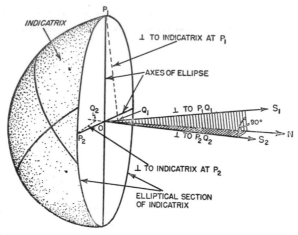

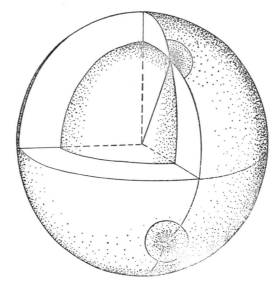

Fig. 12. Diagram showing relationship between a wave normal and its associated rays.

Fig. 13. Ray-velocity surfaces in three dimensions.

dimples and the center are directions of the *secondary optic axes*. The dimples are outlined by circles which represent the line of contact of the outer shell and a plane tangent to the shell.

Figure 14 portrays considerably exaggerated sections of the ray velocity surfaces in the planes of symmetry.

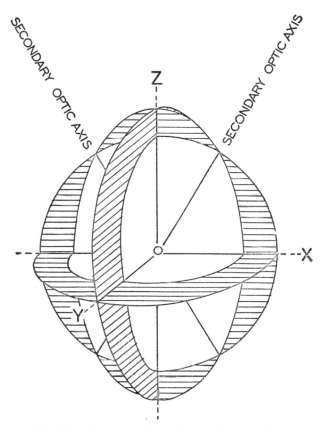

Fig. 14. Symmetry planes of ray-velocity surfaces.

Optic Orientation of Orthorhombic Crystals

The three planes of symmetry of the indicatrix demand that certain conditions regarding its orientation be fulfilled in biaxial crystals. That is, the position of the indicatrix with reference to the symmetry elements of a crystal cannot be such as to be out of harmony with the morphologic symmetry of the crystal. Optical properties as related to crystallographic directions must show the same geometrical distribution or variations as other physical properties, such as hardness, luster, or cleavage.

Orthorhombic crystals have three mutually perpendicular unequal axes and, in the dipyramidal class, three planes of symmetry. This symmetry requires the indicatrix to be oriented so that its three mutually perpendicular axes, the X, Y, and Z axes, coincide with the a, b, and c axes of the crystal. Any deviation from this principle would result in lowering the symmetry of the crystal, thus placing it in the monoclinic or triclinic system. The parallel orientation of indicatrix axes and crystallographic axes results in coincidence of the optical and morphologic planes of symmetry. Moreover, the optic plane must lie in one of the three crystallographic planes of symmetry.

The following orientations are possible:

1. Optic plane parallel to (010) and

$$X = a \qquad X = c$$
$$Y = b \quad \text{or} \quad Y = b$$
$$Z = c \qquad Z = a$$

2. Optic plane parallel to (100) and

$$X = b \qquad X = c$$
$$Y = a \quad \text{or} \quad Y = a$$
$$Z = c \qquad Z = b$$

3. Optic plane parallel to (001) and

$$X = a \qquad X = b$$
$$Y = c \quad \text{or} \quad Y = c$$
$$Z = b \qquad Z = a$$

Figure 15 illustrates an orthorhombic crystal for which the orientation and certain other optical data for a particular wave length may be expressed as follows:

	n	Orientation	Bisectrices	
X	n_X	c	Bxa	Negative
Y	n_Y	a	—	$2V = 18°$
Z	n_Z	b	Bxo	

Optic Orientation of Monoclinic Crystals

Monoclinic crystals have three unequal axes. The a and c crystal axes intersect at acute and obtuse angles and lie, in the prismatic class, in a plane of symmetry. The b axis is normal to the symmetry

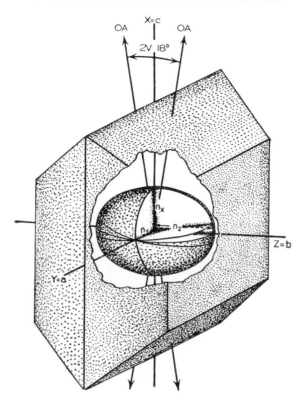

Fig. 15. Negative orthorhombic crystal in which $X = c$, $Y = a$, and $Z = b$. Optic plane is parallel to (100).

plane. The symmetry of a monoclinic crystal requires the following possibilities with respect to the orientation of the indicatrix for a particular color of light:

1. The X axis is parallel to the b crystallographic axis. The optic plane is parallel to the b axis but may occupy any position with respect to the a and c axes but only one position for monochromatic light in a given crystal species.

2. The Y axis parallels the b crystallographic axis. The optic plane lies in the (010) plane, and the X and Z axes, mutually perpendicular, may lie in any position with respect to the a and c axes but in a definite position for each crystalline substance.

3. The Z axis parallels the b crystallographic axis, and the optic plane is parallel to the b axis and may occupy any position with respect to the a and c axes but only one position for a given crystal.

Figure 16 shows one possibility for a monoclinic crystal illuminated by monochromatic light. The Y axis of the indicatrix is parallel to

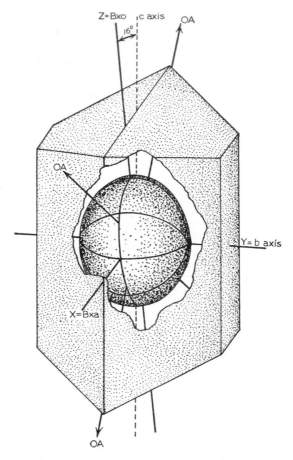

Fig. 16. Monoclinic crystal showing the orientation of the indicatrix for a particular wave length of light. Optic plane is parallel to (010). $Z \wedge c = 16$ degrees.

the b axis of the crystal. The optic orientation and certain other data may be tabulated as follows:

	n	Orientation	
X	n_X		Negative
Y	n_Y	b	$2V = 80°$
Z	n_Z	$\wedge c = 16°$	

Optic Orientation of Triclinic Crystals

Triclinic crystals have no planes of symmetry. Accordingly, the indicatrix may occupy any position with respect to the crystallographic axes, but the position is fixed for a given crystal and a particular color of light.

The orientation of the indicatrix in triclinic crystals is seen to best advantage in stereographic projections. Measurements commonly are made with a universal stage, and the results are plotted so as to show the angular relationships between prominent crystal faces and the important directions of the indicatrix. By means of a stereonet it is possible to rotate a projection into any desired position.

Crystallographers use ϕ and ρ to indicate the angular positions of linear directions or the normals to crystal faces. ϕ is the angle of azimuth measured from the zero meridian, commonly the pole of the (010) face of a crystal, and it is positive in a clockwise direction from 0 to 180 degrees. In the counterclockwise direction from the zero meridian, ϕ is negative. ρ is the angular inclination of a direction or a normal to a face with respect to the north-south axis of the spherical projection and is plotted as the angular distance of a pole from the center of the projection.

The crystallographic study of axinite by Peacock[6] provides an excellent example of the interrelationships of optical and other crystallographic constants in a triclinic crystal. The accompanying table is based on Peacock's data. Figure 17 illustrates the relationships expressed in the table in a three-dimensional drawing.

In Fig. 17 windows have been cut away to show the orientation of the indicatrix for sodium light in an axinite crystal, the center of which is coincident with the center of a hollow sphere enveloping the crystal. Projection of the optical directions and the normals to the crystal faces to the surface of the sphere gives a spherical projection of the poles of the directions and crystal faces. The great circles passing through the poles are zonal lines on the surface of the sphere.

Figure 18 is a stereographic projection of the same data into the equatorial plane of the spherical projection in Fig. 17. The brushes passing through the points of emergence of the optic axes (OA) suggest that the X axis is the acute bisectrix. The zones shown in Fig. 18 correspond to those shown on the surface of the spherical projection in Fig. 17.

[6] M. A. Peacock, "On the Crystallography of Axinite . . . ," *Am. Mineralogist,* Vol. 22, pp. 588–624, 1937.

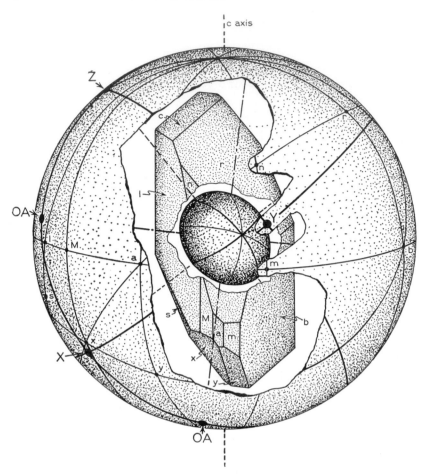

Fig. 17. Spherical projection of crystallographic data for axinite. Both the sphere and the crystal of axinite inside it have been cut away to show in three dimensions the interrelationships of the spherical projection, the axinite crystal, and the indicatrix for sodium light. (Crystallographic data from Peacock, *Am. Mineralogist,* 1937.)

Huygenian Constructions in Biaxial Crystals

Figure 19 shows a particular orientation of the ray-velocity surfaces in an orthorhombic crystal. Only the planes of symmetry of the ray-velocity surfaces are indicated. Figure 20 illustrates three Huygenian constructions for a crystal similar to the one in Fig. 19. The sections in Fig. 20 are parallel to planes of symmetry of the crystal. Any section other than one including two axes of the indicatrix would require a three-dimensional drawing because the rays for the refracted

Crystallographic Constants for Axinite

(Selected from more complete data by Peacock)

Triclinic; pinacoidal

Axial angles: $\alpha = 91° \, 51\frac{1}{2}'$; $\beta = 98° \, 04'$; $\gamma = 77° \, 14'$

Forms		ϕ	ρ	Forms		ϕ	ρ
c	001	89° 23	8° 04′	r	011	8 03	45 21
b	010	0 00	90 00	y	$\bar{1}01$	−75 45	49 13
a	100	102 38	90 00	n	111	62 51	57 41
m	110	60 28	90 00	x	$\bar{1}11$	−41 09	59 39
M	$1\bar{1}0$	135 25	90 00	s	$\bar{1}21$	−26 10	68 34
l	$1\bar{2}0$	151 01	90 00				

Optical Elements

	ϕ	ρ	$n_{(Na)}$		
X	−42°	56°	1.683		
Y	59	75	1.688	±0.002	Negative $2V = 81°$
Z	168	39	1.692		

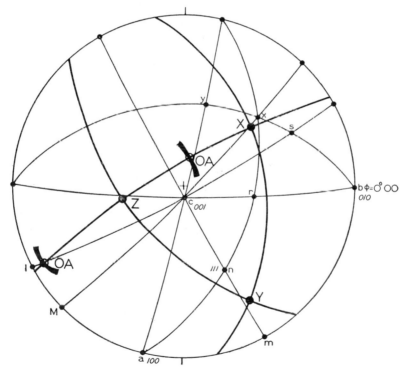

Fig. 18. Stereographic projection of optical and other crystallographic data for axinite. Plane of projection is the equatorial plane of the spherical projection shown in Fig. 17.

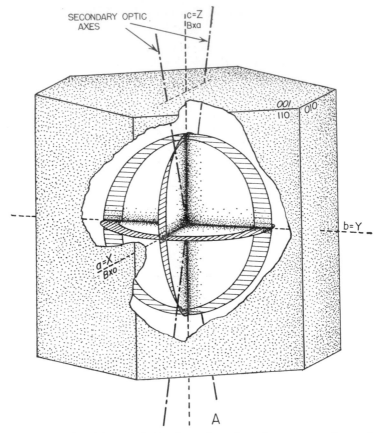

Fig. 19. Orthorhombic crystal showing orientation of symmetry planes of ray-velocity surfaces in a positive crystal in which $X = a$, $Y = b$, and $Z = c$.

light waves do not lie in the same plane, although the planes including the vibration directions are mutually perpendicular. In this particular crystal, the orientation is $X = a$; $Y = b$; $Z = c$. The crystal is optically positive.

In the drawings the relative velocities of the waves in the wave trains moving along the rays are indicated by the spacing of the dots and arrows. The arrows indicate the direction of vibration of waves whose ray-velocity surfaces in the plane of the drawing are ellipses. The arrows are not perpendicular to the direction of propagation in the crystal but, rather, parallel to the tangent to the ray-velocity surface at the point of intersection with the ray. The waves vibrating normal to the drawing are indicated by dots. These waves produce circular ray-velocity surfaces in the sections of the drawings.

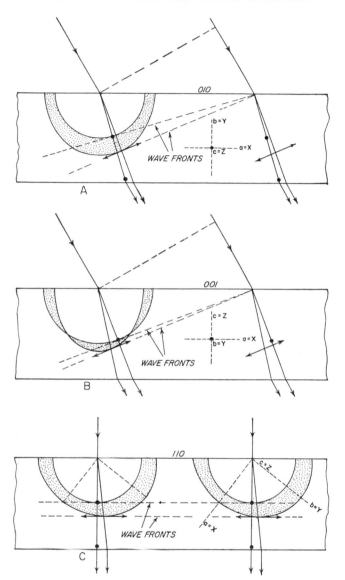

Fig. 20. Huygenian constructions for an orthorhombic crystal similar to the one in Fig. 19.

        A. Light falling with inclined incidence on (010).
           Plane of incidence parallel to (001).
        B. Light falling with inclined incidence on (001).
           Plane of incidence parallel to (010).
        C. Light falling with perpendicular incidence on (110).
           Plane of incidence parallel to (001).

Extinction Angles in Biaxial Crystals

The purpose of measuring extinction angles is the location of the directions of the traces of mutually perpendicular vibration planes of light waves that emerge from a crystal and the correlation of directions of vibration of the waves with identifiable crystal directions and planes. This procedure, in effect, gives information regarding the orientation of the indicatrix. Extinction angles measured from crystal axes or crystal planes when one of the axes or one of the planes of symmetry of the indicatrix is parallel to the axis of the microscope generally provide the most useful type of information. Crystals are at extinction when the traces of the planes of vibration of the emergent light waves are parallel to the planes of vibration of the upper and lower polars.

Extinction angles in any section of a crystal of known properties can be calculated by complex formulae described by Johannsen[7] and Rosenbusch and Wülfing.[8] In this book only simple graphical methods employing stereographic projections will be reviewed.

Graphical (and mathematical) solutions are based on the relationships stated in the *law of Biot-Fresnel*. This law states that the vibration directions, or, more precisely, the directions of the traces of the planes of vibration, of the waves transmitted by a biaxial crystal plate for perpendicularly incident light waves bisect the angles between two planes which are normal to the plate and include the wave normal and the directions of the optic axes. In Fig. 21 suppose that an elliptical section has been cut through the center of the indicatrix for a particular color of light and that the indicatrix is enveloped by a sphere whose center coincides with the center of the indicatrix. *ON* is the direction of the single wave normal for two sets of waves vibrating in mutually perpendicular directions and, in their wave fronts, traveling perpendicular to the section of the indicatrix. *N* is the point of emergence of the wave normal on the surface of the sphere. *A* and *B* are the points of emergence of the optic axes on the sphere, and *AN* and *BN* are arcs of great circles drawn from *A* and *B* to *N*.

According to the Biot-Fresnel law, the angles formed by the great circles joining the points of emergence of the optic axes and the point of emergence of the wave normal on a section cut normal to *ON*, the wave normal, are bisected by the traces of the vibration planes of the two sets of waves moving along the normal. Note that each section of

[7] A. Johannsen, *Manual of Petrographic Methods*, McGraw-Hill Book Co., 1918.

[8] H. Rosenbusch and E. A. Wülfing, *Mikroscopische Physiographie*, Vol. I, Part 1, Stuttgart, 1921/24.

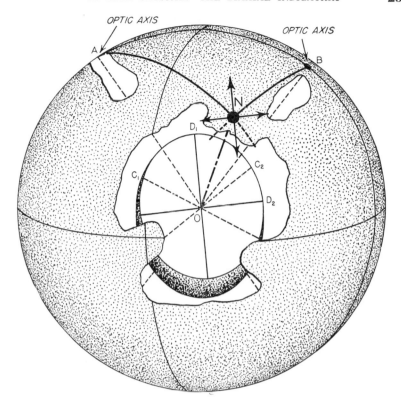

Fig. 21. Diagram used in proving Biot-Fresnel law.

the sphere defined by such a great circle includes an optic axis and the wave normal. In Fig. 21 OC_1 and OC_2, two radii of the elliptical section of the indicatrix, are also the radii of the circular sections lying in the section of the indicatrix perpendicular to ON. Inasmuch as all radii of the circular sections are equal, OC_1 and OC_2 are equal and, therefore, must lie symmetrically on either side of OD_1 and OD_2, the semimajor and semiminor axes of the elliptical section of the indicatrix. Now, the mutually perpendicular vibration planes of the two sets of waves moving along ON include OD_1 and OD_2. Accordingly, the vibration planes bisect the angles between the planes including ON and the optic axes.

Stereographic constructions using a stereonet (see p. 310) show how extinction angles as measured from crystal directions or planes vary as a function of variation of the direction of the crystal section and variation in the optical properties. Figure 22 shows the relationships in a crystal of a monoclinic amphibole for which $Z \wedge c = 20$ degrees

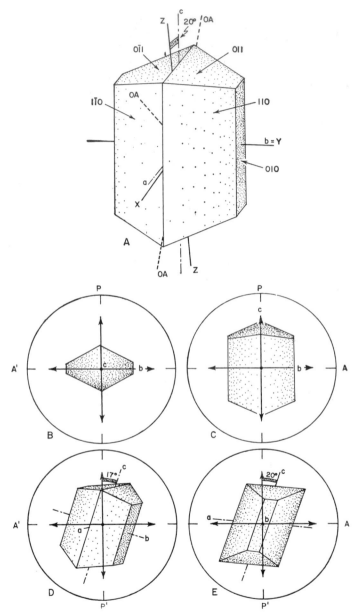

Fig. 22. Extinction angles in monoclinic crystal in several orientations.

    A. Clinographic projection showing optic orientation.

    B. Crystallographic *c* axis parallel to microscope axis.

    C. Crystallographic *b* and *c* axes parallel to microscope stage.

    D. Crystal resting on {110} face.

    E. Crystal resting on {010} face.

in the obtuse angle β and the optic plane lies in {010}. The crystal is assumed to have an optic angle of 85 degrees. The extinction angles that may be measured in the crystal for various orientations are indicated in Fig. 22B–E. Figure 22A is a clinographic projection showing the crystal faces, the crystal axes, and the optic orientation. In Fig. 22B the crystal is viewed under the microscope in a direction parallel to the c axis, and the extinction angle as measured from {010} is zero. In Fig. 22C the crystal is resting on the microscope stage in a position such that the b and c axes are both parallel to the stage. For this orientation the extinction angle as measured from either the {010} face or the direction of the c axis again is zero. In Fig. 22D it is assumed that the crystal has rolled over so as to rest on a prism face, {110}. The c axis is still parallel to the microscope stage, but the b axis is inclined to it. The extinction angle between the direction of the c axis as determined by the edges of intersection of the faces parallel to the c axis and the nearest extinction position is 17 degrees. Finally, in Fig. 22E the crystal is oriented so that the b axis is parallel to the axis of the microscope, and $Z \wedge c = 20$ degrees.

The extinction angle of 17 degrees in the crystal in Fig. 22D was predicted from the constructions in Figs. 23 and 24. Figure 23 is a stereographic plot of the crystal faces and directions shown in Fig. 22A. To obtain the extinction angle in a section cut parallel to {110} or in a crystal resting on {110}, as in Fig. 22D, great circles 1 and 2 are drawn through the poles of {110} and the poles of the optic axes (OA). Great circles 3 and 4 are drawn so as to bisect the angles between great circles 1 and 2. The angle of 17 degrees between the pole of the c axis and the intersection of the trace of the {110} plane with great circle 3 gives the extinction angle measured from the direction of the c axis to the nearest extinction position in a crystal resting on {110}.

Figure 24 shows a manipulation which produces straight lines in the stereographic plot for the great circles passing through the optic axes and a normal to the {110} face. The crystal is assumed to be lying on the microscope stage in the position indicated in Fig. 22C, and the poles for this position are indicated by open circles on the plot. Now, the crystal is rotated so as to rest on a {110} face as in Fig. 22D, and in the projection the poles of the crystal faces and directions are rotated so as to occupy the positions indicated by the solid circles. In the rotated position the pole for {110} is in the center of the plot; that is, it is polar. To obtain the vibration directions for the light waves emerging from the crystal, straight lines 1 and 2 are drawn through the pole for {110} and through the poles for the optic axes. The bisectors of the angles thus obtained locate the traces of

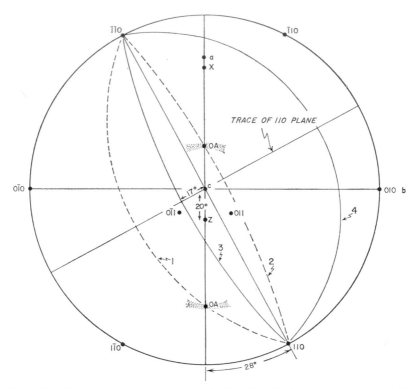

Fig. 23. Stereographic plot of crystal in Fig. 22. Projection from upper half of spherical projection.

the planes of vibration of the emergent light waves. When these are parallel to the vibration planes of the polars, the crystal will be at extinction. As for Fig. 22, $Z \wedge c$ turns out to be 17 degrees.

The extinction angle of 20 degrees measured from the c axis for a crystal oriented so that the b axis is parallel to the microscope axis (Fig. 22E) is, for this particular crystal, a maximum angle in the zone {100: 010}. If the optic angle, 2V, were 60 degrees instead of 85 degrees, constructions similar to those described above would indicate an extinction angle of 24 degrees for a crystal lying on {110}. For a 2V of 40 degrees the extinction angle is 30 degrees, and so on. An infinite number of possibilities is suggested when various extinction angles are determined graphically for all possible kinds of biaxial crystals. However, in monoclinic crystals a prismatic habit is common, and there are numerous occasions when an opportunity is presented to measure extinction angles from the direction of the c axis, parallel to the long dimension of the crystals. The statement

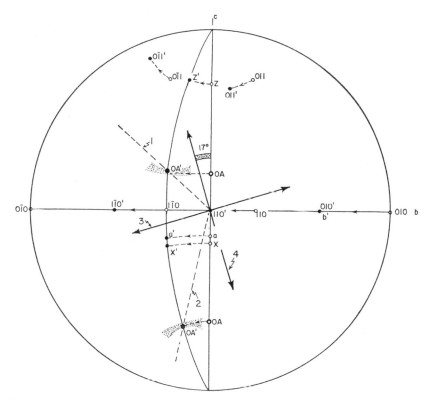

Fig. 24. Stereographic plot of crystal in Fig. 22. Projection from upper half of spherical projection.

is sometimes made that in such crystals the maximum extinction angle is measured in sections parallel to {010}, a statement that for certain combinations of optical properties and optic orientation is not in agreement with the facts. Accordingly, in all biaxial crystals, including monoclinic crystals, maximum extinction angles as they are employed to identify critical optical and crystallographic directions should be used with caution.

Measurement of an exact extinction position for a crystal illuminated with monochromatic light is a relatively simple procedure. However, in white-light illumination exact measurements may be difficult or impossible because of the fact that the indicatrices for different colors may have different optic angles and different crystallographic orientations. In orthorhombic crystals the X, Y, and Z axes of all the indicatrices are parallel to the crystallographic axes, but variations in the optic angles may result in incomplete extinction in random sections. In monoclinic crystals sharp extinction is seen in crystal sections cut parallel to the b crystal axis because one of the indicatrix axes for every color is parallel to the b axis. In other sections different indicatrix orientations and optic angles tend to prevent complete extinction. In triclinic crystals the indicatrix for each color has a different orientation, and the lack of parallelism of the axes and variations in the optic angles may prevent complete extinction in all sections of a crystal. If the differences in the optic angles and orientations are slight, extinction positions in white light may be located with sufficient accuracy for routine work, but, if the differences are great, a monochromatic-light source must be used to obtain reliable results.

Determination of Refractive Indices and Optic Orientation of Biaxial Crystals

The three principal refractive indices of biaxial crystals are most conveniently determined by the immersion method. By proper manipulation the indices can be measured without the aid of interference figures, although interference figures assist in locating fragments that have proper orientations. The use of interference figures in index measurement is described in a subsequent section of the book. To obtain n_X, the minimum refractive index, several fragments showing maximum interference colors are rotated to the extinction position for which the relief, Becke line, etc., indicate that the refractive index of the crystal is at a minimum. In determining which grains have a maximum interference color, give consideration to the variation of the maximum interference color with varying thickness of the fragments. By successive immersions the minimum refractive index is matched, and, when it is thought that a match has been obtained, the fragments are rolled by moving the cover glass or by other means to be certain that the fragments are actually in an orientation that yields the minimum index. The maximum refractive index, n_Z, is obtained in a similar manner. Several fragments showing a maximum interference color are rotated into the extinction position for which the refractive index is a maximum, and by successive immersions the maximum index is matched with the immersion medium.

To measure n_Y, the intermediate principal index, fragments are located which show a black or gray first-order interference color during a complete rotation of the microscope stage. If, after the upper polar is removed, the refractive index of the fragment relative to that of the immersion medium does not change as the stage of the microscope is rotated, it is known that the fragment has the proper orientation for the measurement of n_Y. Such a fragment is oriented so that one or the other of the optic axes is parallel or nearly parallel to the axis of the microscope. By successive immersions of fragments in this orientation n_Y is measured.

Cleavages may prevent crystal fragments from lying in a desired position, and it may become necessary to roll the fragments or to support them with ground cover glass. A special technique for measuring refractive indices of fragments that have conspicuous cleavages or have unusual shapes is described in Chapter 17.

It is generally desirable to ascertain the position of the indicatrix for a particular color with reference to prominent crystal directions, usually the crystal axes. In orthorhombic crystals the X, Y, and Z axes of the indicatrix are parallel to the crystallographic axes, but in monoclinic crystals only one axis is parallel to a crystallographic axis, and in triclinic crystals none of the axes of the indicatrix coincide with the crystallographic axes.

For example, suppose that in a monoclinic crystal with prismatic {110} cleavage the extinction angle of a fragment showing a maximum order interference color is 20 degrees, measured from the c axis as determined by intersecting cleavage surfaces. In the extinction position the grain is lying so that X or Z is parallel to the plane of vibration of the lower polar and Y is parallel to the microscope axis. Measurement of the refractive index tells whether it is X or Z. Or, as an alternative, the grain is rotated to the 45-degree position from the extinction position and the relative velocities of the waves as they vibrate in mutually perpendicular planes in the crystal fragment are determined by means of an accessory plate. If, in the 45-degree position, the fast direction of the accessory plate (direction of vibration of the lower index component of the plate) is parallel to the slow direction of the crystal fragment (direction of vibration of the higher index component of the crystal fragment) subtractive effects are noted, and it is known that the direction of the Z axis of the indicatrix has been located. Similarly, additive effects resulting from the insertion of an accessory plate when the fragment is 45 degrees from the extinction position indicate that the fast direction of the accessory plate is parallel to the X axis.

If the Z direction makes an angle of 20 degrees with the direction of the intersection of the cleavage, the relationship is expressed by the equation $Z \wedge c = 20$ degrees. When X and Z lie in the symmetry plane of the crystal, Y of necessity lies parallel to the b crystallographic axis.

Interference Colors

Interference colors in biaxial crystals, as in uniaxial crystals, depend on the thickness, orientation, and birefringence of crystal plates or fragments. Abnormal interference colors result from differential absorption of light, or they may be an expression of the fact that the crystal is optically abnormal in certain respects. For example, certain rare substances may be uniaxial for one color of the spectrum and biaxial for the other colors.

Absorption of Light by Biaxial Crystals

Differential absorption of light by crystals results in *pleochroism*. Some biaxial crystals, when viewed in plane-polarized light, change color during rotation of the microscope stage. Ordinarily, the pleochroism or absorption is determined in the directions of the X, Y, and Z axes of the indicatrix.

Thus the absorption formula of a certain crystal might be

$$X = \text{weak}$$

$$Y = \text{strong}$$

$$Z = \text{very strong}$$

and is indicated as $X < Y < Z$. The pleochroism might be expressed in the following terms:

$$X = \text{pale green}$$

$$Y = \text{dark green}$$

$$Z = \text{dark brown}$$

Interior and Exterior Conical Refraction

Interior and exterior conical refraction are of secondary importance in most practical applications of crystal optics but are of considerable theoretical interest and serve to demonstrate certain relations between the indicatrix and ray-velocity surfaces. In the development of the subsequent theory it should be remembered that the primary optic axis is a *direction of equal wave-normal velocity* and the secondary optic axis is a *direction of equal ray velocity*.

Interior conical refraction can be demonstrated by the experiment suggested in the three-dimensional drawing in Fig. 25A. A plate of

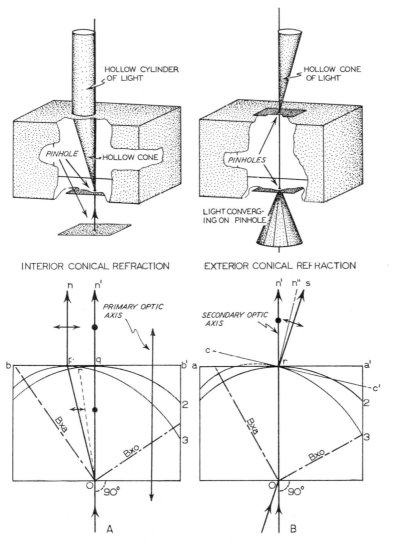

Fig. 25. Diagrams showing the nature of interior and exterior conical refraction.

A. Interior conical refraction in three dimensions and cross section.
B. Exterior conical refraction in three dimensions and cross section.

a biaxial substance is cut exactly at right angles to the primary optic axis (parallel to a circular section of the indicatrix), and monochromatic light waves are allowed to fall with perpendicular incidence on a pinhole in a metal sheet covering the base of the plate. All the light waves do not travel straight through the plate as might be expected, but they constitute a hollow cone with its apex at the pin-hole. Upon leaving the crystal plate, the light waves in the cone are refracted so as to form a hollow cylinder, the diameter of which is equal to the diameter of the base of the interior cone. The presence of the hollow cylinder is determined by holding a flat surface in the path of the cylinder and observing a ring of light, the diameter of which does not change as the surface is raised or lowered.

The explanation of interior conical refraction is suggested in the line drawing in Fig. 25A. The plane of the drawing is the optic plane. Curves 2 and 3 are sections of ray-velocity surfaces; Or is the direction of the secondary optic axis; Oq is parallel to the direction of the primary optic axis and is perpendicular to bb', the wave front tangent to the ray-velocity surfaces at p and q. In three dimensions the wave front is tangent to the outer shell of the ray-velocity surfaces along a circle marking the lip of the dimple at the point of emergence of a secondary optic axis (see Fig. 13).

Light waves perpendicularly incident at O enter the crystal and travel through the crystal in a wave front for which Oq is the wave normal (wave-front normal). Light waves in rays associated with the wave front travel along either Op or Oq, depending upon their direction of vibration. If the waves are in phase, they reach bb' at the same instant, despite the difference in lengths of the paths that the waves follow. In three dimensions the waves following all rays constitute a hollow cone in the crystal. The traces of the planes of vibration of the waves are shown in plan in Fig. 26. Upon leaving the crystal the waves are refracted so as to travel in a direction normal to the crystal plate and parallel to the direction of travel of the incident light waves. The emergent light waves constitute a hollow cylinder of light above the plate.

Exterior conical refraction is demonstrated by the experiment shown in the three-dimensional drawing in Fig. 25B. A crystal plate is cut exactly at right angles to the secondary optic axis of a biaxial crystal. Pinholes on the upper and lower surfaces of the plate are aligned so that only the light waves passing through the plate in the direction of the secondary optic axis can emerge. A cone of monochromatic light is caused to converge on the pinhole on the lower surface. The light waves in the cone will be refracted so as to travel along rays in all directions through the crystal plate, but only the light waves that are refracted so as to follow rays parallel to the secondary optic axis emerge from the plate through the upper pinhole.

Under the above conditions the emergent light waves constitute a hollow cone outside and above the crystal plate. The apex of the cone is at the upper pinhole. The presence of the cone can be demonstrated by placing a flat surface parallel to the plate in the path of the emergent light waves so as to produce a ring of illumination at right angles to the axis of the cone. As the flat surface is raised or lowered, the diameter of the ring changes, thus demonstrating that the light waves actually comprise a cone above the crystal.

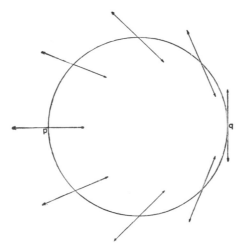

Fig. 26. Traces of vibration planes of light waves in interior conical refraction.

An explanation of exterior conical refraction is offered in the line diagram in Fig. 25B, a section in the optic plane. Light waves converging at O and refracted so as to travel along rays parallel to the secondary optic axis emerge at the pinhole at r. Or is the direction of the secondary optic axis, and aa′ and cc′ are wave fronts in the crystal tangent to the ray-velocity surfaces 2 and 3 at r. Curve 2 is a section of the ray-velocity surface for light waves vibrating perpendicular to the plane of the drawing, and curve 3 is a section of the ray-velocity surface for waves vibrating in the plane of the drawing; rn′ is the wave normal in the crystal for the wave front aa′, and rn″ is the wave normal for the wave front cc′.

Light waves following a ray and vibrating perpendicular to the plane of the drawing travel in the same direction as their associated wave normal On′ and emerge from the plate without refraction. Light waves vibrating in the plane of the drawing are refracted upon leaving the plate so as to travel along rays that make a small angle with rn″. If the crystal had a ray index of refraction of unity for the light waves vibrating in the plane of the drawing, the light waves on emergence would travel in a direction parallel to rn'', but, because this is not so, it should be expected that the wave normal in the crystal and the wave normal of light waves in the emergent rays are not coincident. In effect rn' and rs are the wave normals of the emergent light waves in the plane of the drawing.

All light waves emerging at r constitute a hollow cone, the so-called *cone of external refraction*. Inasmuch as the laws of refraction are operative, the light waves in the exterior cone travel in directions that correspond to the directions of travel of light waves in the incident cone for which the angles of incidence are equal to the angles of refraction of the emergent light waves.

The above explanations hinge on the fact that the directions of the primary and secondary optic axes do not exactly coincide in biaxial crystals. The angle between the two types of optic axes is generally small—less than 2 degrees. Moreover, the apical angles of the cones of interior and exterior conical refraction are of the same order of magnitude. One of the most noticeable effects of refraction of either type is seen in crystal sections cut at right angles to an optic axis. Such grains are not completely dark in all positions between crossed polars, a fact which demonstrates that a slight path difference is produced upon emergence for various light waves moving through a crystal in the direction of a secondary optic axis.

From a theoretical point of view, interior and exterior conical refraction demonstrate the validity of the ray and wave-front concepts of light movement through crystals.

Wooster[9] presents a more rigorous analysis of interior and exterior conical refraction and considers the phenomena as the result of ordinary double refraction of light moving through crystals in directions nearly parallel to the primary and secondary optic axes. He notes that the light circles obtained during experimentation actually consist of two circles separated by a circle of darkness. According to his analysis, only the circle of darkness corresponds to the situation of conical refraction.

[9] W. A. Wooster, *A Textbook on Crystal Physics*, Cambridge University Press, 1938.

13

In the absence of the accessory substage lens of short focal length, the plane-polarized light waves incident on the crystal plate on the microscope stage follow paths which are essentially parallel. Actually the paths of the waves converge slightly because they have passed through a lens of long focal length just above the lower polar. Plane-polarized light waves entering the crystal fragment are, in general, resolved into two sets of waves of different velocities and vibrating in mutually perpendicular planes. The more or less complex waves resulting from the combination of these sets of waves as they leave the crystal are again resolved in the analyzer, which permits light waves vibrating in only one direction to pass through. If the path difference between the emergent waves produced by the crystal plate for monochromatic light is one wave length or any whole number of wave lengths, the result between crossed polars is darkness. If a fractional path difference is produced by the crystal plate, the crystal plate is illuminated in all positions except the extinction positions. Maximum illumination is observed in the 45-degree positions when the path difference is $p\lambda/2$, where p is a whole odd number. In white light the interference color that is seen is dependent on the thickness, orientation, and birefringence of the crystal plate.

Under the conoscope the observed effects depend upon thickness and birefringence as under the orthoscope, but the light waves transmitted by the crystal travel in a great many directions, and the orientation of the crystal for the various angles of incidence of the light waves converging above the substage condensing lens used in conoscopic observations is in effect different for each angle of incidence. The path difference produced in the emergent waves that have traveled in one direction through the crystal in general is not the same as the path difference produced for waves traveling in another direction.

In all constructions in this chapter no attempt is made to show how the light waves leaving the crystal combine to produce more or less complex wave motions. Instead, the light waves are treated as if they pass through the microscope vibrating in the planes determined by their passage through the crystal.

A crystal plate under the conoscope produces an interference figure consisting of curved bands of light called *isochromatic curves* and of black or gray brushes called *isogyres*. In biaxial crystals, as in uniaxial crystals, the appearance and behavior of the isochromatic curves and isogyres as the stage of the microscope is rotated depends to a large extent on the orientation of the crystal plate with respect to the light waves in the several azimuths of the incident cone.

Isochromatic Curves

Isochromatic curves in biaxial crystals may be explained fully only by complex mathematical derivations. Emphasis is placed here on the more important visual concepts and the simpler mathematical concepts that lead to an elementary understanding of the nature of these curves. Detailed mathematical treatments are presented by Johannsen,[1] Rosenbusch and Wülfing,[2] and Wooster.[3]

The isochromatic curves in biaxial interference figures may be regarded as sections of nested Bertin's surfaces of equal path difference (equal phase difference) for emergent light waves and are similar in principle to the isochromatic curves in uniaxial interference figures. However, the geometry of Bertin's surfaces for biaxial crystals is complicated by the fact that there are two optic axes and that the

[1] A. Johannsen, *Manual of Petrographic Methods,* McGraw-Hill Book Co., New York, 1918.

[2] H. Rosenbusch and E. A. Wülfing, *Mikroscopische Physiographie,* Vol. I, Part 1, Stuttgart, 1921/24.

[3] W. A. Wooster, *A Textbook on Crystal Physics,* Cambridge University Press, 1938.

optic angle differs for different crystals as a function of the relative values of the three principal refractive indices.

The particular use of Bertin's surfaces lies in the fact that they indicate the path differences between sets or families of waves *emerging* from the crystal. The path differences upon emergence are most easily calculated if the movement of light energy through the crystal is considered only in terms of the advance of wave fronts in the directions of their normals, a procedure that stresses the advance of families of waves vibrating in a particular direction and does *not* consider the particular paths followed by the individual waves as they advance along their rays. The interference effects that are seen at any point in the interference field are the result of convergence to a focus above the objective lens of all the individual emergent waves that in the crystal constitute wave fronts having a common wave normal (see Fig. 1, p. 161). Some crystallographers prefer to discuss the nature of the relative retardation produced by the crystal in terms of phase differences in the emergent wave fronts. In this book the retardation is measured by the path difference in wave lengths between the waves that constitute the emergent wave fronts, a treatment that is consistent with the theory developed in previous chapters.

No path difference is produced between emergent waves that, in traveling through the crystal, constitute a wave front whose normal is parallel to a primary optic axis. The crystal has a refractive index of n_Y for all such waves. Path differences are produced between emergent waves that, in their wave fronts, have advanced through the crystal in any direction other than that of an optic axis. These path differences result from the fact that the velocities of advance of wave fronts in the direction of a particular wave normal are different for the two sets of waves that vibrate in mutually perpendicular directions and constitute the wave fronts.

The path difference between the emergent waves is expressed as $p\lambda$, where p is a whole or fractional number and λ is the wave length of the emergent waves (equal to the wave length of the incident waves but *not* equal to the wave lengths of the waves in the crystal). The path difference is proportional to t, the distance that the wave fronts for two sets of waves in their wave fronts have advanced through the crystal in the direction of a normal common to both wave fronts, and to the difference in the refractive indices of the crystal for the two sets of waves comprising the wave fronts. This relationship is expressed as

$$p\lambda = t(n' - n'')$$

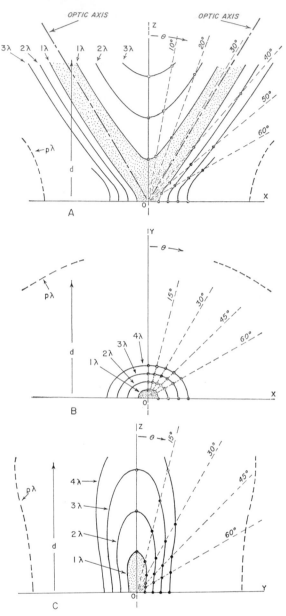

Fig. 1. Curves of equal path difference (equal retardation) in symmetry planes of biaxial indicatrix.

    A. XZ (optic) plane.
    B. XY plane.
    C. YZ plane.

where n' and n'' are the refractive indices of the crystal for the two sets of waves. In terms of the thickness of the crystal plate, d, and the angle, θ, that the wave normal makes with a perpendicular to the crystal plate, the value for t is given by

$$t_\theta = \frac{d}{\cos \theta}$$

Curves of equal path difference (equal phase difference) are most easily computed for sections in the symmetry planes of the indicatrix.

In Fig. 1 the construction of curves of equal path difference for emergent waves in the three planes of symmetry of an indicatrix is used as a device to illustrate the nature of the Bertin's surfaces for a particular biaxial crystal. The curves are derived from a positive indicatrix for which $n_X = 1.5$, $n_Y = 1.6$, and $n_Z = 2.0$. The birefringence for this indicatrix is 0.5, an extremely high birefringence, but it is useful in exaggerating the relationships for easier pictorial representation. The calculated optic angle for the indicatrix is $63° 30'$.

In Fig. 1A the curves of equal path difference in the XZ plane of the indicatrix were obtained for path differences of $p\lambda$, where p is a whole number. Points on the curves were calculated by assuming various angles of θ between the wave normals and the Z axis of the indicatrix and using the equation

$$t_\theta = \frac{p\lambda}{n_Y - n''}$$

where the value of n'' was calculated for each angle θ from the equation

$$(n'')^2 = \frac{(n_X)^2 \cdot (n_Z)^2}{(n_X)^2 \sin^2 \theta + (n_Z)^2 \cos^2 \theta}$$

The curves that were derived correspond to curves of darkness in an interference figure observed in monochromatic light.

In Fig. 1B and C the curves of equal path difference were obtained for the other two symmetry planes of the indicatrix by similar calculations. In the XY plane t was calculated from the formula

$$t_\theta = \frac{p\lambda}{n_Z - n''}$$

and in the YZ plane from the formula

$$t_\theta = \frac{p\lambda}{n'' - n_X}$$

The curves in Fig. 1 are the basis for the construction of the three-dimensional diagram in Fig. 2, which shows nested Bertin's surfaces for 1λ, 2λ, 3λ, and 4λ path differences. The Bertin's surfaces are intersected by a plane perpendicular to the Z axis, the acute bisectrix, and the sections of the Bertin's surfaces in this plane indicate the

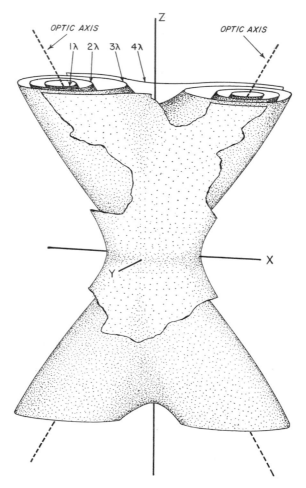

Fig. 2. Nested Bertin's surfaces for path differences (retardations) of 1λ, 2λ, 3λ, and 4λ.

shapes of the curves of darkness that would be seen in an acute bisectrix interference figure in monochromatic light. Figure 3 indicates the general outline of a single Bertin's surface for a particular path difference, and Fig. 4 shows the curves resulting from intersection of the Bertin's surface with the planes of symmetry of the indicatrix. The curves in Fig. 4 are similar to the curves calculated for Fig. 1.

Now, consider a crystal plate cut normal to the acute bisectrix and observed under the conoscope. The color curves that are seen can be regarded as sections of nested Bertin's surfaces and will have shapes de-

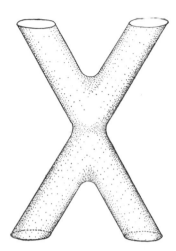

Fig. 3. Bertin's surface.

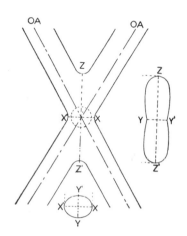

Fig. 4. Sections in symmetry planes of Bertin's surface.

pending on the thickness of the crystal plate, the values for the principal refractive indices, and the magnitude of the optic angle. If a monochromatic-light source is used, dark areas are seen in the interference figure where the optic axes emerge because no path difference is produced for light waves in wave fronts whose wave normals in the crystal are parallel to the primary optic axis. The dark areas around the points of emergence of the optic axes in the interference picture have been called *melatopes*.[4] Around the points of emergence of the optic axes a succession of light curves alternate with curves of darkness. The light curves correspond to sections of Bertin's surfaces for fractional path differences, and the curves of darkness correspond to sections of Bertin's surfaces of $p\lambda$, where p is a whole number. Considering only the light curves and ignoring the areas that are blotted out by the isogyres, the sequence and shapes of the curves might be similar to those shown in Fig. 5. Curves of this type have been called *Cassinian curves*.

The effects of variations in thickness of the crystal plate on the

[4] Johannsen, *op. cit.*

shapes of the light curves are indicated in Figs. 6 and 7. In Fig. 6 the shapes of the curves for two sections of different thickness are indicated in a tilted perspective view. In Fig. 7 the curves for sections of a Bertin's surface in two crystal plates of different thickness are

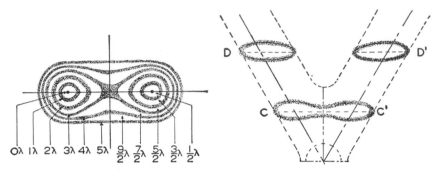

Fig. 5. Section through nested Bertin's surfaces. Section normal to acute bisectrix.

Fig. 6. Sections of Bertin's surface.

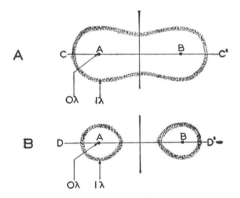

Fig. 7. Cassinian curves for path difference of 1λ.

A. Thin plate.
B. Thicker plate.

shown in plan and correspond to the sections indicated in Fig. 6, although on a different scale. For substances with the same optic angles but different birefringences more light curves are observed in the substance of higher birefringence than in the substance of lower birefringence in plates of the same thickness.

The effects of variations in the optic angle can be predicted by considering the shapes of the Bertin's surfaces for different optic angles. Substances in which the optic angles are small produce nearly circular curves that may surround the area in which the optic axes emerge. As the optic angle increases, the curves change shape, and for a particular path difference the curves may appear as two approximately circular segments, each around the point of emergence of an optic axis, or they may form a single continuous curve surrounding the area within which both of the optic axes emerge. For large optic angles the points of emergence of the optic axes in the interference figure may lie outside of the field of view, and only segments of the curves are seen. The number of color curves that are seen and the disposition of the points of emergence of the optic axes also are functions in part of the numerical apertures of the condensing and objective lenses of the microscope.

In white light the succession of colors about the optic axes normally is the same as the succession in Newton's scale. Black or gray at the points of emergence of the optic axes (melatopes) grades outward into gray, white, yellow, orange, red, etc. In some crystals notable variation in the optic angle and in the crystallographic orientations of the indicatrices as a function of the wave length of light causes a distortion of the color curves resulting from the systematic superimposition of color curves corresponding to sections of Bertin's surfaces of somewhat different shapes and orientations. These effects are explained more fully in Chapter 15, which is concerned with various kinds of dispersion in biaxial crystals.

Isogyres

Under the orthoscope, between crossed polars, a biaxial crystal plate extinguishes four times during a 360-degree rotation. However, in interference figures of biaxial crystals observed under the conoscope, extinction produces black bars or brushes which change position as the stage of the microscope is rotated. These black areas are called *isogyres* or *curves of equal vibration direction* and appear in the form of crosses, bars, or hyperbolic segments. A complete interference figure consists of isogyres superimposed on isochromatic curves. Isogyres are curves determined by the *loci of points in the interference field for which the traces of the planes of vibration of the waves resulting from interference are parallel or nearly parallel to the planes of vibration of the upper and lower polars.*

Precise analysis of all the factors that contribute to the formation of isogyres in biaxial interference figures requires a complex mathematical treatment of the kind described by Kamb.[5] Less complicated approaches to an understanding of the isogyres are based on the use of

[5] W. B. Kamb, "Isogyres in Interference Figures," *Am. Mineralogist,* Vol. 43, pp. 1029–1067, 1958.

skiodromes or the application of the law of Biot-Fresnel. In such approaches an effort is made approximately to locate in the interference field the interference waves that vibrate in planes that are parallel or nearly parallel to the planes of vibration of the upper and lower polars. The skiodrome works reasonably well in explaining isogyres in bisectrix and optic axis figures but, as Kamb emphasizes, it yields an incorrect interpretation of the optic normal figure. However, both the skiodrome and constructions based on the law of Biot-Fresnel permit easily visualized graphical analyses, and both are described in spite of their recognized limitations. Detailed descriptions of the theory of skiodromes are found in Johannsen[6] and Rosenbusch and Wülfing.[7]

Biaxial Skiodromes

We may assume that wave fronts for a particular color advance with equal velocity along the primary optic axes of a biaxial indicatrix and that the component waves vibrate in the circular section at right angles to the direction of the optic axes. Now, suppose that we know the direction and velocity of propagation along its wave normal of a particular wave front for waves of a particular color that are *not* vibrating in a circular section and we wish to locate the positions of the wave normals for all other wave fronts with the same wave-normal velocity. The velocity of a wave front is inversely proportional to the refractive index of the crystal for the waves constituting the wave front so that when we locate a curved section of the indicatrix containing radii equal to the radius giving the refractive index of the crystal for the waves in the wave front in question, we have located the possible vibration directions of waves in a group of wave fronts that advance through the crystal with equal wave-normal velocity.

Figure 8 shows a curved section of the indicatrix containing equal radii. The wave normals corresponding to the radii constitute a cone, and all wave fronts moving along the various wave normals in the cone advance with the same velocity.

The intersection of the cone of wave normals and the surface of a sphere whose center is coincident with the center of the indicatrix produces a *spherical ellipse,* the center of which in Fig. 8 is the acute bisectrix and the foci of which are the poles of the optic axes. A spherical ellipse is analogous to a plane ellipse in that the sum of the distances from the foci measured over the surface of the sphere to

[6] Johannsen, *op. cit.*

[7] Rosenbusch and Wülfing, *op. cit.*

all points on the ellipse is constant. For each group of wave fronts of constant velocity of advance through the crystal there is a corresponding spherical ellipse. Moreover, a second set of spherical ellipses with their centers at the pole of the obtuse bisectrix can be

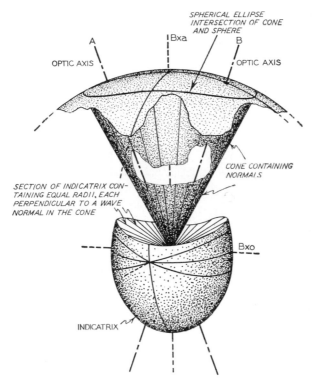

Fig. 8. Diagram showing origin of spherical ellipse about points of emergence of the optic axes on a spherical projection.

constructed and intersect the ellipses about the acute bisectrix. The foci of this second set of ellipses are the poles of the optic axes on either side of the obtuse bisectrix.

The two sets of ellipses on the surface of the sphere at each point of intersection *intersect at right angles.* Each ellipse gives the *loci of the points of emergence on the sphere of all wave fronts of a given wave-normal velocity.* Stated another way, each ellipse gives the *loci of the points of emergence on the sphere of the wave normals for the various sets of waves for which the crystal has a constant refractive index.* By construction, the *trace of the plane of vibration* of waves in the wave front emerging at a particular point on a spherical ellipse is perpendicular to the ellipse at the point of emergence. Thus, perpendiculars (or tangents) drawn to the ellipses at the point of intersection of two ellipses on the sphere give the traces of the mutually perpendicular vibration planes of the two sets of waves in the

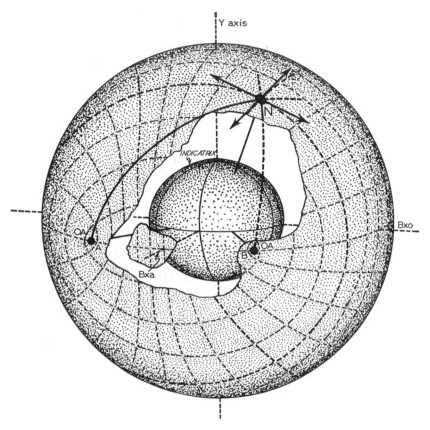

Fig. 9. Diagram showing relationship between an indicatrix and the spherical ellipses indicating the loci of the points of emergence of waves of equal velocity. Vibration directions for light emerging at a point N are indicated by arrows.

wave fronts emerging at the intersection. Figure 9 portrays the relationships discussed above. N is a spherical projection of a wave normal at the intersection of two spherical ellipses. The traces of the planes of vibration of the waves in the wave fronts advancing along the wave normal are indicated by the doubly terminated arrows. The traces of the planes of vibration can be determined also by constructions based on the law of Biot-Fresnel (see p. 232).

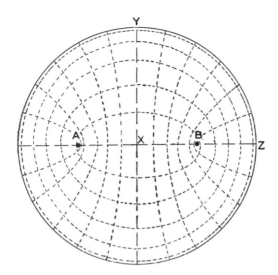

Fig. 10. Skiodrome of a biaxial crystal. Plane of projection is *YZ* plane.

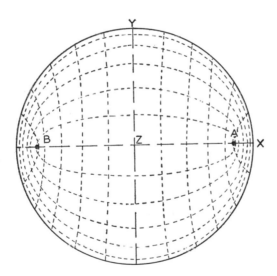

Fig. 11. Skiodrome of a biaxial crystal. Plane of projection is *XY* plane.

The spherical ellipses showing the loci of points of emergence of wave fronts of equal wave-normal velocity have been called *isotaques*. An orthographic projection of the isotaques into any plane of the spherical projection is called a *skiodrome*.

Figures 10 to 12 are skiodromes for a biaxial negative crystal with

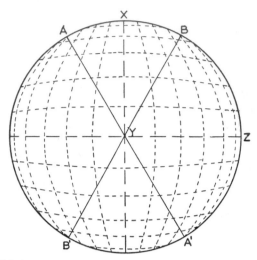

Fig. 12. Skiodrome of a biaxial crystal. Plane of projection is XZ plane.

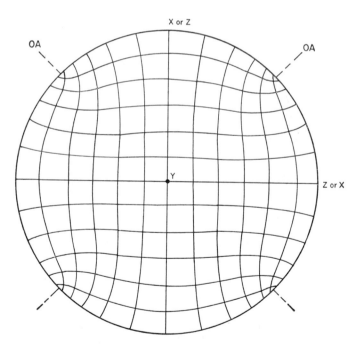

Fig. 13. "Extinction direction net" for optic normal figure for crystal with optic angle of 90 degrees. (After W. B. Kamb, *Am. Mineralogist,* Vol. 43, p. 1066, 1958.)

a $2V$ of 60 degrees. In Fig. 10 the plane of projection is normal to
X, the acute bisectrix. A and B are the points of emergence of the
optic axes. Figure 11 shows the skiodrome for the same crystal with
the plane of the projection perpendicular to Z, the obtuse bisectrix.
The plane of projection in Fig. 12 lies in the optic plane, the XZ
plane. For comparison with Fig. 12, an "extinction direction net"
constructed by Kamb[8] for predicting the locations of the isogyres in

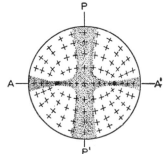

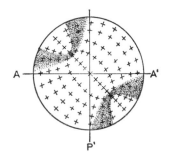

Fig. 14. Vibration directions obtained
from skiodrome of acute bisectrix figure.
Parallel position.

Fig. 15. Vibration directions obtained
from skiodrome of acute bisectrix figure.
Forty-five-degree position.

the interference figure for a crystal plate cut normal to the Y axis
of the indicatrix and having an optic angle of 90 degrees is shown in
Fig. 13.

The problem of determining the nature of the isogyres in an interference figure of a biaxial crystal plate in any position is solved by
ascertaining the locations of wave normals for wave fronts in which
the constituent waves vibrate in planes, the traces of which are parallel
or nearly parallel to the planes of vibration of the upper and lower
polars. This is easily done on a skiodrome. It will be noted that the
curves on the skiodrome do not intersect at right angles in the
outer portion of the skiodrome. However, the effect in the outer
portion of the skiodrome may be disregarded because of the limited
field of view of the conoscope.

Figures 14 and 15 illustrate the use of the skiodrome in predicting
the positions of the isogyres. The traces of the vibration planes of
the light waves in the interference field are obtained from a skiodrome
normal to the acute bisectrix of a biaxial crystal.

[8] Kamb, *loc. cit.*

Planes of Vibration from Biot-Fresnel Constructions

Locations of the traces of the planes of vibration of waves in the field of the interference figure are easily determined in stereographic constructions based on the law of Biot-Fresnel and employing a stereonet.

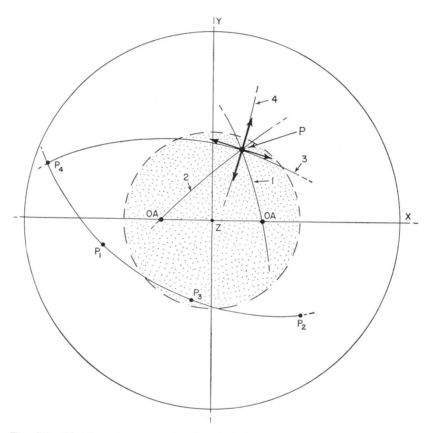

Fig. 16. Biot-Fresnel construction for obtaining traces of planes of vibration of light waves emerging at *P* in acute bisectrix figure of a biaxial positive crystal. Projection from upper half of spherical projection.

The results differ somewhat from those obtained for skiodromes in that the assumption is made that the vibration directions in the interference field can be represented in stereographic projection rather than by an orthographic projection of a spherical projection.

Figures 16 and 17 show constructions obtained with the aid of a stereonet. The stippled areas represent the approximate area of the interference field, an area that depends on the optics of the microscope. An optic angle of 60 degrees is assumed for the crystal. In Figs. 16 and 17 P is the point of emergence of a wave normal in the interference field. According to the law of Biot-Fresnel (see p. 232) the traces of the planes of vibration of the waves in the wave fronts

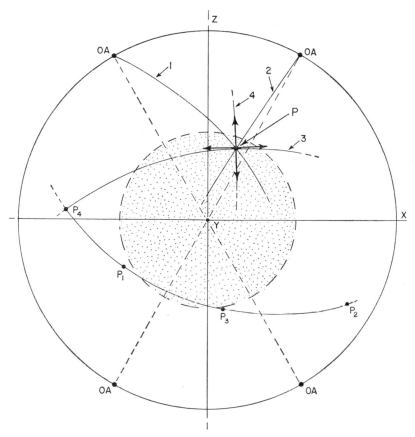

Fig. 17. Biot-Fresnel construction for obtaining traces of planes of vibration of light waves emerging at P in optic normal figure of a biaxial positive crystal. Projection from upper half of spherical projection.

traveling along the wave normal bisect the angles between the planes determined by the great circles passing through the poles of the optic axes and through the pole of the wave normal. Great circles 1 and 2 are so drawn, and at the same time the poles of these circles, P_1 and P_2, are located 90 degrees from the circles. The pole P_3, stereographically halfway between P_1 and P_2, is the pole of a great circle that gives one bisector of the angle between circles 1 and 2, and the pole P_4, 90 degrees stereographically from P_3, is the pole of the other bisecting great circle. The heavy double arrows are drawn tangent to the bisecting great circles at P and give, approximately, the traces of the planes of vibration of the two sets of waves advancing in their wave fronts along the wave normal.

In Fig. 16 the plane of projection is normal to the acute bisectrix. In Fig. 17 the plane of projection is perpendicular to the optic normal.

The Acute Bisectrix Figure

A biaxial crystal section cut normal to the acute bisectrix gives, if the optic plane is parallel to either the upper or lower polar, a black cross superimposed on color curves. As the stage of the microscope is rotated, the cross splits into two hyperbolic segments whose positions are determined by the optic angle and the position of the optic plane with reference to the polars. This is illustrated in Figs. 18 and 19. (See also Figs. 14 and 15.) If the section is very thin or the birefringence is low, only gray or white of the first order may appear adjacent to the isogyre.

Real and Apparent Optic Angles

The acute angle between the optic axes is designated as $2V$, the optic angle. V is the angle between the acute bisectrix and either axis. In general, light waves traveling along the optic axis are refracted when they leave the crystal and under the conoscope the points of emergence of the optic axis appear farther apart than they would if no refraction took place on emergence.

Refraction on emergence gives rise to an apparent optic angle, $2E$, which bears a simple relationship to $2V$. In Fig. 20 AA' and BB' indicate the directions of the optic axes in a crystal plate cut normal to the acute bisectrix. Light waves in a wave front entering the crystal plate at A' with an angle of incidence i are refracted through an angle r. The crystal has an index of n_Y for light waves traveling in their wave front in the direction $A'A$. Accordingly,

$$\frac{\sin i}{\sin r} = n_Y$$

Inasmuch as

$$i = E$$

and

$$r = V$$

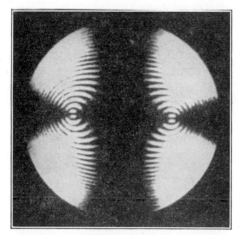

Courtesy McGraw-Hill Book Co.

Fig. 18. Acute bisectrix figure in parallel position. Monochromatic light. (Johannsen.)

Courtesy McGraw-Hill Book Co.

Fig. 19. Acute bisectrix figure in 45-degree position. Monochromatic light. (Johannsen.)

$$\frac{\sin i}{\sin r} = n_Y = \frac{\sin E}{\sin V}$$

or

$$\sin V = \frac{\sin E}{n_Y}$$

or

$$V = \sin^{-1} \frac{(\sin E)}{n_Y}$$

Figure 21 shows the relationship between $2V$ and $2E$ for various values of n_Y. The curves are a simple expression of the fact that light waves traveling along an optic axis are refracted less upon leaving crystals in which n_Y is low than they are upon leaving crystals for which the value of n_Y is higher.

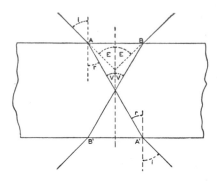

Fig. 20. Relationship of $2E$ to $2V$.

The angle V may be calculated from the indices of refraction, but, if the indices are not accurately determined, considerable error is introduced into the solution. If n_Y is known, it is possible to determine the optic angle of a mineral from an acute bisectrix figure by measuring the distance between the points of emergence of the optic axes with a micrometer eyepiece. Use is made of a value called *Mallard's "constant."*

For a given combination of lenses the following equation is valid:

$$D = K \sin E$$

where D is half the scalar distance between the points of emergence of the optic axes as seen under the conoscope, K is Mallard's constant,

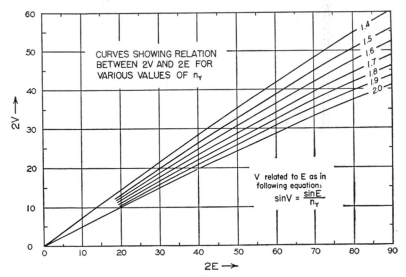

CURVES SHOWING RELATION BETWEEN 2V AND 2E FOR VARIOUS VALUES OF n_Y

V related to E as in following equation:
$$\sin V = \frac{\sin E}{n_Y}$$

Fig. 21. Diagram showing relationship between $2V$ and $2E$ for various values of n_Y.

and E is one-half the apparent axial angle in air. D is measured in terms of scale divisions in a micrometer eyepiece. Suppose that a crystal has a known $2E$ of 70 degrees and gives an acute bisectrix figure for which the points of emergence of the optic axes are 20 scale divisions of the micrometer eyepiece apart. Then

$$K = \frac{10}{\sin 35°} = 17.4 = \text{Mallard's constant}$$

Now

$$\frac{\sin E}{\sin V} = n_Y$$

So that for the particular combination of lenses used in the measurement

$$\sin V = \frac{D}{K \cdot n_Y} = \frac{D}{17.4 \cdot n_Y}$$

If a particular microscope and a certain combination of lenses are in constant use for measurement of $2E$ angles and calculation of $2V$ by use of Mallard's constant, the investigator will find it convenient to construct a chart for graphical solution of the relationship. Formulae for construction and descriptions of the use of $2V$–$2E$ charts may be found in publications by Winchell[9] and Tobi.[10]

Obtuse Bisectrix Figure

A crystal section cut normal to the obtuse bisectrix gives, under the conoscope when the optic plane is parallel to the vibration directions of either polar, an isogyre in the form of a black cross. But, because the points of emergence of the optic axes in the interference field are generally outside of the field of view, slight rotation of the microscope stage causes the cross to break into two segments which leave the field very rapidly on further rotation. This is understood if reference is made to the skiodrome in Fig. 11.

The color curves in an obtuse bisectrix figure have the same general shape as those in an acute bisectrix figure, but ordinarily only segments are seen. These segments maintain the same shapes during rotation of the microscope stage.

---

[9] H. Winchell, "A Chart for Measurement of Interference Figures," *Am. Mineralogist*, Vol. 31, pp. 43–50, 1946.

[10] A. C. Tobi, "A Chart for Measurement of Optic Axial Angles," *Am. Mineralogist*, Vol. 41, pp. 516–519, 1956.

Optic-Axis Figure

The optic-axis figure is seen in crystals cut normal to either optic axis. Properly oriented crystals under the petrographic microscope appear gray or black during a complete rotation of the microscope stage between crossed polars, because no path difference upon emergence is produced for waves in wave fronts traveling along a primary optic axis.

The optic-axis figure may be considered as one-half of an acute bisectrix figure; commonly it consists of a single isogyre which goes

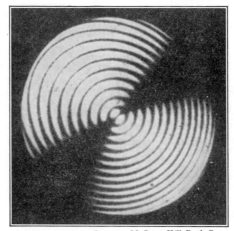

Courtesy McGraw-Hill Book Co.

Fig. 22. Optic-axis figure in 45-degree position. Monochromatic light. (Johannsen.)

through the same general changes of shape and position as either of the segments of the acute bisectrix figure on rotation of the microscope stage. Figure 22 shows a photograph of an optic-axis figure in the 45-degree position.

Figure 23 shows diagrammatically the relationship between an acute bisectrix figure and an optic-axis figure. The observer is looking in a direction parallel to one of the optic axes, and, when the optic plane is parallel to either the upper or lower polar, the isogyre in the interference field is a straight bar. Figure 24 illustrates the effects of rotation of the microscope stage and demonstrates the reason for the change of the straight bar in the parallel position to a hyperbolic curve in the 45-degree position. Of special importance is the observation that *in the 45-degree position the convex side of the curved isogyre faces toward the acute bisectrix.*

Figures 23 and 24 are not true representations of actual conditions, for, if it were possible to see the whole area indicated in the drawing,

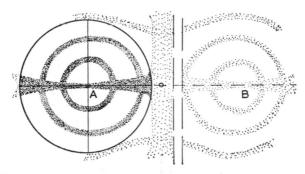

Fig. 23. Relationship between optic-axis figure and acute bisectrix figure. Parallel position.

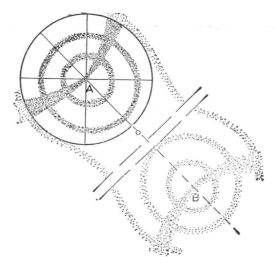

Fig. 24. Relationship between optic-axis figure and acute bisectrix figure. Forty-five-degree position.

the color curves around either optic axis would be highly asymmetrical with respect to each other.

Wright[11] has shown that it is possible to estimate $2V$ from the curvature of the isogyre in an optic-axis figure in the 45-degree position.

[11] F. E. Wright, *The Methods of Petrographic-Microscopic Research,* Carnegie Inst. of Washington, Pub. No. 158, p. 168, 1911.

If the isogyre remains straight in all positions during rotation, the optic angle, $2V$, is 90 degrees. As the angle between the brushes of the isogyre approaches 90 degrees, the optic angle approaches zero. The curvature of medial lines of isogyres for several values of $2V$ are shown in Fig. 25.

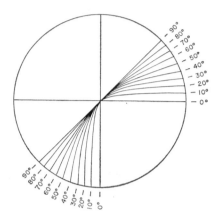

Fig. 25. Curvature of isogyres in optic-axis figures for various angles of $2V$. (From T. C. Phemister, *Jour. Geol.*, 32, p. 402, 1924.)

Optic-Normal Figure

Sections cut perpendicular to the optic normal, the Y axis of the indicatrix, give broad, poorly defined isogyres, with or without color curves. When the X and Z directions parallel the traces of the vibration planes of the polars, a diffuse cross appears which breaks into hyperbolic segments on slight rotation of the microscope stage. The segments leave the field rapidly in the quadrants containing the acute bisectrix as the stage is rotated. The figure is similar to the flash figure seen in uniaxial crystals cut parallel to the c axis and is rarely used to determine optical sign.

The nature of the figure may be estimated by referring to the skiodrome illustrated in Fig. 12 or the extinction direction net in Fig. 13 and to a section of a Bertin's surface parallel to the XZ plane.

CHAPTER 14. DETERMINATION OF OPTIC SIGN IN BIAXIAL CRYSTALS

Determination of optic sign in biaxial crystals may be made by various methods not involving the use of interference figures. It is possible to obtain sign by measuring the indices of refraction or by determining whether the optic angle, $2V$, lies about the X or Z axis. But sign determination from interference figures is relatively simple. In thin sections or in fragments in immersion media, an experienced observer can determine sign quickly and at the same time estimate the optic angle. Moreover, by use of interference figures the orientation of the indicatrix with reference to the polars may be ascertained, thus facilitating refractive index measurements.

Determination of Sign from Acute Bisectrix Figures

Figure 1 indicates the relationships between an acute bisectrix figure and the principal directions of the indicatrix. A centered acute bisectrix figure is seen under the conoscope in sections cut normal to the acute bisectrix. Determination of optic sign consists essentially of ascertaining whether the Z axis or the X axis is the acute bisectrix. The optic sign may be determined in either the parallel or 45-degree position.

In an acute bisectrix figure the traces of the vibration planes of the two sets of waves emerging at any point N (Fig. 2) can be located approximately by connecting the points of emergence of the optic axes and the point of emergence of the light waves at N with straight lines. This construction is based on the Biot-Fresnel law (see p. 232).

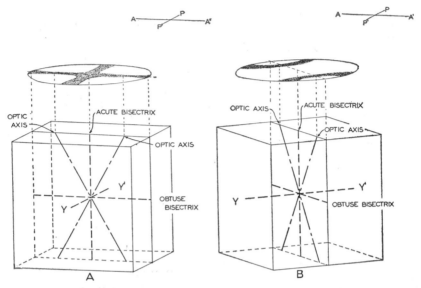

Fig. 1. Relation of acute bisectrix figure to indicatrix.

A. Parallel position.   *B.* Forty-five-degree position.

The directions bisecting the angles between the two lines at their intersection give the traces of the vibration planes of the two components.

The traces of the vibration planes can be obtained also from a skiodrome in which the plane of projection includes the obtuse bisectrix and the Y axis.

As an illustration of the use of the construction shown in Fig. 2, suppose that an accessory plate is inserted over the interference figure in such a manner that the fast direction of the plate is in quadrants 2 and 4; that is, the direction of the trace of the plane of vibration of the faster waves in the accessory plate lies in quadrants 2 and 4. The fast direction of the accessory plate is nearly parallel to the trace of the plane of vibration, c, of one set of waves emergent at N and is nearly at right angles to the trace of the plane of vibration, d, of the other set of waves emerging at N. Now, assume that the insertion of the plate causes additive effects in quadrants 1 and 3, and, simultaneously, subtractive effects in quadrants 2 and 4. Additive effects result from an increase in the path difference between the two sets of waves emergent from the crystal, and subtractive effects are caused by a decrease in the path difference. Inspection of the diagram indicates that waves vibrating in c vibrate more nearly parallel to the obtuse bisectrix than the waves in d. Also, the waves in d vibrate more nearly parallel to the Y axis than to the obtuse bisectrix. Inasmuch as the accessory plate demonstrates that the waves vibrating in c are faster

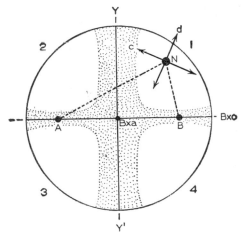

Fig. 2. Approximate method of locating traces of vibration planes of light emerging at any point N.

than the waves vibrating in d, waves traveling along the acute bisectrix and vibrating parallel to the obtuse bisectrix are faster than the waves vibrating parallel to Y. Accordingly, Z is the acute bisectrix, and the crystal is positive.

Use of the accessory plate in the manner described above indicates that the index of refraction of the crystal for the waves vibrating parallel to the obtuse bisectrix (the faster waves) is less than the index of refraction of the crystal for the waves vibrating parallel to the Y axis (the slower waves).

In negative crystals an accessory plate produces additive effects in quadrants 2 and 4 and subtractive effects in quadrants 1 and 3.

The Biot-Fresnel law can be used to obtain the traces of the vibration planes in an interference figure in any position of rotation of the microscope stage. However, in the 45-degree position the determination of sign may be made more easily by considering the interaction of the accessory plates and light waves emerging along and near the trace of the optic plane.

Suppose that in an interference figure in the 45-degree position the trace of the optic plane is northwest-southeast, parallel to the fast direction of an accessory plate. Suppose, moreover, that the accessory plate produces additive effects in the portion of the interference figure between the isogyres and subtractive effects outside the isogyres. Two

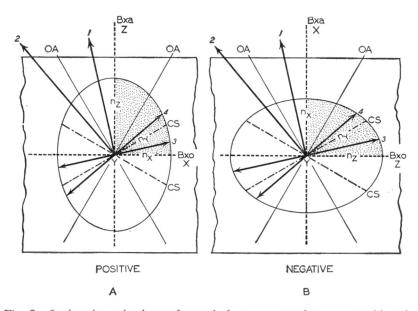

POSITIVE

A

NEGATIVE

B

Fig. 3. Sections in optic planes of crystal plates cut normal to an acute bisectrix.

sets of waves moving along the acute bisectrix (Fig. 3) vibrate at right angles to the direction of transmission and parallel to the obtuse bisectrix and the Y axis, respectively. If the effects are additive in the center of the interference figure, the waves vibrating in the optic plane and parallel to the fast direction of the accessory plate are faster than the waves vibrating parallel to the Y axis, and, accordingly, the refractive index of the crystal is lower for waves vibrating parallel to the obtuse bisectrix than it is for waves vibrating parallel to the Y axis. Therefore, the obtuse bisectrix is X and the acute bisectrix is Z, and the mineral is positive (Fig. 3A).

Now consider light waves vibrating in mutually perpendicular planes and, in their wave fronts, advancing in the direction of a wave normal, 1, in or near the optic plane and between the acute bisectrix and an optic axis. The waves in one wave front vibrate parallel to the Y axis of the indicatrix and in the other wave front perpendicular to the wave normal and in the XZ plane somewhere between the circular section and the obtuse bisectrix. In positive crystals the index of refraction for waves vibrating between the circular section and the obtuse bisectrix in the optic plane is lower than the refractive index for waves vibrating parallel to Y, and, accordingly, are faster. If the trace of the vibration plane for these waves is parallel to the fast direction of the accessory plate, the effect at the point of emergence of the wave normal is additive. Using the same type of reasoning it can be shown that in positive crystals the effects on the concave sides of the isogyres are subtractive if the fast direction of the accessory plate is parallel to the trace of the optic plane in an acute bisectrix figure.

If the optic plane of a positive crystal is perpendicular to the fast direction of the plate, the effects are the reverse of those described above.

Optic sign in acute bisectrix figures of negative crystals (Fig. 3B) is determined by demonstrating that X is the acute bisectrix.

Good results will be obtained if the mica plate and quartz wedge are used for interference figures displaying isochromatic curves and if the gypsum plate is used for diffuse figures with only first-order color curves. The effects of the introduction of accessory plates over acute bisectrix figures in both the parallel and 45-degree positions are shown in Figs. 4, 5, and 6. All examples are optically positive; negative crystals give opposite results.

The observer may have difficulty in finding a perfectly centered acute bisectrix figure. In the figures that are seen, two conditions, or a combination of these, may arise: (1) The optic plane may be normal to the plane of the section, but the acute bisectrix is inclined. This condition is illustrated in Fig. 7. (2) The optic plane may be inclined, but the acute bisectrix and the optic normal both lie in a plane of symmetry between the isogyres. This condition is shown in Fig. 8. In general, however, both acute bisectrix and optic plane are inclined with respect to the section. The nature of an uncentered acute bisectrix figure of this type is illustrated in Fig. 9. Figures 10 and 11 show the effects of rotation of the microscope on the isogyres of the two types of off-center acute bisectrix figures shown in Figs. 7 and 8.

If the position of the optic plane is determinable, acute bisectrix figures, even though considerably off center, may be used for sign determination.

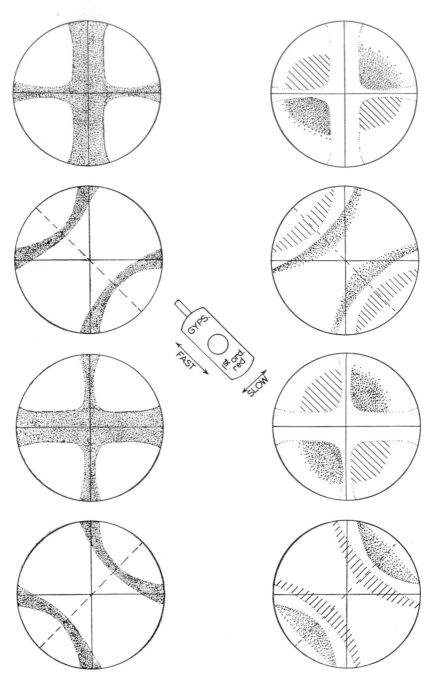

Fig. 4. Effect of inserting gypsum plate on positive acute bisectrix figures. Stippling, blue; hatching, yellow. The student may wish to color the appropriate areas to emphasize the effects.

Fig. 5. Effect of insertion of mica plate on positive acute bisectrix figures.

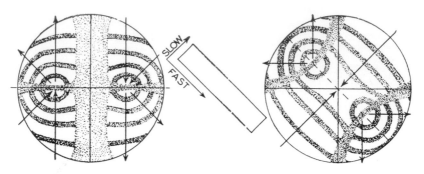

Fig. 6. Movement of color curves upon insertion of quartz wedge over positive acute bisectrix figures.

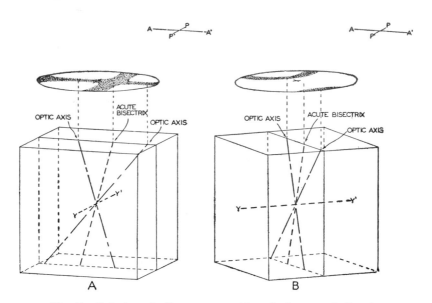

Fig. 7. Relation of off-center acute bisectrix figure to indicatrix.

A. Parallel position.
B. Forty-five-degree position.

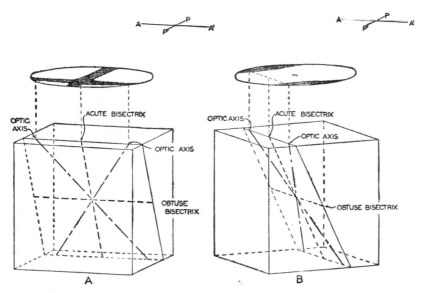

Fig. 8. Relation of off-center acute bisectrix figure to indicatrix.

A. Parallel position.

B. Forty-five-degree position.

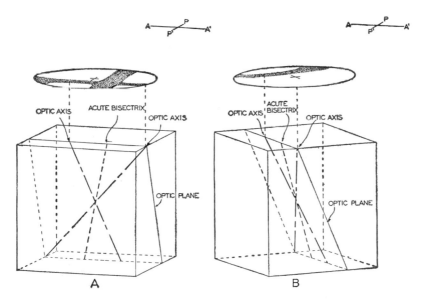

Fig. 9. General example of off-center acute bisectrix figure.

A. Parallel position.

B. Forty-five-degree position.

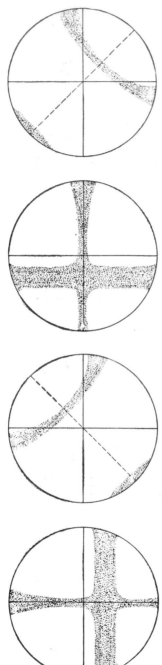

Fig. 10. Effect of clockwise rotation of microscope stage on a type of off-center acute bisectrix figure. (See Fig. 7.)

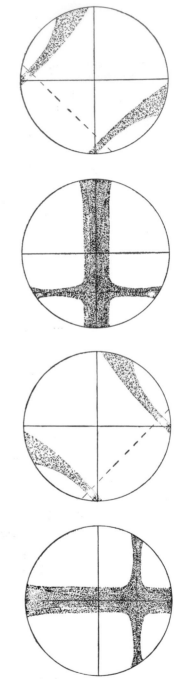

Fig. 11. Effect of clockwise rotation of microscope stage on a type of off-center acute bisectrix figure. (See Fig. 8.)

Determination of Sign from Obtuse Bisectrix Figures

In obtuse bisectrix figures a black cross is observed in the zero and 90-degree positions. As the microscope stage is rotated, the cross rapidly breaks up into segments which leave the field in the quadrants containing the trace of the optic plane. If the observer recognizes the fact that he is looking along the obtuse bisectrix, rather than the acute bisectrix, the sign may be easily determined. But the effects obtained by introducing the accessory plates will be *opposite* from those obtained from an acute bisectrix figure. If 2V equals 90 degrees, there is no distinction between the acute and obtuse bisectrix figures.

Determination of Optic Sign from Optic-Axis Figures

The optic-axis figure, more than any other, is used to determine the sign of biaxial crystals because of the ease of finding crystal sections which give this figure. It is difficult, at times, to obtain a perfectly centered figure, and it becomes necessary to use uncentered figures. The theory will be developed first for centered figures and then for uncentered figures.

Figure 12A and B illustrates the relation of the optic-axis figure to the indicatrix in a crystal plate. When the trace of the optic plane is parallel to the plane of vibration of either the upper or lower polar, the isogyre is a straight bar, Fig. 12A. On rotating the crystal 45 degrees, a curved isogyre with the convex side toward the acute bisectrix results, Fig. 12B. If 2V equals 90 degrees, the bar remains straight during a complete rotation of the microscope stage.

The interference figure in the 45-degree position permits the determination of sign. This is explained by reference to Fig. 13, which shows sections parallel to the optic planes of biaxial positive and biaxial negative crystals, both with an arbitrarily assigned 2V of 60 degrees.

In Fig. 13A suppose that two sets of light waves vibrating in mutually perpendicular planes advance in their wave fronts along a wave normal, 1, lying in the optic plane between the direction of the acute bisectrix and an optic axis. The light waves emerge in the interference figure on the convex side of the isogyre. One set of waves vibrates parallel to the Y axis of the indicatrix, and for this set the crystal has a refractive index of n_Y. The other set vibrates in the optic plane at right angles to the wave normal and somewhere between

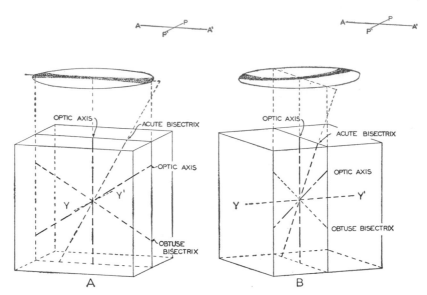

Fig. 12. Relation of optic-axis figure to indicatrix.

A. Parallel position.
B. Forty-five-degree position.

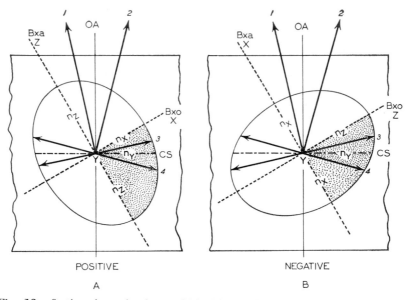

Fig. 13. Sections in optic planes of biaxial crystals cut normal to an optic axis.

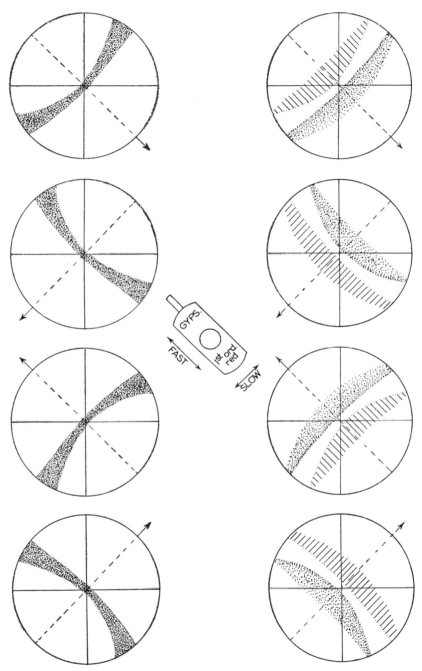

Fig. 14. Effect of insertion of gypsum plate on positive optic-axis figures. Stippling, blue; hatching, yellow. The student may wish to color the appropriate areas to emphasize the effects.

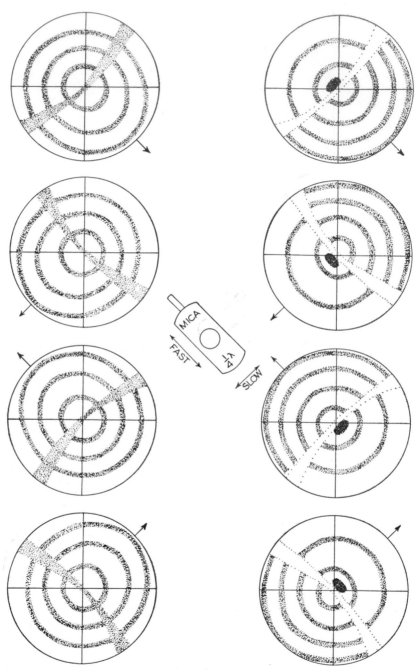

Fig. 15. Effect of insertion of mica plate on positive optic-axis figures.

the circular section and the obtuse bisectrix. If the crystal is positive, the waves vibrating in the optic plane are faster than the waves vibrating parallel to Y, and for these waves the crystal has a refractive

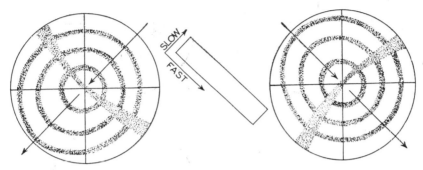

Fig. 16. Movement of color curves upon insertion of a quartz wedge over positive optic-axis figures.

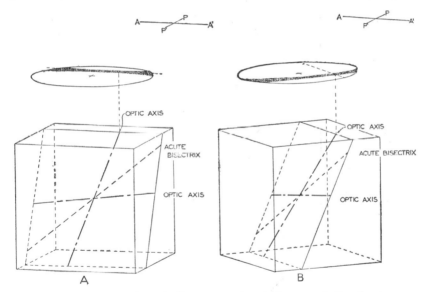

Fig. 17. Relation of off-center optic-axis figure to indicatrix.

A. Parallel position.

B. Forty-five-degree position.

index somewhere between n_Y and n_X. Accordingly, if the fast direction of an accessory plate is parallel to the trace of the optic plane, additive effects will result in the interference figure on the convex side of the isogyre, and it is determined that X is the obtuse bisectrix and Z

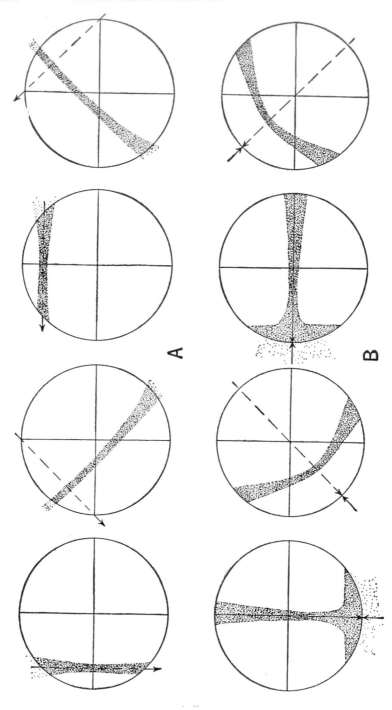

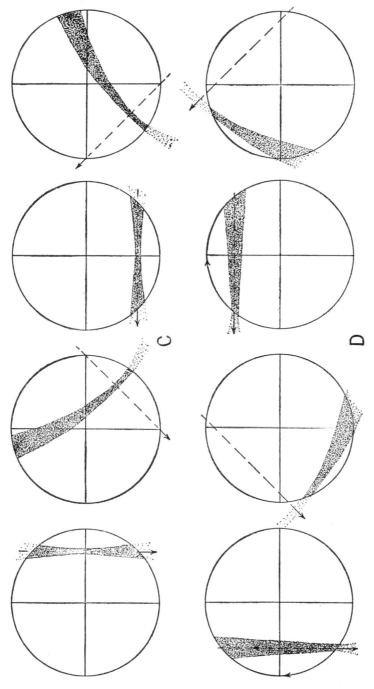

Fig. 18. Effect of clockwise rotation of microscope stage on various types of off-center optic-axis figures. Dashed line is trace of optic plane. Arrows point toward acute bisectrix.

is the acute bisectrix. An opposite effect is seen on the concave side of the isogyre because the waves vibrating in the optic plane are also vibrating between the acute bisectrix and a circular section. For these waves the crystal has an index somewhere between n_Y and n_Z.

Figure 13B shows the construction in the optic plane for an optically negative crystal.

In any event, the changes on the opposite sides of the isogyre upon insertion of an accessory plate will be opposite in nature. The specific changes depend on the position of the isogyre and the construction of the accessory plates.

Figures 14, 15, and 16 illustrate the changes that take place in optic-axis figures when various accessory plates are inserted into the microscope. All examples are positive; opposite effects will be noted in negative crystals.

In the usual type of off-center optic-axis figure, the optic plane as well as the optic axis is inclined with respect to the surface of the section, as shown in Fig. 17. This drawing permits visualization of the changes that take place during rotation of the crystal. If it is possible to locate the position of the trace of the optic plane and the approximate position of the acute bisectrix, the problem of sign determination becomes no more difficult than the determination of sign in centered figures. The effects on introduction of the accessory plates are similar, whether the figure is centered or uncentered.

In Fig. 18 various possibilities are indicated. A study of these possibilities together with a visualization of the relations suggested in Fig. 17 permits the solution of most problems of sign determination in optic-axis figures.

Use of Interference Figures in Index Measurement

Interference figures reveal the directions of the axes of the indicatrix and assist in measurement of the principal indices of refraction. In an acute bisectrix figure it is known that the Y direction is perpendicular to the optic plane, which includes the points of emergence of the optic axes (the melatopes). Moreover, when the optic sign is ascertained, the direction of the X or Z axis is discovered. For example, in a positive crystal the refractive indices for the two sets of waves traveling parallel to the acute bisectrix and vibrating in mutually perpendicular planes are n_X and n_Y; n_Z may be measured in a crystal which shows an obtuse bisectrix figure. Crystals which give negative acute bisectrix figures yield n_Y and n_Z. Perfectly centered optic-axis figures yield indices equal to n_Y in all positions of rotation of the microscope stage.

CHAPTER 15 DISPERSION IN BIAXIAL CRYSTALS

Dispersion is an expression of the fact that the refractive indices of nonopaque substances vary with the wave length of light and the fact that passage of light through crystals conforms rigidly to the requirements of crystal symmetry.

In biaxial crystals all three principal refractive indices undergo dispersion that is not necessarily proportional and results in dispersive effects involving the optic angles. Moreover, there are additional dispersive effects which depend on different orientations of the indicatrices for different colors. Dispersion introduces certain peculiarities into interference figures of biaxial crystals observed in white light. These peculiarities are attributable to the fact that for each wave length of light there exists an indicatrix which has its own characteristic refractive indices, optic angle, and optic orientation.

Figure 1 illustrates *dispersion of the refractive indices,* or *refractive index dispersion,* for a biaxial crystal. The principal refractive indices, n_X, n_Y, and n_Z, are plotted as a function of the wave length of light. The wave length is plotted on a logarithmic scale to obtain straighter curves than would be obtained with an arithmetic scale, a procedure that permits easier extrapolation and interpolation of plotted data.

An important manifestation of dispersion in biaxial crystals is the presence of color fringes on the isogyres of interference figures. These fringes may be pronounced or barely visible, depending upon whether the dispersion is strong or weak. The amount of dispersion as seen in interference figures may be expressed as follows: *perceptible* if the isogyres show faintly visible colored borders; *weak* if a little more easily seen; *strong* if very apparent; and *extreme* if the color fringes cover a large part of the field of the microscope.

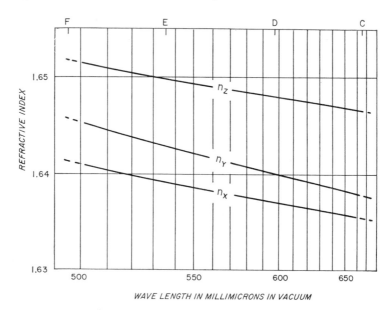

Fig. 1. Dispersion curves for a colorless biaxial crystal.

Dispersion of the indices of refraction in biaxial crystals results in *dispersion of the optic axes*. The reason for this is apparent when it is considered that the optic angle, $2V$, may be computed from the indices. Accordingly, if the principal indices for various wave lengths of light are different and do not vary in simple proportion with the wave length, the optic angles differ. Dispersion of the optic axes in biaxial crystals is expressed by a formula which states whether the optic angle for red is greater or less than the optic angle for violet. These colors are chosen because they are at the extremes of the spectrum for white light and because they are the colors commonly seen in the color fringes. If $2V$ for red is greater than $2V$ for violet, the dispersion formula is $r > v$; $r < v$ expresses the reverse relationship. The violet is actually a bluish violet and sometimes almost a pure blue.

In addition to dispersion of the indices and $2V$, there are several types of dispersion which depend on crystal symmetry. Recognition of the type of dispersion in a crystal helps to classify the crystal in its proper crystal system. Dispersion dependent on crystal symmetry in the monoclinic and triclinic systems is commonly designated as *dispersion of the bisectrices*.

Dispersion as described in the following pages is of the kind commonly observed in colorless or nearly colorless biaxial crystals. Dispersion in crystals that strongly absorb some or most of the transmitted colors and that may or may not be markedly pleochroic usually is of a very complex nature and is not amenable to simple geometric portrayal.

Dispersion in Orthorhombic Crystals

In orthorhombic crystals the X, Y, and Z axes of the indicatrices for all colors of light coincide with the three mutually perpendicular crystallographic axes. This results from the symmetry requirements of the orthorhombic system, which, in the dipyramidal class, has three mutually perpendicular planes of symmetry. Dispersion of the indices, that is, variation of the indices with the color of light, causes variation in the optic angle, $2V$. This type of dispersion is called *rhombic* or, perhaps better, *orthorhombic dispersion*. It is the principal type of dispersion observed in interference figures of orthorhombic crystals.

The origin and nature of rhombic dispersion is suggested by Fig. 2, which shows diagrammatically the dispersion effects produced in an acute bisectrix figure viewed in white light. Dispersion of the indices has caused dispersion of the optic axes for all colors of light, but the figures show only the positions of the optic axes of red and violet. Arbitrarily it has been assumed that the optic angle, $2V$, for red is greater than the optic angle for violet (that is, $r > v$) and that the crystal is optically positive with $X = b$, $Y = a$, and $Z = c$.

In the parallel position, Fig. 2A, the optic plane is parallel to the plane of vibration of the analyzer (in most microscopes), and the points of emergence of the optic axes in the interference field lie in the trace of the vibration plane of the analyzer, AA', and in the horizontal brushes of the isogyre. No color fringes are produced adjacent to the isogyre, but, if the dispersion is strong, the isochromatic curves (not shown) will be somewhat blurred in both the parallel and 45-degree positions by systematic superimposition of a series of curves centered about the optic axes for the various colors. In the 45-degree position, Fig. 2B, rotation has caused the isogyre in Fig. 2A to break

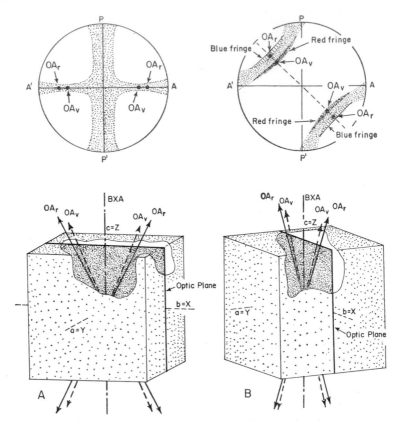

Fig. 2. Rhombic (orthorhombic) dispersion in an orthorhombic crystal. Distribution of isogyres and color fringes on isogyres in interference figures are shown for the crystal plate with optic orientation indicated in block diagrams. OA_r, optic axis for red; OA_v, optic axis for violet. $r > v$.

A. Parallel position.
B. Forty-five-degree position.

up into two hyperbolic segments, and color fringes will be noted on the concave and convex sides of the isogyres, as indicated.

The fact that violet (or blue) fringes appear at the points of emergence of the optic axes for red and red fringes appear at the points of emergence of the optic axes for violet needs explanation. This phenomenon is understood if it is realized that no path difference is produced for red light moving along an optic axis for red. Consequently the red color, in effect, is removed from white light at the points of emergence of its optic axes in the interference field, and a color near the opposite end of the spectrum appears, that is, blue.

The same type of reasoning applies to violet light. That is, a red color appears at the points of emergence of the optic axes for violet light.

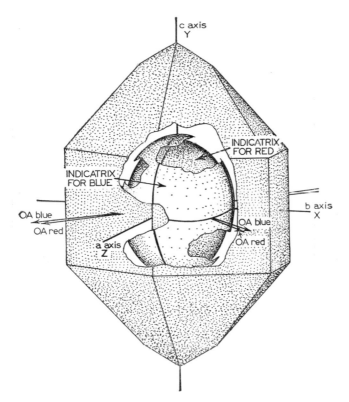

Fig. 3. Orthorhombic crystal showing orthorhombic (rhombic) dispersion. Crystal is positive, and $2V$ is near 90 degrees.

Between the red and blue fringes a normal black or gray isogyre is present where the path differences for the intermediate colors of the spectrum are insufficient to produce color effects.

In crystals in which $r < v$, the color fringes are reversed.

Figure 3 is a three-dimensional drawing of an orthorhombic crystal cut away to show the indicatrices for red and blue (violet). Note that the optic orientation for both indicatrices is the same but that dispersion of the optic axes is present.

In certain rare orthorhombic crystals the dispersion is so extreme that a very unusual effect is produced. In brookite at 25° C the optic plane for short wave lengths lies in the bc plane. As the wave length of the incident light increases the optic angle decreases, and near 555 m_μ the crystal is uniaxial with a $2V$ of zero. For wave lengths greater than 555 m_μ, the optic angle opens up in the ab plane so that the optic planes for colors at opposite ends of the spectrum are crossed. This type of dispersion is called *crossed axial plane* dispersion. Figure

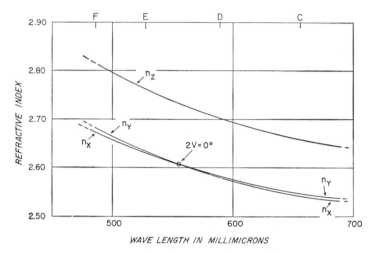

Fig. 4. Dispersion curves for brookite.

4 shows how the refractive indices change with the wave length of light in brookite. Figure 5 is a diagrammatic three-dimensional drawing showing the orientations of indicatrices for red and blue (violet) in brookite. For both indicatrices $Z = b$.

In describing the optic orientation of crystals such as brookite, it is necessary to specify the wave length (in vacuum) of the light used in the determination.

Dispersion in Monoclinic Crystals

Monoclinic crystals in the prismatic class have a single plane of symmetry, which includes the a and c crystal axes; the b crystallographic axis is normal to the symmetry plane. Because of the symmetry requirements of monoclinic crystals, one axis of the indicatrix for each wave length of light must coincide with the b crystallographic axis, and the other axes of the indicatrix must lie in the crystallographic symmetry plane. Three possibilities arise: (1) The acute bisectrix parallels the b axis, and the obtuse bisectrix and the optic normal lie in the crystallographic plane of symmetry. The b axis

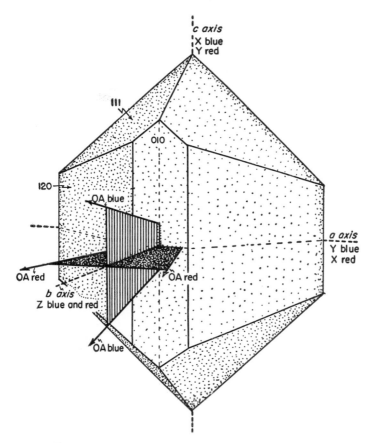

Fig. 5. Crossed axial plane dispersion in brookite.

serves, in effect, as an axis or rotation for the indicatrices of the various colors. Interference figures in white light show *crossed dispersion* in an acute bisectrix figure. (2) The obtuse bisectrix parallels the *b* axis, and the acute bisectrix and the optic normal lie in the crystallographic plane of symmetry. This orientation results in *horizontal dispersion* in the acute bisectrix figure observed in white light. (3) The optic normal parallels the *b* axis, and the acute and obtuse bisectrices lie in the crystallographic plane of symmetry. Acute bisectrix figures show *inclined dispersion* in white light.

In monoclinic crystals showing strong or extreme dispersion not only are prominent color fringes observed on the isogyres, but also the isochromatic curves may have a peculiar appearance resulting from the systematic superimposition of sets of color curves developed around the points of emergence in the interference field of the optic axes for the various colors of white light. The distribution of the color curves may be understood by considering the effects of super-

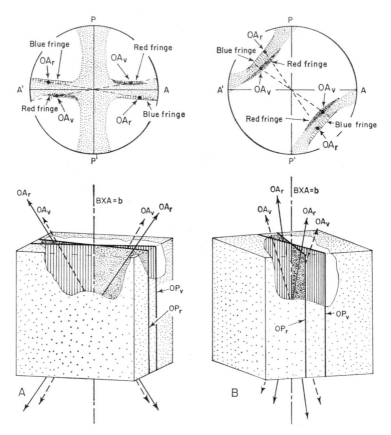

Fig. 6. Crossed dispersion in a monoclinic crystal. Distribution of isogyres and color fringes on isogyres in interference figures are shown for the crystal plate with optic orientations for the indicatrices for red and violet indicated in the block diagrams. OA_r, optic axis for red; OA_v, optic axis for violet; BXA, acute bisectrix. $r > v$.

        A. Parallel position.
        B. Forty-five-degree position.

imposition of the different kinds and shapes of color curves that would be observed if the interference figure were viewed in light of different colors provided by a succession of different monochromatic-light sources. The superimposed color curves can also be regarded as corresponding to the sections of a series of Bertin's surfaces derived from indicatrices with different optic angles and having some what different orientations. Color curves in interference figures are not indicated in the illustrations in this chapter.

Figure 6 shows the space relationships that result in *crossed dispersion*. This phenomenon is seen in monoclinic crystal plates which give acute bisectrix figures in sections cut normal to the *b* crystallographic axis. The *b* axis serves as an axis of rotation, and the axial planes for

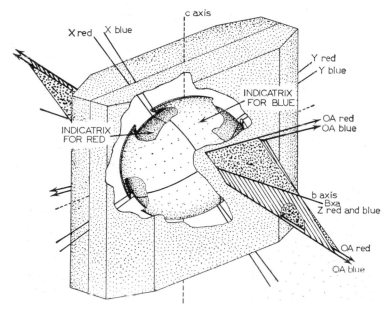

Fig. 7. Monoclinic crystal that would show crossed dispersion in an acute bisectrix figure.

the various wave lengths of light assume various positions between the extreme positions occupied by the axial planes for red and violet. As in orthorhombic dispersion, the red color fringes determine the locations of the optic axes for violet.

Crossed dispersion in the parallel position, Fig. 6*A*, produces similar color fringes on diagonally opposite sides of the isogyres. In Fig. 6, $r > v$, as determined by the fact that the blue fringes are spaced farther apart than the red fringes. In the 45-degree position, Fig. 6*B*, when $r > v$, the red fringes border the convex sides of the isogyres and lie on a diagonal line passing through the center of the field. The blue fringes display the same relation but lie on the concave sides of the isogyres. When $r < v$, the color fringes are reversed.

Figure 7 is a three-dimensional drawing of a monoclinic crystal that would show crossed dispersion in a plate cut normal to the *b* crystallographic axis.

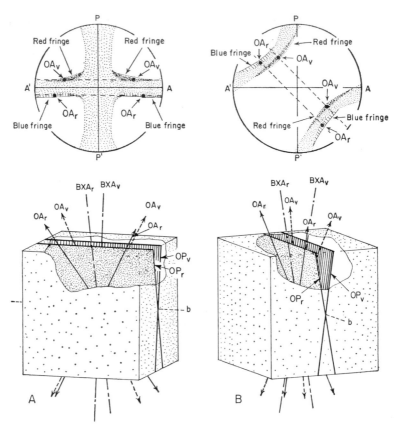

Fig. 8. Horizontal dispersion in a monoclinic crystal. Distribution of isogyres and color fringes on isogyres in interference figures are shown for the crystal plate with optic orientations for the indicatrices for red and violet indicated in the block diagrams. OA_r, optic axis for red; OA_v, optic axis for violet; OP_r, optic plane for red; OP_v, optic plane for violet; *BXA*, acute bisectrix. $r > v$.

A. Parallel position.
B. Forty-five-degree position.

Symmetrical crossed dispersion, when identified in acute bisectrix figures, suggests to the observer that he is looking along the *b* crystallographic axis of a monoclinic crystal.

Figure 8 illustrates *horizontal dispersion*. This type of dispersion is seen in interference figures of monoclinic crystal sections cut normal to the plane of crystallographic symmetry and approximately normal to the acute bisectrices for the various colors. In such sections the obtuse bisectrix parallels the b crystallographic axis. The b axis serves as an axis of rotation, and the optic planes for the various colors assume intermediate positions between the extreme positions of the axial planes of red and violet. In the example shown, $r > v$.

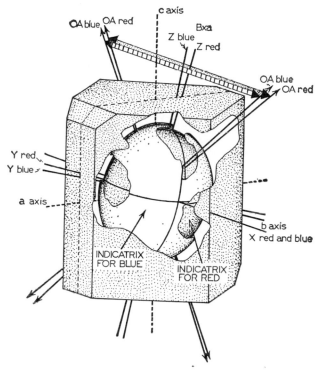

Fig. 9. Diagram of a monoclinic crystal that shows horizontal dispersion in an acute bisectrix figure.

Dispersion of the bisectrices is evident in that the points of emergence of the bisectrices for various colors do not coincide.

In the parallel position, Fig. 8A, the spreading of the traces of the axial planes by rotation of the axial planes about the b axis causes fringes of the same color to appear in similar symmetrical positions on the isogyres. The color fringes are symmetrical with respect to the symmetry plane of the crystal. When the red fringes are spaced farther apart than the blue fringes, $r < v$.

Observation of horizontal dispersion in an acute bisectrix figure leads to the conclusion that a crystal is monoclinic and that the obtuse bisectrix parallels the *b* crystallographic axis.

Figure 8*B* shows horizontal dispersion in the 45-degree position. A crystal section cut approximately normal to the acute bisectrices of the monoclinic crystal in Fig. 9 shows horizontal dispersion.

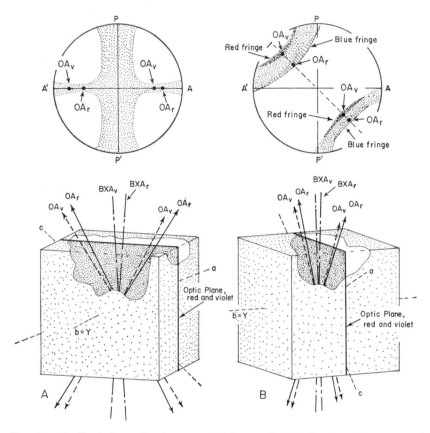

Fig. 10. Inclined dispersion in a monoclinic crystal. Distribution of isogyres and color fringes on isogyres in interference figures are shown for the crystal plate with optic orientations for the indicatrices for red and violet indicated in the block diagrams. OA_r, optic axis for red; OA_v, optic axis for violet; *BXA*, acute bisectrix. $r < v$.

Inclined dispersion produces color effects similar to those shown in Fig. 10. If the optic normal, *Y*, is parallel to the *b* crystallographic axis, the crystal axis serves as an axis of rotation about which the indicatrices for the various colors rotate until they assume characteristic positions for a given crystal, resulting in dispersion of the bisectrices. The extremes of rotation are the positions assumed by the bisectrices for red and violet. In crystals showing inclined dispersion, both the acute and obtuse bisectrices lie in the crystallographic plane of symmetry.

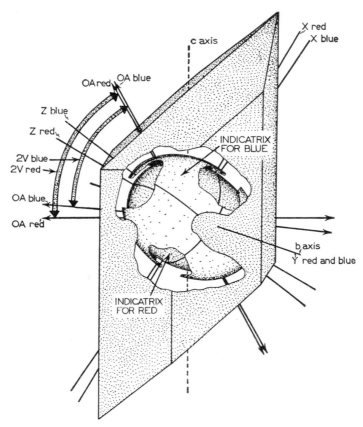

Fig. 11. Diagram of a monoclinic crystal that shows inclined dispersion in an acute bisectrix figure.

A section cut from a crystal in the parallel position, Fig. 10*A*, gives an acute bisectrix figure for which the isogyre does not differ in appearance from that in a figure showing no dispersive effects. This is explained by the fact that the optic axes for all colors lie in the same plane, the optic plane, and in the parallel position no opportunity is afforded for color fringes to appear. However (Fig. 10*B*) color fringes are seen in the 45-degree position. Many possibilities must be considered, each of which depends on the difference between the axial angles for red and violet and the extent to which the bisectrices are rotated with respect to each other. Figure 10 illustrates an example in which $r < v$, and the angular difference between the bisectrices is such that the red fringe appears on the convex side of one isogyre and on the concave side of the other. However, the red fringe, under certain circumstances, might appear on the convex or concave sides of both isogyres. In the latter example, the red and violet fringes on one isogyre would be narrower and spaced closer together than on the other isogyre. If the spacing were exactly the same, the dispersion would be orthorhombic. The isogyres and color fringes in inclined dispersion are symmetrical with respect to the trace of the optic plane but are not symmetrical with respect to a plane normal thereto. Again this relationship is accounted for by the fact that monoclinic crystals have only one plane of symmetry.

Figure 11 illustrates a monoclinic crystal that would show inclined dispersion in an acute bisectrix figure.

Dispersion in Triclinic Crystals

Triclinic crystals have no planes of symmetry. Accordingly, it is theoretically possible for the indicatrix for each color to assume any position in a crystal, and dispersion of the optic axes, indices, and the bisectrices produces unsymmetrical color fringes in interference figures. Usually the dispersive effects can be described only by assuming a combination of two or more types of monoclinic dispersion.

Probably the best way to visualize dispersion in triclinic crystals is to study the effects in stereographic projection. In general, however, it is sufficient to note the amount of dispersion and to ignore the geometry of the color fringes.

CHAPTER 16 SYSTEMATIC MICRO-SCOPIC EXAMINATION OF NONOPAQUE SUBSTANCES

There are many techniques for the microscopic examination of nonopaque substances. The particular technique that is employed depends upon the purpose of the investigation. If it is desired merely to identify a substance by its optical properties, the steps in the procedure are kept to a minimum. If, on the other hand, a precise determination and description of all optical properties is required, the procedure may become very complicated. Optical techniques do not always permit unequivocal identification of crystalline chemical compounds or minerals. One of the chief reasons for this is that many of the optical data appearing in published descriptions and determinative tables are incomplete, and the investigator may have difficulty in locating a described substance having identically the same properties as the material he is studying.

The optical properties of pure, crystalline chemical compounds or minerals and the end members of solid-solution series generally are constant and diagnostic. However, many mixed crystal series characterized by limited or complete solid solution display a partly or completely continuous gradation of optical and other physical properties. In such series optical data should be plotted on curves showing the optical properties as they are related to composition. In multicomponent isomorphous series, a diagram showing the relationship between chemical composition and optical properties of necessity must be very complex. In order to express adequately the composition, it might be required to assume the presence of three or more end members and to use polyhedral diagrams.

In spite of difficulties that may be encountered in optical studies because of isomorphism or solid solution, the optical technique still remains as one of the most facile methods for identification of non-opaque substances, particularly if the observer has had experience that has sharpened his judgment as to the effects of isomorphous substitution of one substance for another as based on a knowledge of crystal chemistry.

Preferences as to the optical equipment that should be used in measurement of optical constants differ widely. The simplest equipment consists of a petrographic or chemical microscope with the usual lens combinations and accessory plates and a set of standardized liquid immersion media. For certain purposes a universal stage has no substitute, but most workers prefer to dispense with complicated accessory devices and use only the simplest basic equipment. For accurate work a variable or fixed source of monochromatic light is required, but in routine identification of substances white light generally suffices.

In determinative work, preliminary study of physical properties both in hand specimen and under the microscope serves a useful purpose and may assist in the identification of a substance which cannot be distinguished from another substance on the basis of optical properties alone.

In this chapter attention is given to procedures for the examination of single crystals or aggregates of crystals by the immersion method. More elegant methods for studying crystals by crystal rotation techniques are outlined in Chapter 17.

Optical Examination of Crystals or Fragments in Immersion Media

Particular attention should be paid to the preparation of samples for examination by the immersion technique. Finely divided powders or small, loose crystals may not require preliminary crushing or grinding. However, many coarsely crystalline materials must be reduced to powder before immersion in liquid index media.

The method employed in powdering a sample preparatory to optical examination determines to a considerable extent the ease or difficulty with which the optical constants may be measured. If a substance has no cleavage, simple crushing and grinding with a small steel or agate mortar and pestle is satisfactory. However, if one or more cleavages are present, the powder is produced by crushing or grinding, depending upon what is desired in the subsequent optical measurements. A cleavable substance crushed by a series of sharp blows with the pestle yields fragments with flat faces, and, when immersed in a liquid index medium, the fragments tend to roll over so as to lie on the flat faces. This result may or may not be desirable. If, on the other hand, the sample is pulverized by a combination of pressure and a gyratory motion of the pestle, the fragments tend to be rounded and are more likely to assume random orientations on the glass slide.

Fibrous and micaceous substances and certain substances with two or more eminent cleavages present a special problem. These substances may be supported in desired positions in immersion media by mixing them with finely powdered cover glass before placing them in the liquid, or they may be subjected to special treatment. Many fibrous and micaceous substances are relatively soft and, if held between two glass slides, may be shaved into thin slices with a razor blade by using the edges of the glass slides as guides. A very small portion of the fibrous or micaceous substance is allowed to extend beyond the edges of the slides, and by successive cuttings several fragments that will lie in the desired position in the liquid immersion may be obtained. Platy or fibrous minerals may be examined by sprinkling fragments on a gel-coated slide before adding the immersion liquid. The gel should not be miscible with the immersion liquid. A solution of water glass generally provides a suitable gel coating on the glass slide.

Many investigators classify the powder by sizes by screening after grinding. A 100-mesh or 60-mesh screen serves this purpose, but for routine work screening of the sample is not generally required. A very small amount of the powder is added to the immersion medium on a glass slide, or the powder is placed on the slide and the immersion liquid is added. A cover glass is placed on top of the immersion for protective purposes. Additional liquid may be introduced under the cover glass by capillarity by touching a drop of liquid to the edge of the cover glass.

To determine all optical constants repeated immersions may be required. A single crystal may be transferred from one slide to another and rolled into the desired positions by gentle manipulation of the cover glass with the point of a pencil. If a powder is available, it is preferable to use only a few fragments and to roll selected grains so as to obtain desired orientations. If too much powder is added to the index liquid, it will not be easy to observe interference figures because of the difficulty of isolating single grains in the field of the microscope.

Amorphous substances and *isotropic crystals* have only one refractive index for a specified wave length. For certain types of work it is desirable to ascertain the refractive indices for several standard wave lengths of light. Strained isotropic substances are more or less birefringent.

Uniaxial substances belong to the tetragonal or hexagonal systems and possess two principal refractive indices. The index for the ordinary component n_O can be measured in all grains; the index for the extraordinary component n_E can be measured only in grains showing a maximum interference color and yielding a centered flash figure.

The optic sign may be determined when the refractive indices have been measured; or it may be determined in crystals in which the direction of the c axis is known or in an optic-axis figure obtained from a grain that remains gray or black during a complete rotation of the microscope stage. In plane-polarized light, with the upper polar removed, various features such as crystallization, cleavage, etc., may be noted; and, once the directions of O and E have been located, the absorption formula, or dichroic formula, may be noted.

The optical data may be summarized conveniently according to the scheme suggested in the following examples:

	n_{546}	n_{589}	n_{670}	Dichroism	
O	$2.032 \pm .001$	$2.013 \pm .001$	$1.990 \pm .001$	Pink	Uniaxial positive; absorption $O > E$, weak
E	$2.048 \pm .001$	$2.029 \pm .001$	$2.005 \pm .001$	Colorless	

	n	
O	$1.713 \pm .003$	Uniaxial negative
E	$1.705 \pm .003$	Colorless

Biaxial substances crystallize in the orthorhombic, monoclinic, and triclinic systems and have three principal indices of refraction. The maximum and minimum refractive indices, n_X and n_Z, are measured in grains showing a maximum interference color and yielding centered flash figures; n_Y may be measured in grains that remain dark between crossed polars during a complete rotation of the microscope stage and give centered optic-axis figures, or it may be measured at right angles to the optic plane in crystals giving symmetrical bisectrix figures. In positive crystals giving centered acute bisectrix figures, n_X may be measured in the trace of the optic plane; in negative crystals, n_Z may be measured in the same manner.

Fragments yielding off-center interference figures permit measurement of one refractive index, if the figures show any symmetry. For example, in off-center bisectrix or optic axis figures in which the isogyres in the 45-degree position are symmetrical with reference to the trace of the optic plane (the optic plane is parallel to the microscope axis) n_Y may be measured when the normal to the optic plane is parallel to the lower polar. In off-center bisectrix figures for which the optic plane is inclined but for which the isogyres in the 45-degree position are symmetrical with regard to a line normal to the trace of the optic plane and passing through the point of emergence of the bisectrix, n_X or n_Z may be measured in a direction parallel to the trace of the optic plane. Whether it is n_X or n_Z depends on which bisectrix is involved and whether the mineral is positive or negative.

Optic sign may be determined from the refractive indices or from interference figures. The acute bisectrix figure should be examined carefully for dispersion of the optic axes and bisectrices. Horizontal, inclined, and crossed dispersion indicate monoclinic crystallization and give valuable clues as to the optic orientation. Triclinic crystals produce asymmetrical triclinic dispersion. The interference figures also may be used to estimate or measure $2V$ and $2E$, or these values may be computed from the refractive indices.

Optic orientation is determined by establishing the relationship between the crystallographic directions and the X, Y, and Z directions of the indicatrix. If it is not possible to identify crystallographic directions by cleavages or crystal outline, complete determination of optic orientation by the immersion technique alone is impossible.

The absorption formula and pleochroism are noted for the X, Y, and Z directions of the indicatrix at the time that the refractive indices are being measured or during the process of determining the optic orientation.

The optical data may be summarized as indicated in the following examples for orthorhombic and monoclinic crystals:

	n_{Na}	Orientation	Pleochroism	
X	$1.702 \pm .001$	c	Pink	Orthorhombic
Y	$1.722 \pm .001$	b	Colorless	Biaxial positive $2V = 84°$
Z	$1.750 \pm .001$	a	Rose	Dispersion $r < v$, weak Absorption $Z > X > Y$

	n	Orientation	
X	$1.568 \pm .003$	b	Monoclinic Biaxial positive $2V = 26°$ Dispersion $r < v$, weak Nonpleochroic
Y	$1.569 \pm .003$		
Z	$1.587 \pm .003$	$\wedge c = 21°$	

Triclinic crystals require special treatment. The optic orientation may be shown by means of a stereographic projection which includes the poles of important crystal faces and the poles of important directions of the indicatrix. The optical and morphological crystallographic data may also be given in tables which summarize the angular relationships of all pertinent data in terms of ϕ and ρ angles (see p. 13).

The accompanying outline gives a summary of a procedure that might be followed in part or entirely in the routine optical examination of nonopaque substances by the immersion method.

Outline Procedure for Examining Nonopaque Substances by the Immersion Method

I. Preliminary megascopic examination.
   a. Ascertain as many of the following properties as feasible:
      1. Crystallization and crystal habit.
      2. Color.
      3. Luster.
      4. Fracture.
      5. Cleavage.
      6. Hardness.
      7. Specific gravity.
      8. Fusibility.

II. Exploratory microscopic examination.
   a. With the upper polar not inserted determine as many of the following properties as feasible in a liquid immersion:
      1. Crystallization and crystal habit.
      2. Color by transmitted light. Selective absorption or pleochroism, if present.
      3. Fracture.
      4. Cleavage.
      5. Relief and refractive index relative to immersion medium.
   b. With upper polar not inserted observe whether inclusions or alterations are present.
   c. With upper polar inserted.
      1. Find out if the substance is isotropic or anisotropic.

2. Observe twinning if present. If the substance is twinned, note the type of twinning.

3. Observe the interference color in anisotropic substances and appraise its relationship to thickness, orientation, and birefringence.

III. If a substance is isotropic, measure the refractive index for white light or one or more specified wave lengths.

IV. If a substance is anisotropic, make the following observations:

a. Examine an interference figure to determine whether the substance is uniaxial or biaxial, if this is not already known.

b. For uniaxial substances determine the following:

1. Optic sign by any of several available methods.
2. Sign of elongation or flattening.
3. Refractive indices for white light or for one or more standard wave lengths.
4. Birefringence, measured or computed as difference between maximum and minimum refractive indices.
5. Absorption formula and dichroism.

c. If a substance is biaxial, determine the following:

1. Optic sign. If sign is determined from an acute bisectrix interference figure, note the amount and type of dispersion. This procedure helps in determining the crystal system of the substance.
2. Sign of elongation or flattening.
3. Refractive indices for white light or for one or more standard wave lengths.
4. Optic orientation, if crystallographic directions can be identified.
5. $2V$ and $2E$, either calculated from refractive indices or measured in interference figures.
6. Pleochroism and absorption formula.

V. If data obtained in above tests do not suffice for determination, additional chemical or X-ray tests may be needed.

CHAPTER 17 CRYSTAL ROTATION METHODS

In the routine examination of powders or crystals by the immersion method, measurement of the indices of refraction and determination of the optic orientation are expedited by rolling the grains into desired positions by gently moving the cover glass with a pencil point or a needle. Appropriate orientations are checked by noting the relief relative to the immersion medium and by noting extinction angles, interference colors, interference figures, and other optical characteristics. Inequidimensional fragments may be supported by crushed cover glass or may be ground or cut so that the grains will assume a variety of orientations on the object slide. However, many investigators prefer to use equipment that will permit controlled rotation of crystals into any desired position and feel more confident of the accuracy of the results because of a more certain knowledge of the geometrical relationships between crystal directions and the axis of the microscope. Any device that can be attached to the microscope stage to permit rotation of a crystal about one or more axes other than the axis of the microscope is called a *universal stage,* or a *stage goniometer,* and it is possible to obtain such devices with one, two, three, four, or five axes of rotation to be attached to the stages of most kinds of polarizing microscopes.

The modern four- and five-axis stages are constructed so that it **is** possible to rotate crystal plates or fragments into positions that permit measurement of optic orientation, $2V$, the pleochroic formula, dispersion, optic sign, and twin laws in a single section of a crystal. With appropriate auxiliary equipment refractive indices may be measured quickly and accurately. The universal stage is also used extensively in petrofabric studies in which mineral orientations in rocks are measured and analyzed statistically.

Information obtained from universal-stage measurements is conveniently plotted with the aid of stereographic and equal-area nets, which are graphical devices of considerable versatility. A brief discussion of these nets and their uses is included in this chapter.

Emphasis is placed in this chapter on the use of the one-circle stage for the measurement of optical properties by the immersion method and the use of the multiaxis stage for the examination of petrographic thin sections. No effort will be made to describe the equipment and procedures used for the double variation method of refractive index measurement because this has been done so completely by Emmons.[1] Instead, the use of the four-axis universal stage for thin-section examination will be outlined. The four-axis stage requires that a constant graphical record be kept of all important manipulations, and it minimizes errors, especially when the operator is relatively inexperienced.

Stereographic Net

The plane of projection in stereographic projections is the equatorial section of the spherical projection (see p. 14). The poles of crystal faces or directions on either the upper or lower hemisphere of the spherical projection are projected into the equatorial plane as if viewed from either the north or south pole, depending upon whether the poles on the sphere are assumed to lie on the south or north hemisphere. Stereographic projections are based on the upper or lower hemispheres of the spherical projection.

Graphical solutions in stereographic projections are greatly expedited by using a stereographic net, such as the one shown in Fig. 1.[2] A sheet of translucent vellum is placed over the net so that it can be rotated about the center of the network. A pin at the center of the net and passing through the vellum will serve as an axis of rotation,

---

[1] R. C. Emmons, *The Universal Stage,* Geol. Soc. Amer., Memoir 8, 1943.

[2] Stereographic nets and "surface-true" nets (equal-area nets) may be obtained from E. Leitz, Inc., 468 Fourth Ave., New York 16, N. Y.

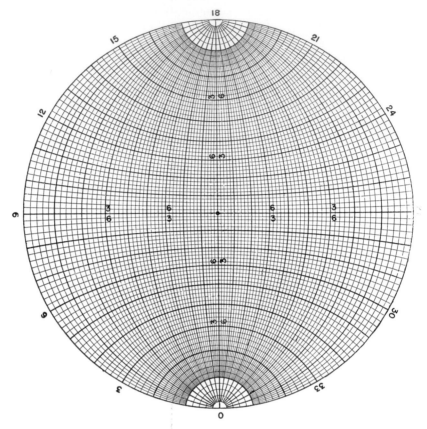

Fig. 1. Stereographic net for plotting data in stereographic projection and for rotating plotted points into new positions.

or use may be made of a more elaborate stereographic net with a rotating peripheral mount.

Equal-Area Net

Data similar to those plotted on stereographic projections may be analyzed statistically if plotted on equal-area projections. Plotting of data is facilitated by the use of the equal-area net shown in Fig. 2. The net differs from an ordinary stereographic net in that areas enclosed by intersecting lines on the net are nearly equal over the area of the net at any given "latitude." The poles of perpendiculars to planes or the pole of any direction may be plotted if the azimuth and the inclination from the vertical are known.

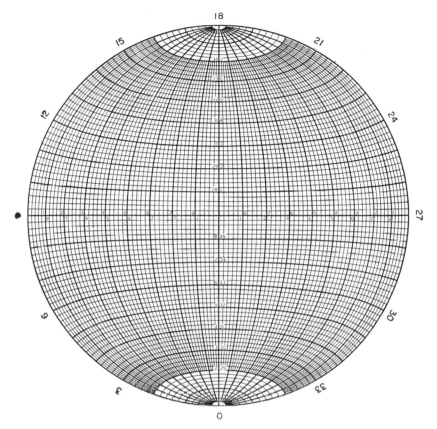

Fig. 2. Equal-area net.

According to standardized procedure the lower rather than the upper hemisphere of the spherical projection is used as the basis for plotting points in the equal-area projection, a practice that differs from many methods employing the stereographic projection.

One-Axis Universal Stage

Joel[3] describes the use and construction of a one-axis universal stage (one-circle stage goniometer) to measure refractive indices and to determine the orientation of the indicatrix for uniaxial and biaxial crystals by an orthoscopic technique. A crystal is mounted on a glass fiber and is attached to the horizontal spindle of the instrument. A

[3] N. Joel, "A Method to Determine the Indicatrix of Small Crystals," *Mineralogical Mag.*, Vol. 29, pp. 206–214, 1950.

divided circle on the knob of the spindle permits measurement of the angle of rotation about the horizontal axis of the stage, and combined rotations of the crystal about the horizontal axis and the vertical axis of the microscope permit rotation of each of the principal axes of the indicatrix into a north-south direction in a horizontal plane. In the north-south position (parallel to the plane of vibration of the lower polar) the appropriate refractive index may be measured in an im-

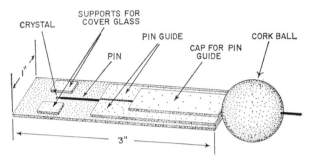

Fig. 3. One-axis crystal rotation device constructed from glass microslides, a pin, and a cork ball.

mersion cell. A record of the rotations about the horizontal and vertical axes, as plotted in a stereographic projection, permits determination of the orientation of the indicatrix relative to the axis of the spindle.

An inexpensive and easily constructed single-axis stage that serves many of the functions of a one-axis universal stage is described by Rosenfeld[4] and is essentially a one-axis universal stage without a divided circle for angular measurements. Figure 3 shows such a stage as modified by the author for use in his own laboratory. An ordinary 1 by 3 inch glass microslide is used as the base. From another slide two sections of glass are cut and are cemented to the base with water glass or cellulose acetate cement to provide a slot that will act as a pin guide. The width of the slot is determined by the diameter of the pin, such as a corsage pin, that will be inserted in the slot. Near the opposite end of the base two small squares (or triangles) of glass are cemented to the base to provide a support for a cover glass for an immersion cell. The pin is cut to an appropriate length and a cork ball, or an ordinary cork bottle stopper, is attached to one end

[4] J. L. Rosenfeld, "Determination of All Principal Indices of Refraction on Difficultly Oriented Minerals by Direct Measurement," *Am. Mineralogist*, Vol. 35, pp. 902–905, 1950, and written communication.

to facilitate rotation of the pin. With the aid of a hand magnifier or a low-power stereoscopic microscope a crystal or fragment of greatest diameter less than the diameter of the pin is cemented to the pin point with water glass, and the pin is inserted into the slot. The cork is adjusted so that the crystal will lie within the immersion cell, and the cork is outside the edge of the microscope stage. A piece of string is placed in the slot over the pin to insure a tight fit of the pin in the slot, and the pin guide is then capped with another section of

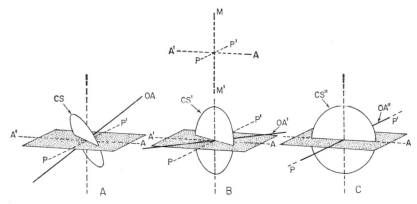

Fig. 4. Rotation of a uniaxial crystal into desired critical positions. *CS* is a circular equatorial section of the indicatrix. *OA* is the optic axis.

A. Random orientation.
B. Crystal rotated about horizontal axis, *AA'*, to place optic axis in horizontal plane (stippled).
C. Crystal rotated about vertical axis, *MM'*, to place optic axis in a north-south direction, *PP'*, in the horizontal plane.

glass slide, which is not cemented to the mount. The whole device is held in place with the spring clamps on the microscope stage and is moved to a position where the immersion cell is in the center of the stage, and the crystal can be viewed through the microscope. Liquid immersion media can be introduced into the immersion cell by capillarity and can be removed by using absorptive cellulose tissue, so that a single mount can be used for a succession of observations and measurements. If desired, acetone may be used to flush and clean the immersion cell and the crystal between successive immersions.

The theory of the one-axis universal stage method is explained with the aid of Figs. 4 through 9. In Fig. 4 a uniaxial crystal is rotated first about a horizontal axis, *AA'*, and then about a vertical axis, *MM'*, in order to place the optic axis in a horizontal plane (stippled) and then in a north-south direction for the measurement of the refractive index, n_E. It is assumed that the plane of vibration of the lower polar also is north-south. Figure 4A shows the indicatrix in a random orientation. The circular equatorial section, CS, of the indicatrix contains radius vectors, all of which are equal to n_O. The optic axis,

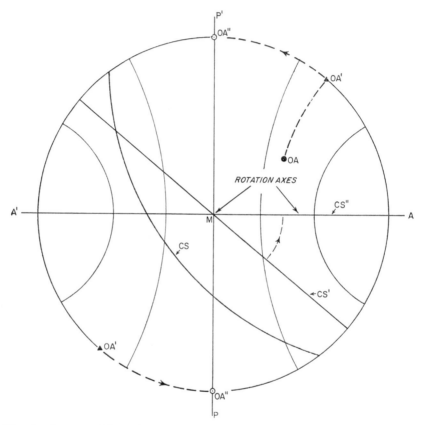

Fig. 5. Stereographic projection of operations performed in Fig. 4. CS, CS', and CS'' are successive positions of the circular equatorial section of the indicatrix. OA, OA', and OA'' are successive positions occupied by the optic axis. Based on projection from upper hemisphere.

OA, normal to the circular equatorial section, contains the vector, n_E. Rotation about the horizontal axis, AA', will bring the optic axis into a horizontal plane as in Fig. 4B, and rotation about a vertical axis, MM', brings the optic axis into a north-south direction, PP', as in Fig. 4C. The crystal in this position will be at extinction between crossed polars because the vibration directions for the E and O components are parallel to the planes of vibration of the polarizer and analyzer. The ordinary index, n_0, can be measured in any orientation provided that the crystal is rotated to extinction and the trace of the

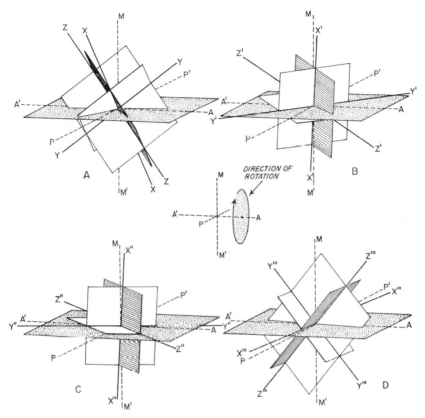

Fig. 6. Rotation of a biaxial crystal about a horizontal axis, AA', so as to place each of the indicatrix axes (X, Y, and Z) in a horizontal plane (stippled). Planes are planes of symmetry of the indicatrix. Optic plane is indicated by hatching. Rotation away from the observer.

> A. Random position.
> B. Y axis in horizontal plane.
> C. Z axis in horizontal plane.
> D. X axis in horizontal plane.

intersection of the circular equatorial section with the horizontal plane is north-south.

The operations indicated in Fig. 4 are shown in stereographic projection (upper hemisphere) in Fig. 5. The directions AA', PP' are the same in both figures.

In special orientations for uniaxial crystals the horizontal axis of rotation may happen to be parallel or perpendicular to the optic axis. If it is parallel, rotation about the horizontal axis at the extinction position will not relieve the extinction. If the horizontal axis is perpendicular to the optic axis, again a rotation about the optic

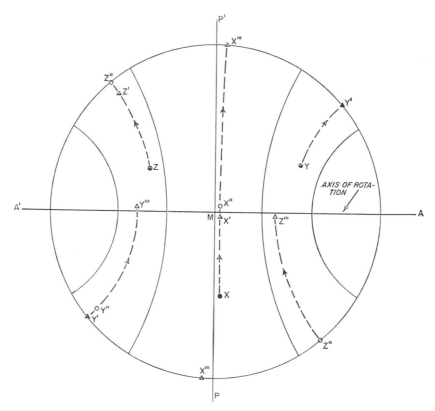

Fig. 7. Stereographic plot of operations in Fig. 6. X, X', X'', X''', Y, Y', Y'', Y''', and Z, Z', Z'', Z''' indicate successive positions occupied by the indicatrix axes during rotation about the horizontal axis, AA'. Based on projection from upper hemisphere.

axis at the extinction position will not relieve the extinction. In the 45-degree position on the microscope stage, when the optic axis is normal to the horizontal axis of rotation, the crystal can be rotated about the horizontal axis from a position where the interference color is a maximum (optic axis horizontal) to a position where the interference color is a minimum (optic axis parallel to axis of microscope). In a random orientation for the indicatrix rotation about either the horizontal or vertical axis of a grain at extinction position will relieve the extinction.

Figure 6 shows that it is possible to rotate any of the principal axes of an indicatrix for a biaxial crystal into a horizontal plane parallel to the stage of the microscope. The X, Y, and Z axes and the planes of symmetry of the indicatrix are shown in a random position in Fig. 6A. Rotation about the horizontal axis, AA', in a direction away from the observer successively places each of the axes of the indicatrix in the horizontal plane. The same operation is indicated in Fig. 7, a stereographic projection. If desired, the extinction positions for any

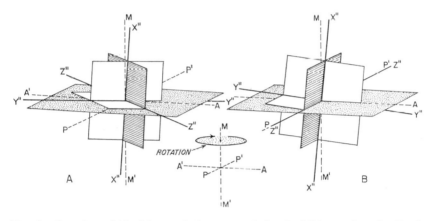

Fig. 8. Rotation of biaxial crystal about a vertical axis, MM', to place the Z axis in a north-south direction in a horizontal plane.

A. Same position as in Fig. 6C.
B. Position after rotation.

position of rotation of the crystal could be calculated by reference to the Biot-Fresnel construction, but in this discussion attention is given to the indicatrix in only certain critical orientations.

After rotation of the X, Y, or Z axis into the horizontal plane, rotation about the vertical axis, MM', will bring the crystal to extinction when the intersections of the symmetry planes of the indicatrix with the horizontal plane are north-south and east-west. Figure 8 shows a rotation about the vertical axis, MM', to bring the Z axis into a north-south direction. In this position the crystal is at extinction, and, if the vibration plane of the lower polar is north-south, the value for n_Z can be measured. Rotation about the vertical axis is indicated in the stereographic projection in Fig. 9. Similar operations would permit rotation of X or Y into extinction positions where it would be possible to measure n_X and n_Y.

If the horizontal rotation axis is east-west and normal to a plane of symmetry of the indicatrix (parallel to X, Y, or Z), the crystal will be at extinction between crossed polars and rotation about the

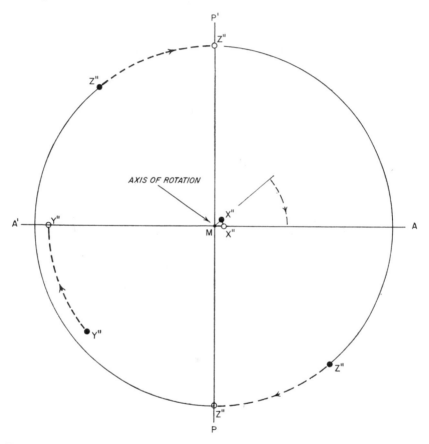

Fig. 9. Operation in Fig. 8 shown in stereographic projection. Solid circles indicate poles before rotation and open circles locate poles after rotation. Based on projection from upper hemisphere.

horizontal axis will not relieve the extinction. Rotation about either the horizontal or vertical axis will relieve extinction in crystals in which the indicatrix directions are inclined to the horizontal rotation axis.

The successful use of a one-axis stage depends upon the ability of the observer to determine that the indicatrix is in particular critical orientations on the stage of the microscope. Preliminary examination in immersion media by ordinary methods may give some clues as to the orientation and may permit measurement of some or all of the properties. As a matter of fact, use of the one-axis stage commonly is justified only when material is scarce or the crystal or its fragments, because of habit or cleavage, have unusual shapes that prevent measurement of properties by more routine methods.

An anisotropic crystal on the stage of the microscope can be placed in an extinction position by rotation about either a horizontal or a vertical axis or by combined rotation about both axes. Considering all possible orientations of the indicatrix and all possible rotations to positions of extinction, it is seen that there can be practically an infinite number of extinction positions for a particular crystal as it is rotated about both horizontal and vertical axes. The problem, then, becomes one of locating extinction positions for which important directions of the indicatrix have assumed orientations that will permit meaningful measurements of properties. In crystal-rotation methods, observation of interference color, relief, interference figures, and other properties assists in identifying crystals that are in appropriate critical orientations. Rosenfeld[5] has noted that when the indicatrix is in a position such that one of the principal refractive indices can be measured, an interference figure in the general case will show an isogyre symmetrically disposed about the east-west cross hair of the ocular (assuming that the plane of vibration of the lower polar is north-south).

In uniaxial crystals n_O always can be measured in one of the extinction positions. If the crystal is immersed in an index liquid and, after each of a succession of rotations about the horizontal axis, it is possible to rotate the crystal about the vertical axis to an extinction position in which the relief is the same as for previous rotations to extinction, the observer is assured that, for each such extinction position, the trace of the intersection of the circular equatorial section of the indicatrix with the horizontal plane is north-south and that n_O can be measured. After the immersion medium has been changed so that it matches n_O, it will be seen that, at 90 degrees from the position where n_O is measured, the Becke line or oblique illumination will indicate that n_E is greater or less than n_O. If n_E is greater, the crystal is positive, and, if it is less, the crystal is negative. The crystal is rotated about both the horizontal and vertical axes to a succession of extinction positions by small increments of rotation until the relief of the crystal in a liquid of refractive index equal to n_O is at a maxi-

[5] Rosenfeld, *loc. cit.*

mum. In this position the optic axis is exactly or nearly in a horizontal plane and north-south, where the full value of n_E can be measured by successive immersions. The direction of the optic axis can be preserved by recording the vertical and horizontal angles on the one-axis universal stage or by sticking a pin parallel to the optic axis into the cork ball on the device illustrated in Fig. 3. In the last stages of index measurement additional slight rotations about both vertical and horizontal axes are made so that the observer can be certain that he is obtaining the full value of n_E, whether it be a maximum or minimum value for the crystal.

If it happens that the crystal is mounted so that the horizontal axis is parallel to the optic axis, rotation about the horizontal axis, when it is east-west or north-south and the crystal is at extinction, will cause no change in the relief of the crystal in the immersion liquid, but the relief in one extinction position will differ from that in the other position. If the optic axis is perpendicular to the horizontal axis, rotation about the horizontal axis when it is east-west will cause the relief to change. Both n_O and n_E can be measured in this position by rotation about the horizontal axis. When the horizontal axis is north-south and is perpendicular to the optic axis, n_O can be measured in all positions of rotation about the horizontal axis.

In biaxial crystals the crystal should be immersed in a liquid with an index somewhere between the maximum and minimum indices as determined by preliminary examination on a glass slide. The crystal should be rotated in small increments about both horizontal and vertical axes to a succession of extinction positions until the relief for a particular extinction position is at a maximum. By the Becke line method or by oblique illumination it is determined whether the index in the position of maximum relief is greater or less than that of the immersion liquid. At the position of maximum relief, when the index is higher than that of the liquid, the Z axis is actually or nearly in a north-south direction in a horizontal plane. X is in this direction if the refractive index of the crystal is less than that of the liquid. In either event the location of the axis of the indicatrix is recorded by noting the appropriate angles on the universal stage and the microscope stage or by sticking a pin into the cork ball on the simpler type of stage so that it is parallel to the indicatrix direction. By similar manipulations the other axis (X or Z) is located, and the appropriate refractive index is measured. In the last stages of measurement additional slight rotations are made to ascertain that, for the minimum refractive index, the true value of n_X is being obtained and that, for the maximum index, the full value of n_Z is determined. When the directions of the X and Z axes are located accurately by means of recorded angles or pins in the cork ball, n_Y can be measured by rotating the crystal to a position where the Y axis is in a north-south direction in a horizontal plane, a position where the X and Z axes lie in a vertical east-west plane. Accuracy of orientation in all positions can be checked by noting interference figures.

In a special case the crystal may have been mounted so that an axis of the indicatrix is parallel to the horizontal axis of rotation. In this case rotation about the horizontal axis at an extinction position will not relieve the extinction. One refractive index can be measured when the horizontal axis is north-south, and the other two indices can be measured by rotating the crystal about the horizontal axis when it is in the east-west position.

Construction and Adjustment of the Multiaxis Universal Stage

Figure 10 is a photograph of a typical four-axis stage. Figure 11 indicates diagrammatically the basic elements of the four- and five-axis stages. Both types have an inner glass plate on which the slide mount and the glass hemispheres may be placed so that a thin section may be rotated on any or all of four or five axes of the stage. All rotations are measured on conveniently located graduated circles or arcs of circles. There is considerable difference of opinion as to the proper designation of the axes, but for general purposes the axes may be referred to as east-west, north-south, or vertical. A useful notation for the four-axis stage is as follows:

Inner vertical axis	A_1
North-south axis	A_2
Outer vertical axis	A_3
East-west axis	A_4
Axis of microscope stage	A_5

At rest positions A_1, A_3, and A_5 are parallel to the tube of the microscope, and A_2 and A_4 are mutually perpendicular and lie in a horizontal plane.

Emmons[6] designates the axes for the five-axis stage as follows:

Inner vertical axis	(I. V.)
Inner east-west axis	(I. E-W)
North-south axis	(N-S)
Outer vertical axis	(O. V.)
Outer east-west axis	(O. E-W)
Microscope axis	(M.)

[6] Emmons, *op. cit.*

Courtesy E. Leitz, Inc.

Fig. 10. Four-axis universal stage.

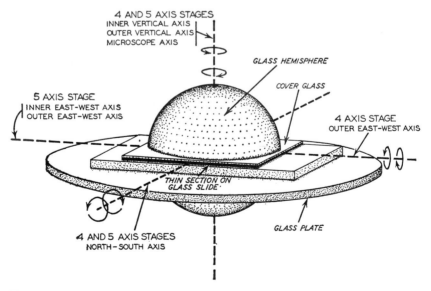

Fig. 11. Thin section mounted between glass hemispheres on universal stage. Diagram indicates rotation axes for four- and five-axis stages.

Figure 12 is a diagrammatic plan view indicating the positions of the rotation axes, the graduated circles, and the indices for the graduated circles of a four-axis stage at the starting or rest position.

The universal stage commonly is equipped with several pairs of glass hemispheres of different refractive indices. For a particular mineral the hemispheres are used which have a refractive index nearest the index or several indices of the mineral. This increases the angle through which a section may be turned before total reflection results,

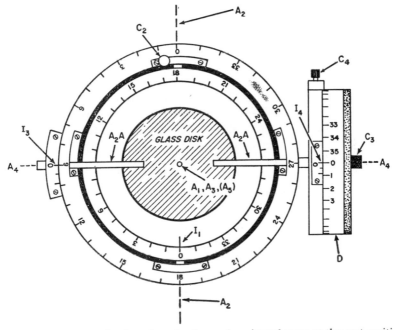

Fig. 12. Diagrammatic plan view of a four-axis universal stage at the rest position. A_1, A_2, A_3, and A_4 are the rotation axes of the universal stage, and A_5 is the axis of the microscope stage. C_2, C_3, and C_4 are the arresting screws for A_2, A_3, and A_4. A_2A indicates the graduated vertical arcs for A_2. I_1, I_2, and I_4 are the indices for the graduated circles for A_1, A_2, and A_4. D is the graduated drum for rotating the stage about A_4.

and it removes or reduces the necessity for making angular corrections dependent upon differences in the indices of the crystal and the glass hemisphere. Methods of making angular corrections for precise work are described in a later section of this chapter.

Universal stages equipped with small hemispheres permit direct observation of interference figures. The small hemispheres assist in precise measurement of optic angles and determination of critical optical orientation by use of interference figures but are not as useful as larger hemispheres in routine examination of thin sections of polymineralic aggregates.

Universal stages with a Schmidt guide slide (parallel ruler) mounted in the metal holder for the upper glass hemisphere permit traverses across the thin section at fixed intervals and enable the operator to move the section so as not to disturb its orientation relative to the axes of the universal stage.

Special microscope objectives are required for use with the universal stage so that the microscope can be focused on a slide between the glass hemispheres.

The universal stage is mounted on the microscope stage after removing the central disk of the microscope stage to provide room for free movement. A drop or two of cedar oil or glycerin is placed on the glass disk in the center of the stage, a thin section is placed in position, two or three drops of oil are placed on top of the section, and the upper hemisphere is fastened down on the slide with the screws. The lower hemisphere is now attached to the lower side of the glass disk using several drops of oil to remove the air film between the hemisphere and the disk.

The microscope is now focused on a point in the thin section, the microscope stage is rotated, and the objective is centered in the usual fashion. The glass plate of the four-axis stage is set horizontal by rotation to the zero positions on A_2 (north-south) and A_4 (east-west), and the A_1 and A_3 axes are brought into coincidence with A_5 by focusing on a point in the slide, rotating the inner circle about A_1, manually moving the universal stage over the microscope stage to the desired position, and then tightening the holding screws.

Next, the height of the thin section is adjusted so that A_2 and A_4 lie in the plane of the section and intersect in a point with A_1, A_3, and A_5. A point on the slide is placed at the intersection of the cross hairs and the glass disk is raised or lowered by an adjusting screw below the disk until the point in the slide remains stationary during rotation on A_2 and A_4.

With the indices for A_1, A_2, and A_4 set at zero on their respective graduated circles and (for many universal stages) the index for A_3 set at 90 degrees, the microscope stage is rotated so that A_2 and A_4 (mutually perpendicular) coincide with the cross hairs. The microscope is focused on a dust particle on the surface of the upper hemisphere, and the microscope stage is rotated until the dust particle moves parallel to the cross hairs upon rotation of A_2 and A_4. The reading on the graduated circle of the microscope stage is noted as the zero position for A_5 and is permanently marked by a stopping device. In many microscopes further adjustment of the universal stage will enable the operator to set the stop so that the zero mark on the microscope stage is also the zero position for A_5.

The manipulations for the five-axis stage are similar to those described above except that it must be remembered that there are two horizontal east-west axes.

For accurate work the light source must be carefully centered. This may be done by inserting the Bertrand-Amici lens and adjusting the mirror and light source until the light is centered in the microscope tube. A strong light cut down by iris diaphragms in the objectives and elsewhere in the microscope works well.

Measurement and Plotting of Crystal Planes

At the outset of measurements with the universal stage it should be determined whether the results are to be plotted on a net as if the poles of the planes and directions are on the upper or lower hemisphere of the spherical projection. The procedure that is selected is strictly arbitrary. Instead of using the upper half of the spherical projection as a basis for operations with the stereographic net, the procedure followed in earlier sections of this chapter, all subsequent plots will be based on constructions based on the lower hemisphere of the spherical projection.

A useful manipulation is the measurement and plotting of the attitudes of the planes and poles of cleavages, crystal faces, composition planes of twins, and similar planes in crystals. Plotting is expedited by placing a sheet of tracing vellum over the net, drawing a circle having the same diameter as the net on the vellum, and setting a needle through the center of the circle into the center of the net. A zero point is then arbitrarily indicated on the circle on the vellum by an arrow.

The plane in question in a particular mineral grain is moved, with the aid of a parallel ruler, to the center of the microscope field, and the inner circle is rotated about A_1 until the trace of the plane coincides with the axis parallel to the east-west cross hair (parallel to A_4). Now the grain is rotated about A_4 until the trace of the plane is as sharp or thin as it is possible to make it, and readings on the graduated circles for A_1 and A_4 are recorded. Suppose that the grain is rotated to the left 43 degrees on A_1 and tilted away from the observer 23 degrees on A_4 to obtain the desired result. This information is plotted on the projection as indicated in Fig. 13A.

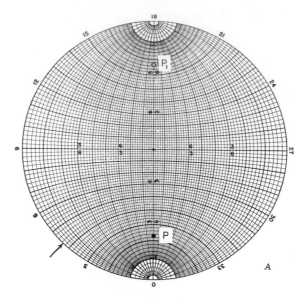

Fig. 13A. Method for plotting pole, P, of plane set vertical and parallel to A_4 by rotation 43 degrees to left on A_1 and, then, rotation on A_4 23 degrees away from observer. Arrow indicates zero position on vellum overlay. Plot based on stereographic projection of bottom half of spherical projection. P_1 shows where pole would fall if upper half were used.

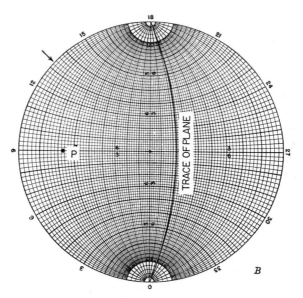

Fig. 13B. Projection in Fig. 13A rotated so that great circle giving trace of plane 90 degrees from pole, P, can be drawn.

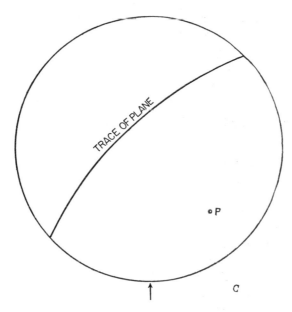

Fig. 13C. Stereographic projection in Fig. 13*A* rotated back to initial position.

The vellum is turned above the net through an angle of 43 degrees to the left from the zero position on the periphery. Then, assuming that the lower hemisphere is the basis for the projection, the pole of the plane is found by plotting a point 23 degrees in from the south end of the north-south diameter of the net. The trace of the plane for which the pole is plotted can be obtained by rotating the vellum sheet until the pole lies on the east-west diameter of the net as in Fig. 13*B*. The great circle 90 degrees from the pole on the east-west diameter is the trace of the plane in the stereographic projection.

Figure 13*C* shows the projection rotated back to the initial position.

Isotropism and Anisotropism

The determination of the nature of the optical indicatrix for a particular crystal is simply performed with a petrographic microscope by examining interference figures. However, on the universal stage the procedure is relatively easy and consists of determining whether the crystal is isotropic or anisotropic and, if it is anisotropic, whether it is uniaxial or biaxial. Proof that an anisotropic crystal is not uniaxial is sufficient indication that it is biaxial.

The procedure given below gives satisfactory results with most sections of crystals in thin sections. If the results are inconclusive for a particular grain, search for another grain of the same substance and try again. All operations are performed between crossed polars. A combination of an objective lens of short focal length and hemispheres of small to moderate diameter permits direct observation of interference figures, is useful in classifying a crystal as uniaxial or biaxial, and helps in determining critical orientations of the indicatrix.

I. If the grain remains dark during rotation about A_1, proceed as follows:

A. Rotate section a few degrees about A_2. Then rotate about A_4. If the section remains dark, the substance is *isotropic*.

B. If the section becomes illuminated, return stage to rest position, and then rotate a few degrees on A_4. If the section is still dark, return stage to rest position, rotate a few degrees on A_1 and then rotate a few degrees about A_4. If the section is anisotropic and remains dark during rotation on A_4 before and after rotation about A_1, the substance is *uniaxial* and is cut normal to the optic axis. If the section is illuminated after rotation on A_4 either before or after rotation on A_1, the substance is *biaxial* and is cut normal to an optic axis.

II. If the section is alternately extinguished and illuminated during rotation about A_1, A_3, or A_5, proceed as follows, after returning stage to rest position.

A. Rotate section to extinction on A_1 and then rotate about A_4.

1. If the grain is illuminated, return A_4 to rest position and rotate section 90 degrees to next extinction position. Now rotate on A_4. If section remains at extinction, it is *uniaxial*. If it becomes illuminated it is *biaxial*.

2. If in operation II*A* the section remains at extinction, return A_4 to the rest position and rotate the section through 90 degrees on A_1 to the next extinction position. Now rotate section a few degrees about A_2, and then return section to extinction by rotation about A_1. If, after this manipulation, the section remains at extinction during rotation on A_4, the substance is *uniaxial*. If the section is illuminated, the substance is *biaxial*.

Measurement of Uniaxial Crystals

In uniaxial crystals the indicatrix is an ellipsoid of revolution. A section of a crystal, oriented so that the optic axis is parallel to the microscope tube, remains dark during rotation about A_5, the axis of the microscope stage. A section lying so that the optic axis is perpendicular to A_5 shows a maximum interference color and extinguishes four times during a complete rotation about A_5. In universal-stage procedure the optic axis is placed parallel to the microscope tube for grains of relatively low interference color and perpendicular to the microscope tube for grains with relatively high interference colors.

I. Suppose that in the rest position a grain of a uniaxial substance such as quartz shows a gray interference color and it is desired to place the optic axis (c axis) parallel to the microscope tube. Proceed as follows:

    A. Turn section to extinction about A_1, and then rotate section about A_4.

        1. If the grain remains dark the optic axis lies in a plane including A_2 and A_5. A_4 is returned to zero, and the microscope stage is rotated 45 degrees about A_5, which relieves the extinction, and the section is rotated about A_4 until again at extinction. This manipulation places the optic axis parallel to the microscope tube, and the grain should remain dark during additional rotation on A_5. If not, repeat the above operation. The scale readings on A_1 and A_4 are noted and plotted on a net, as in the example shown in Fig. 14*A* and *B*. In Fig. 14*A* the A_1 reading was 310 degrees, and A_4 read 337 degrees for a quartz grain.

        2. If in operation I*A* the grain does not remain at extinction on rotation about A_4, the section is turned 90 degrees about A_1, and the above procedure is followed.

        3. If neither of the above steps produces extinction after rotation about A_4, the optic axis cannot be brought into coincidence with the microscope tube, and the optic axis must be placed parallel to A_4.

II. To place the optic axis in a grain showing relatively high interference colors parallel to A_4, turn the section about A_1 to an extinction position where it will remain dark on rotation about A_2, but does *not* remain dark on rotation about A_4. The optic axis then lies in a plane including A_4 and A_5. The section is tilted on A_2 until rotation about A_4 no longer causes illumination.

Figure 15 illustrates a hexagonal crystal (uniaxial) in various critical positions on the universal stage.

Measurement of Biaxial Crystals

A fundamental operation in the measurement of biaxial crystals is rotation of the section so as to bring X, Y, or Z of the optical indica-

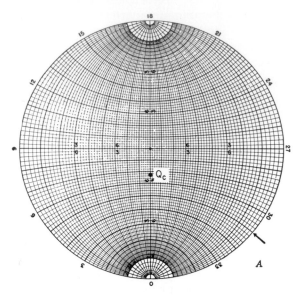

Fig. 14A. Method for plotting pole of optic axis for quartz, Q_c. Scale reading for A_1 is 310 degrees, and for A_4 337 degrees. A_4 was tilted toward the observer 23 degrees (360 minus 337). Projection based on lower half of spherical projection.

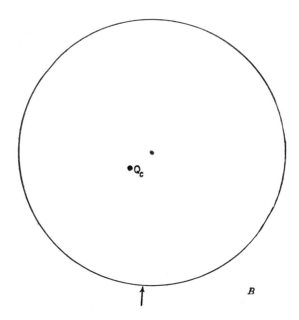

Fig. 14B. Projection in Fig. 14A rotated back to zero position.

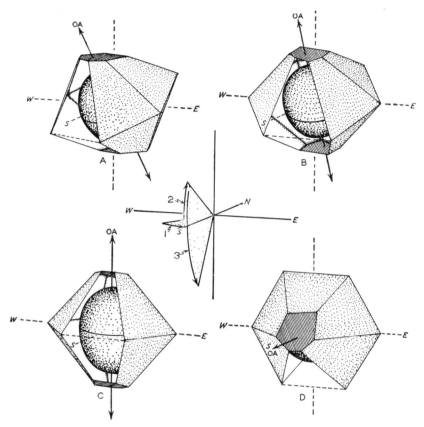

Fig. 15. Hexagonal crystal in various critical positions on universal stage.

A. Original random position. Grain is illuminated.

B. Rotated about A_1 to extinction position. Grain will remain extinguished during rotation on A_4 but not on A_2.

C. Optic axis parallel to A_5. Grain will remain extinguished during rotation about A_5.

D. Optic axis parallel to A_2. Grain will remain at extinction during rotation about either A_2 or A_4.

axis into coincidence with A_4. When one of these axes is parallel to A_4, a symmetry plane of the indicatrix stands in a vertical north-south plane. Plotting of two symmetry planes or their poles on a stereonet permits solution of the problem of the location of the third plane or pole. Special measurements yield the value for $2V$, the optic angle.

In ordinary procedure the symmetry plane that is first located is the one most nearly parallel to the tube of the microscope (A_5).

This is done by rotating the section to each extinction position on A_1 and then turning the section on A_4. Measurement is begun from the extinction position which yields the least illumination upon rotation on A_4.

Following is a procedure which will work for most grains in a section. If a particular grain does not yield satisfactory results, try another grain of the same substance.

1. Rotate the section to extinction on A_1. If the section remains at extinction upon rotation about A_4, then X, Y, or Z is parallel to A_4. In the general case rotation about A_4 will relieve the extinction.

2. If, after rotation about A_1 to extinction, rotation about A_4 relieves the extinction, turn the section on A_4 to a position of maximum illumination, and then reduce the illumination to a minimum by rotation to the left or right on A_2. Return to zero on A_4 and observe. If extinction is not complete, repeat the above rotations about A_1 and A_2 until darkness persists when the section is rotated about A_4. In this position a normal to a symmetry plane of the indicatrix is parallel to A_4. Note the angular readings on A_1 and A_2, and plot the data on a net.

3. Rotate the microscope stage about A_5 to the 45-degree position, and then rotate the section about A_4.

   a. If the Y axis of the indicatrix is parallel to A_4, one or perhaps both of the optic axes may be brought into coincidence with the microscope tube upon rotation about A_4. As an optic axis approaches coincidence with the tube, the interference color falls, and, at the position of coincidence, minimum illumination results. If the section can be turned far enough about A_4 to obtain minimum illumination, record the angle on the scale for A_4, and plot the result to locate the optic axis on the projection.

   b. If the X or Z axis of the indicatrix is brought parallel to A_4 after initial manipulation on A_1 and A_2, rotation about A_4 when A_5 is in the 45-degree position will cause the interference color to rise.

   Allow A_5 to remain in the 45-degree position, and return A_4 to zero. Insert a gypsum plate or some other type of compensator in the slot in the microscope tube, and determine whether the axis parallel to A_4 is X or Z. If the fast direction of the compensator or accessory plate is parallel to X, the effects will be additive because light waves vibrating parallel to X are faster than light waves vibrating parallel to the Z axis. Conversely, parallelism of fast directions of the compensator or accessory plate and the Z axis produces subtractive effects.

c. Rotate the stage about A_5 to the zero position, restore A_2 to zero, rotate A_1 to the second extinction position, and proceed as above to orient a second plane of symmetry in the section of the mineral grain. Determine whether X, Y, or Z is parallel to A_4, note the optic angle, if possible, and plot results with the aid of a net.

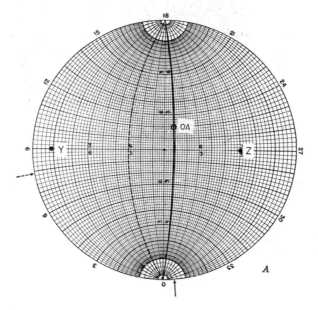

Fig. 16A. Separate operations for plotting poles and planes for a biaxial crystal which yielded the following data: Y axis located parallel to A_4 when $A_1 = 355$ degrees, $A_2 = 9$ degrees to right. An optic axis was located by rotation about A_4 20 degrees away from observer when Y was parallel to A_4. Z axis located parallel to A_4 when $A_1 = 79$ degrees and $A_2 = 30$ degrees to left. Solid index arrow for Y plot; dashed arrow for Z plot.

An example of the above measurements is plotted in Fig. 16A, B, and C. Figure 17 shows a biaxial crystal plate in several critical positions.

Corrections for Rotations

If the average refractive index of a crystal is approximately the same as the index of the glass hemispheres, routine measurements ordinarily do not require corrections for the various rotations about the axes of the universal stage. For more precise work or when the

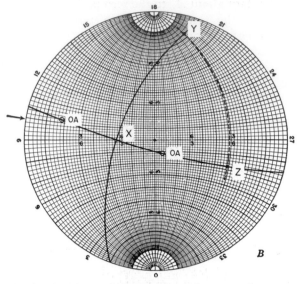

Fig. 16B. Poles for Y and Z and planes normal thereto as they appear on vellum tracing. X has been located at intersection of planes and has been placed on east-west diameter of net to permit plotting the plane normal to X (dashed curve). The projection of this plane is a great circle which includes the poles for Y and Z. An additional optic axis has been located symmetrically with regard to X on the trace of the optic plane.

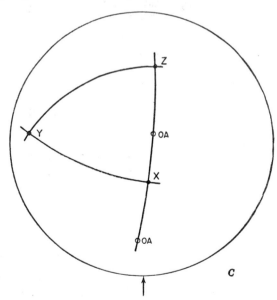

Fig. 16C. Stereographic plot for data in Fig. 16A and Fig. 16B rotated to rest position.

refractive indices of the crystal and the hemispheres differ considerably, corrections may be desirable. Figures 18 and 19 indicate the directions of the paths of light traveling through the hemispheres and

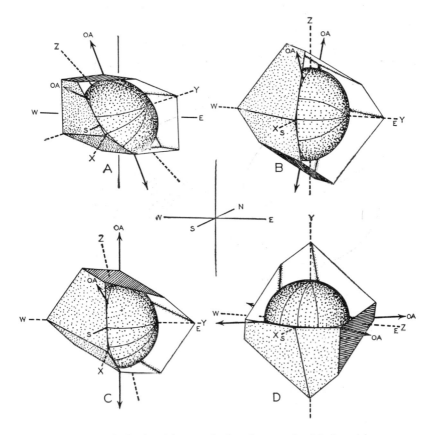

Fig. 17. Orthorhombic crystal plate in several critical positions.

A. Random position.
B. Z axis parallel to A_5. Crystal remains at extinction during rotation on A_4 and A_2.
C. Optic axis parallel to A_5. Crystal remains at extinction during rotation about A_5.
D. Y axis parallel to A_5. Crystal remains at extinction during rotation about A_4 and A_2.

a crystal plate when the refractive indices differ by a significant amount. In Fig. 18 particular refractive indices have been assigned to hemispheres and crystal plate and angle between a vertical axis and the path of light in the crystal has been calculated for an angle of incidence of 30 degrees within the lower hemisphere. The equation that was used is

$$\frac{n_1}{n_2} = \frac{\sin i}{\sin r}$$

where n_1 is the refractive index of the crystal, n_2 is the refractive index of the hemispheres, and r is the angle of refraction in the crystal. Figure 19 shows that the direction of movement of light through the crystal relative to a vertical axis is not altered by mounting the

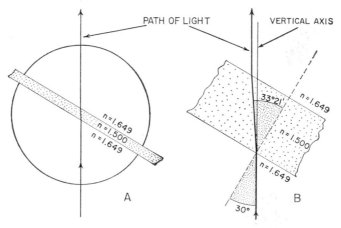

Fig. 18. Refraction of light by crystal plate between glass hemispheres of universal stage.

      A. Plate inclined to vertical axis of microscope.
      B. Enlarged diagram of a portion of Fig. 18*A*.

crystal on a glass slide or by introducing liquid films between the crystal and the hemisphere. The only condition that must be met is that the glass slides and liquid films must have surfaces parallel to their contact with the crystal plate. In Fig. 19*A* the crystal is shown as if it were mounted on an object slide with a cover glass. In Fig. 19*B* the crystal plate is shown in direct contact with the glass hemispheres. In both Fig. 19*A* and Fig. 19*B* the angle of refraction of light within the crystal relative to a vertical axis is the same.

    Measurements of crystal directions such as the *X*, *Y*, and *Z* axes of an indicatrix should give poles that are 90 degrees apart on stereographic projections. If they are not 90 degrees apart after appropriate corrections for rotations have been made, deviations probably are the result of incorrect observation or errors in plotting. In evaluating stereographic plots, poles that are obtained by small rotations about horizontal axes are more likely to be correctly measured and plotted than poles whose location requires large angular rotations. In thin sections, corrections usually are calculated by assuming an average refractive index for the crystal, and, in methods which yield measurements of refractive indices by the immersion methods, the measured refractive index is used to calculate the corrections.

The determination of the correct position of a pole of an optical direction on a stereographic plot can be made by using the Fedorov chart in Fig. 20. This chart is based on Snell's law of refraction and

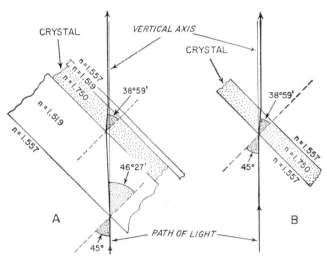

Fig. 19. Diagrams showing that direction of light refracted by crystal between hemispheres on universal stage is not altered by intervening plates or films of substances of different refractive index.

    A. Crystal plate mounted on glass microslide.
    B. Crystal plate in direct contact with hemispheres.

shows refractive indices (circles) and angles between the normal to plane of the inner stage of the universal stage and the vertical axis of the microscope (radial lines). The vertical lines are guide lines only, and their exact spacing is of no significance. To illustrate the use of the chart suppose (Fig. 18) that the normal to the inner stage is inclined 30 degrees to the vertical axis of the microscope stage and that the crystal has a refractive index of 1.500 and the hemispheres an index of 1.649. The radial line for 30 degrees is followed toward the center of the diagram to the circle for index 1.500. From the point of intersection follow a vertical guide line to the circle for index 1.649. The radius through the intersection of the guide line and the circle for index 1.649 corresponds to a corrected angle of about 33 degrees as compared with a calculated angle of 33° 21′. Note that the angle for the crystal is *greater* than the angle measured with the universal stage when the index of the crystal is *less* than the index of the hemispheres. The reverse relationship holds when the refractive index of the crystal exceeds the index of the hemispheres.

The corrected angle that is plotted is always the angle between the perpendicular to the inner stage and the vertical axis of the micro-

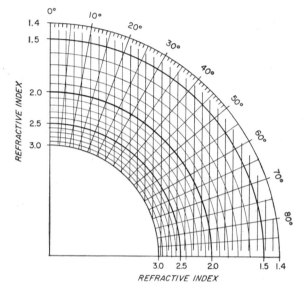

Fig. 20. Fedorov chart for correcting angles between crystal directions and microscope axis when refractive indices of hemispheres and crystal differ.

scope. In plotting measurements on the universal stage, whatever rotations are made, the pole for a particular direction as it is finally plotted is projected into a horizontal plane which is the plane of the inner stage at the rest position. Once the pole is plotted in this plane of projection, the angle between the normal to the inner stage at rest (the center of the stereographic projection) and the pole of the crystal direction is easily read by use of the stereonet. It is this angle which is corrected with the aid of calculations using Snell's law or, more conveniently, by referring to the Fedorov chart. The pole for the corrected angle lies on the same radial line as the uncorrected pole when the stereographic plot shows the locations of the poles as they are plotted in a plane parallel to the inner stage of the stage at rest position.

Twinned Crystals

The universal stage frequently is used for the determination of twin planes, twin axes, and composition planes in anisotropic crystal plates in thin sections. The twinning laws can be derived from the stereo plot or equal-area plot by correlation with identified crystal planes or directions. In tetragonal, hexagonal, and orthorhombic crystals the twin axis is perpendicular to both the twin plane and the composition plane. In monoclinic and triclinic crystals the twin axis may lie in or be perpendicular to the composition plane, depending upon the nature of the twin.

Two graphical methods are in common use for locating the pole of the twin axis in projections. In both methods the X, Y, and Z axes of the indicatrix for twinned segments of the crystal are plotted with the aid of a net. If a particular crystal yields poor results, try another crystal in the same slide.

1. In the first method the stereogram is rotated until poles of two corresponding indicatrix axes such as X_1 and X_2 lie on the same great circle of the net, and a great circle including the poles is traced on the projection. The same procedure is followed for the other corresponding pairs of indicatrix axes. The three circles should intersect at a point or in a small triangle, the center of gravity of which is the pole of the twin axis. The projection is now rotated until the pole of the composition plane lies on the east-west diameter of the net, and a great circle is drawn 90 degrees from the pole to locate the trace of the composition plane. The location of the pole of the composition face may be located crudely by rotation on A_1 and A_4 until the plane is parallel to A_4 and shows a minimum width in the section. The angular readings permit plotting of the pole of the plane as if it were a cleavage or a crystal face.

2. In the second method (after Berek) the projection is rotated over the net until two corresponding axes in the opposed twin segments lie on the same great circle. The number of degrees between the poles is counted off, and the point bisecting the poles is plotted. On the same great circle another point is plotted 90 degrees from the first point. The projection is rotated until one of these points lies on the east-west diameter of the net, and a short arc is drawn along the great circle on which the other point lies. The second point is

now treated similarly. The above procedure is repeated for the other two sets of indicatrix axes and yield arcs which intersect in a point or a triangle whose center of gravity is the pole of the twinning axis. As in the first method the pole of the composition plane can be obtained approximately by rotating the section on A_1 and A_4 until the plane shows minimum width when parallel to the east-west cross hair of the microscope.

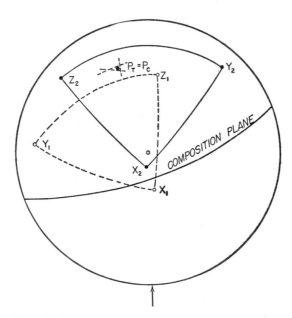

Fig. 21. Rapid method of approximately locating pole of twin axis in a twinned crystal. X_1, Y_1, and Z_1 and X_2, Y_2, and Z_2 are the poles of the indicatrix axes as determined for adjacent segments of a twin. The pole of the twin axis P_T coincides with the pole of the composition plane P_c.

The first method is illustrated in Fig. 21, an example in which the pole of the twinning axis coincides with the pole of the composition plane in a normal twin.

Two general types of results may be expected when the poles of twinning axes are plotted.

1. The twinning axis coincides with or is near to the plotted pole of the composition plane. This result indicates a *normal twin*.

2. The twin axis lies on or close to the arc representing the trace of the composition plane. This indicates a *parallel or complex type of twin*.

Rotation of Projections

The stereonet or the equal-area net can be used to rotate any projection into a desired position. The need for rotation may arise from the fact that the thin section does not cut across a mineral grain so as to give a symmetrical plot with regard to optical or crystal directions or planes.

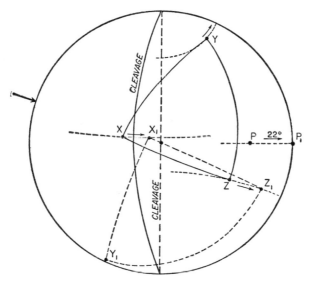

Fig. 22. Rotation of pole for cleavage and poles for indicatrix axes into new position. Solid lines indicate projection before rotation. Dashed lines show projection after rotation.

An example is shown in Fig. 22. In this example the pole of the {010} cleavage has been located in a mineral grain, and it is desired to rotate the diagram so that the pole of the cleavage will lie on the perimeter of the net. The pole is placed on the east-west diameter of the net, where it is seen that a rotation of 22 degrees about the north-south axis is required to produce the desired result. The rotation is accomplished for this pole and for poles of the indicatrix axes by rotating each pole 22 degrees along the stereographic projection of the appropriate lines of latitude derived from the spherical projection.

INDEX

Abbe refractometer, 84
Abbe total reflectometer, **83**
Aberrations, balancing of, **44**
  chromatic, 43
  monochromatic, 43
  spherical, 43
Aberrations of lenses, **43**
Abnormal blue, 149
Abnormal dispersion, 37
Abnormal interference colors, 149, 240
Absorption, biaxial crystals, 240
  differential, 149, 240
  in tourmaline, 149
  uniaxial crystals, 149
Absorption coefficient, 112
Absorption formula, biaxial crystals, 240
  uniaxial crystals, 149
Absorption of light, 112
Accessories, optical, 189
  Babinet compensator, 195
  Berek compensator, 194
  Bertrand ocular, 193
  biquartz wedge, 193
  for determination of order of an inter-
    ference color, 143

Accessories, for measurement, of extinc-
    tion angles, 193
  of path difference, 194
  of phasal difference, 194
  gypsum plate, 191
  mica plate, 192
  quartz wedge, 143, 190
Achromatic light, 59
Achromatic objectives, **53**
Acute bisectrix, 209
Acute bisectrix figure, 262
  off-center, 273
  use in sign determination, 269
Air, refractive index, 38
Allen, R. D., 57
Amici-Bertrand lens, 47, 50
Amici compensating prism, 86
Amorphous substances, definition, **1**
Amplitude, of light wave, 123
  of simple harmonic motion, 27
Analyzer, 45
  function, 141
  interference in, 141
Angle, of extinction, 151, 232
  of incidence, 33, 35

Angle, of reflection, 33
  of refraction, 35
Angles, interfacial, 2
Angles of crystals, measurement, 13, 14
Angular aperture, 51
Anhedral crystals, 1
Anisotropic crystals, interaction with microscope, 127
Anisotropic media, 30
  ray-velocity surfaces, 32
Anisotropism, determined with universal stage, 327
Anomalous interference colors, 149, 240
Anomalous interference figures, 291
Aperture, angular, 51
  numerical, 52
Apochromatic objectives, 52
Apparent optic angle, 262
Apparent relief, 65
Arago-Fresnel laws, 141
Astigmatism, of lenses, 44
Axes, crystallographic, 2
Axes of symmetry, definition, 6
Axial ratio of crystals, 4
Axinite, optic orientation, 227, 228
Axis of lens, 41
Axis of rotary inversion, 6
Axis of symmetry, 6

Babinet compensator, 195
Balancing of aberrations, 44
Banded spectrum, 140
Beam of light, definition, 30
Becke, F., 173
Becke line, 66
  colored, 70, 71
  false, 69
  origin of, 67
Becke-line method of index measurement, 66
Berek compensator, 194
Berek method of plotting twin data, 339
Berman, H., 57, 63
Bertin's surfaces, biaxial crystals, 250
  uniaxial crystals, 169
  uniaxial flash figures, 184
Bertrand-Amici lens, 47, 50
Bertrand ocular, 193
Biaxial crystals, 207
  absorption formula, 240

Biaxial crystals, acute bisectrix figure, 262
  Bertin's surfaces, 247
  birefringence, 210
  determination of optic orientation, 238
  determination of optic sign, 269
  dispersion, 287
  extinction angles, 232
  flash figures, 268
  Huygenian constructions, 229
  in convergent polarized light, 245
  interference colors, 240
  interference figures, 245
  isochromatic curves in interference figures, 246
  isogyres in interference figures, 253
  measurement, of refractive indices, 238
    on universal stage, 329
  obtuse bisectrix figure, 265
  optic-axis figure, 266
  optic-normal figure, 268
  pleochroism, 240
  ray-velocity surfaces, 214
  rotation to measure properties, 317
  wave normals, 215
Biaxial indicatrix, 207
  derived ray-velocity surfaces, 214
  equation, 210
  principal planes, 212
Biaxial interference figures, 245
  acute bisectrix figure, 262, 269
  Bertin's surfaces, 247
  Biot-Fresnel constructions, 260
  isochromatic curves, 246
  isogyres, 253
  obtuse bisectrix figure, 265, 279
  optic-axis figure, 266, 279
  optic-normal figure, 268
  use in index measurement, 286
Biaxial isotaques, 257
Biaxial skiodromes, 254, 257
Biconcave lens, 42
Biconvex lens, 42
Biot-Fresnel constructions, 256
  in biaxial interference figures, 260
Biot-Fresnel law, 232, 270
Biquartz wedge, 193
Birefringence, biaxial crystals, 210
  definition, 141
  from interference color, 142

Birefringence, in uniaxial crystals, 92
  partial, 210
Birefringence chart, 142
Bisectrices, dispersion of, 289
Bisectrix, acute, 209
  obtuse, 209
Borosilicate glass, 62
Brewster's law, 114
Brookite, dispersion, 292

Calcite, cleavage, 153
  double refraction, 103
  optic orientation, 91
  transmission of light, 105
  use in Nicol prism, 111
Calcite experiment, 103
Capacity, refractive, 57
Cassinian curves, 251
Cauchy's equation, 61
Center of symmetry, definition, 6
Centering of objectives, 53
Central illumination, 72
Channeled spectrum, 140
Chromatic aberrations, 43
Chromatic light, 59
Circular polarization, 109
Circular sections of indicatrix, 209
Circularly polarized light, 109, 120
  composition and resolution, 117
Cleavage, 8
  plotted with universal stage, 325
Cleavage fragments, orientation on glass
    slide, 153
Clinographic projection, 19
Closed forms, on crystals, 6
Color, by interference, 126
  by mixing, 59
  by subtraction, 59
Color curves, biaxial interference figures,
    246
  uniaxial interference figures, 165, 177
Color fringes, in immersion methods,
    70
  on isogyres, 288
Color phenomena, in immersion meth-
    ods, 70
Color spectrum, 23, 38
Colored Becke line, 70
Colored light, 59
Coma, of lenses, 44

Combination, crystallographic, 6
Compensating eyepieces, 54
Compensating oculars, 54
Compensating prism, Amici, 86
Compensation, 146
  by quartz wedge, 144
  complete, 146
  mechanism, 145
  partial, 146
Compensator, Babinet, 195
  Berek, 194
  graduated quartz plate, 194
Compensators, 194
Complete compensation, 146
Complex twins, in crystals, 11, 340
Composition and resolution of wave
    motions, 117
Composition of light waves in a plane,
    115
Composition plane, of crystals, 11
Compound lenses, 44
Condensers, substage, 54
Condensing lens, refraction of light in
    conoscope, 162
  substage, 54
Conical refraction, exterior, 240
  interior, 240
Conjugate radii, 216
Conoscope, 49, 50, 160
Constructive interference of light waves,
    116
Contact goniometer, 14
Contact twins, 11
Continuous spectrum, 140
Convergent light, 160
Converging lenses, 41
Corrections for rotations on universal
    stage, 333
Critical angle, 40
  of diamond, 40
  use in index measurement, 83
Crossed axial plane dispersion, 292
Crossed dispersion, 293, 295
Crystal, definition, 1
  ideal, 1
Crystal axes, 2
Crystal faces, plotting with universal
    stage, 325
Crystal forms, 6
Crystal habit, 9

Crystal planes, orientation with universal stage, 325
Crystal projections, 12
Crystal rotation methods, 308
Crystal systems, definitions, 2, 4
Crystal substances, definition, 1
Crystallography, 1
Crystals, anhedral, 1
  anisotropic, 30
  axial ratios, 4
  biaxial, 207
  cleavage, 8
  closed forms, 6
  combinations of forms, 6
  complex twins, 11
  composition plane in twins, 11
  contact twins, 11
  defect lattices, 2
  defects, 2
  euhedral, 1
  imperfactions, 1, 2
  in immersion media, 302
  interfactal angles, 2
  isotropic, 30
  length-fast, 205
  length-slow, 206
  malformed, 2
  measurement of angles, 13
  Miller indices, 5
  mosaic structure, 2
  normal twins, 11
  open forms, 6
  parallel twins, 11, 340
  parameters, 5
  parting, 8
  penetration twins, 11
  perfect, 1
  physical properties, 2
  poles of faces, 13
  polysynthetic twins, 11
  projections, 12
  rational intercepts of faces, 5
  ray-velocity surfaces, 32
  repeated twins, 11
  simple twins, 11
  solid solutions, 2
  subhedral, 1
  symmetry elements, 6
  twin axis, 11
  twin plane, 11

Crystals, twins, 9
  uniaxial, 88
  zones, 13

Dark-field immersion, 78
Defect lattices, 2
Defects, of lenses, 43
Density, related to refractive index, 56
Depth of focus, 52
Destructive interference of light waves, 117
Dextrorotatory crystals, 155
Diamond, critical angle, 40
  refractive index, 40
Dichroism, 149
Differential absorption, 112, 149
Diffuse reflection, 35
Dispersion, 60
  abnormal, 37
  crossed, 293
  crossed axial plane, 292
  horizontal, 293
  in biaxial crystals, 287, 288
  in brookite, 292
  in monoclinic crystals, 292
  in orthorhombic crystals, 289
  in triclinic crystals, 300
  in uniaxial crystals, 92
  inclined, 293
  of the optic axes, 288
  of the refractive indices, 37, 60
  orthorhombic, 289
  partial, 60
  refractive-index, 60
  relative, 60
  rhombic, 289
  rotatory, 157
  total, 60
  triclinic, 300
  wave-length, 60
Dispersion curves, 62, 71
  for biaxial crystals, 288
Dispersion formula, 288
Dispersion methods of refractive index measurement, 79
Dispersion of the refractive indices, biaxial crystals, 287
Dispersive power, 60
Distortion by lenses, 44

Diverging lenses, 41
Dodge, N. B., 78
Double-diaphragm method of index measurement, 78
Double-variation method of index measurement, 80

$2E$, 263
E rays, 96
E waves, 89
Electric vector, 21, 26
Electromagnetic spectrum, 22
Electromagnetic theory of light, 20
Electromagnetic waves, 21
  frequency, 22
  velocity, 22
  visible spectrum, 23
Elements of symmetry, 6
Elongation, sign of, 205
Ellipse, from projected circular motions, 118
  spherical, 254
Elliptical motion, from combined circular motions, 118
Elliptical polarization, 109
Elliptically polarized light, 109, 120
  composition and resolution, 117
Emmons, R. C., 63, 71, 80, 309, 321
Enantiomorphism, 155
Equal-area net, 310
Equal-path-difference curves, biaxial crystals, 249
  uniaxial crystals, 167
Equal-phase-difference curves, biaxial crystals, 249
  uniaxial crystals, 167
Ethyl salicylate, 61
Euhedral crystals, 1
Exterior conical refraction, 240
Extinction angles, biaxial crystals, 232
  measurement with optical accessories, 193
  monoclinic crystal, 234
  uniaxial crystals, 151
Extinction direction net, 187
Extinction position, 127
Extraordinary rays, 96
Extraordinary waves, 89
Eyepieces, Huygens', 53
  Ramsden, 53

False Becke line, 69
Fast component, 144, 189
Fast direction, 190
Fedorov chart, 338
Fermat's principle, 33
Filters, interference, 58
First-order interference colors, 139
First-order red plate, 191
Five-axis universal stage, 309, 321
Fivelings, 12
Flash figure, in biaxial crystals, 268
  in uniaxial crystals, 183
  use in sign determination in uniaxial crystals, 204
Fluorite objectives, 53
Focal distance, 42
Focal length, 42
Focal point, 42
Focus, 42
  depth of, 52
  real, 42
  virtual, 42
Form, crystallographic, 6
Four-axis universal stage, 323
Fourlings, 12
Fracture, 9
  classification, 9
Fraunhofer lines, 58
Frequency of electromagnetic waves, 22, 27
Fresnel-Arago laws, 141
Fresnel-Biot construction, 256
Fresnel-Biot law, 270
  derivation, 232
Fresnel mechanism for rotatory polarization, 157

Gates, R. M., 71
Gladstone and Dale, rule of, 56
Glass, borosilicate, 62
Gnomonic projection, 14
Goniometer, contact, 14
  reflecting, 13
Graphical solutions, with stereographic net, 309
Gypsum plate, 191

Habit, classification, 9
  of crystals, 9
Hartmann equations, 61

Hartmann net, 62, 92
Hexagonal crystals, optic orientation, 90
Hexagonal division of hexagonal system, 4
Hexagonal system, definition, 4
Higher-order white, 140
Horizontal dispersion, 293, 296
Huygenian constructions, biaxial crystals, 228
  uniaxial crystals, 99
Huygens' ocular, 53
Huygens' principle, 33
Hydrogen discharge tube, 58
Hyperplane ocular, 54

Iceland spar, 111
Ideal crystal, 1
Illumination, central, 72
  oblique, 74
Image, real, 42
  reversed by lens, 42
  virtual, 42
Immersion media, 63
  tabulation of properties, 64
Immersion methods, color phenomena, 70
  of refractive index measurement, 62
  summary of procedure, 306
  using auxiliary single-axis stage, 312
Imperfections in crystals, 1, 2
Incidence, angle of, 33
  plane of, 34
Inclined dispersion, 293, 298
Index, refractive, 36
Index liquids, 63, 64
Index measurement, biaxial crystals, 238
  uniaxial crystals, 151
Index media, tabulation of properties, 63, 64
Index of refraction, 36, 38, 125
  accuracy of measurement, 63
  calculation, 55
  determined from critical angle, 83
  dispersion methods of measurement, 79
  measured by central illumination, 72
  measurement, 55
    by Abbe refractometer, 84, 86
    by Becke-line method, 66

Index of refraction, measurement, by double-diaphragm method, 78
  by double-variation method, 80
  by method of perpendicular incidence, 82
  by minimum-deviation method, 80
  by Pulfrich refractometer, 84
  by total reflectometer, 83
  in dark-field illumination, 78
  in liquid immersions, 62
  in oblique illumination, 74
  of air, 38
  relation to density and composition, 56
  related to temperature, 61
Indicatrix, biaxial, 207
  isotropic, 39
  uniaxial, 87
Indices of crystal faces, 5
Indices of refraction, biaxial crystals, 209
  equivalent designations, for biaxial crystals, 209
    for uniaxial crystals, 90
  measured with one-axis auxiliary stage, 315, 319, 320
  measurement, in biaxial crystals, 238
    in uniaxial crystals, 151
    with aid of biaxial interference figures, 286
  symbolism, for biaxial crystals, 209
    for uniaxial crystals, 90
  uniaxial crystals, 88
Initial magnification, 52
Intensities, visual, 139
Intercepts, of crystal faces, 5
Interfacial angles of crystals, 2
Interference, of light waves, 116, 128
  of wave motions, 117
Interference color chart, 142
Interference colors, abnormal, 149
  in biaxial crystals, 240
  in quartz wedge, 138
  order by quartz wedge, 143
  order of, by color bands, 143
  origin, 126
Interference figures, 51
  acute bisectrix figure, 262, 269
  biaxial crystals, 245
  biaxial optic-axis figure, 266, 279
  Biot-Fresnel constructions, 260

Interference figures, color curves, **in** biaxial crystals, 246
  in uniaxial crystals, 165, 180
  flash figure, in biaxial crystals, 268
  in uniaxial crystals, 183, 200
  isogyres, in biaxial figures, 253
  in uniaxial figures, 170, 175
  obtuse bisectrix figure, 265
  off-center biaxial figures, 273, 286
  off-center uniaxial optic-axis figures, 181
  optic-normal figure, 268
  uniaxial crystals, 160, 165
  uniaxial flash figures, 183
  uniaxial optic-axis figures, 179
  use in index measurement in biaxial crystals, 286
Interference filters, 58
Interior conical refraction, 240
Isochromatic curves, biaxial interference figures, 246
  uniaxial interference figures, 165, 177
Isogyres, biaxial interference figures, 253
  curvature in biaxial optic-axis figures, 268
  from uniaxial skiodrome, 176
  location determined by vector analysis, 177
  uniaxial interference figures, 165, 170
Isometric system, definition, 2
Isomorphous series, 301
Isomorphous substances, **2**
Isotaques, biaxial, 257
  uniaxial, 173
Isotropic cross, 163
Isotropic indicatrix, 39
Isotropic media, 30
  ray-velocity surfaces, 32
Isotropic substances, optics, 33
Isotropism, determination on universal stage, 327

Jaffe, H. W., 57
Joel, N., 311
Johannsen, A., 173, 232, 246

Kamb, W. B., 161, 170, 173, 187, 253, 259
Ketteler-Helmholtz equation, 37

Larsen, E. S., 57, 63

Lattice defects, 2
Left-hand crystals, 155
Length-fast crystals, 205
Length-slow crystals, **206**
Lens, axis, 41
  biconcave, 42
  biconvex, 42
  reversal of image, **42**
Lens aberrations, 43
Lenses, 41
  compound, 44
  condensing, 54
  converging, 41
  defects, 43
  diverging, 41
  resolving power, 52
Levorotatory crystals, 155
Lichtenecker equation, 56
Light, achromatic, 59
  chromatic, 59
  colored, 59
  electromagnetic theory, **20**
  linearly polarized, 21
  luminosity, 140
  monochromatic, **23**
  nature of, 20
  omnichromatic, 59
  plane-polarized, 21
  visual intensities, 140
  wave lengths, 24
Light beam, definition, **30**
Light ray, definition, 29
Light sources, 58
Light vector, 26
Light waves, 23, 87
  amplitudes, 123
  composition and resolution in a plane, 115
  path difference, 124
  phasal difference, 124
  vector analysis, 115
  velocity, 22
Linearly polarized light, 21, 109
Longitudinal waves, 24
Lorentz equation, 56
Lorenz equation, 56
Luminosity of light, 140
Luster, 35

Magnetic vector, **21**

Magnification, initial, 52
Mallard's constant, 264
Melatopes, 251
Melilite, 149
Mercury arc, 58
Mertie, J. B., Jr., 212
Merwin, H. E., 79
Meyrowitz, R., 65
Mica plate, 192
Michel-Lévy chart, 142
Microscope, as a conoscope, 49, **50**
  as an orthoscope, 47, 48
  eyepieces, 53
  objectives, 52
  oculars, 53
  polarizing, 45
  transmission of light waves, 127
Microscopic examination, systematic, 301
Millimicron, definition, 23
Minimum-deviation method of index
  measurement, 80
Molecular refractivity, 57
Monochromatic aberrations, 43
Monochromatic light, 23
Monochromatic radiations, 58
Monochromator, 58
Monoclinic crystals, dispersion, 292
  optic orientation, 224
  stereographic plot of extinction angles,
    235
Monoclinic system, definition, 4
Mosaic structure, 2
Multiaxis universal stage, 321
Muscovite, use in mica plate, 192

n_E, definition, 90
Negative biaxial indicatrix, 209
Negative crystals, biaxial, 209
  uniaxial, 90
Negative elongation, 205
Negative uniaxial indicatrix, **90**
Newton's colors, 137
Nicol prism, 47, 111
  construction, 111
  transmission of light, 111
n_O, definition, 89
Nonopaque substances, systematic micro-
  scopic examination, 301
Normal twins, 11, 340
Numerical aperture, 52

n_X, definition, 209
n_Y, definition, 209
n_Z, definition, 209

O rays, 96
O waves, 89
Objectives, achromatic, **53**
  apochromatic, 52
  centering procedure, **53**
  fluorite, 53
  microscope, 52
  oil immersion, 52
Oblique illumination, 74
Oblique-illumination method of index
  measurement, 74
Obtuse bisectrix, 209
Obtuse bisectrix figure, 265
  use in sign determination, **279**
Oculars, 53
  Bertrand, 193
  compensating, **54**
  Huygens', 53
  hyperplane, 54
  Ramsden, 53
Off-center acute bisectrix figures, 273
Off-center biaxial optic-axis figures, 286
Off-center uniaxial optic-axis figures, 181
Oil immersion objectives, 52
Omnichromatic light, 59
One-axis crystal rotation device, 312
One-circle stage goniometer, 311
One-quarter lambda plate, 192
Open forms, on crystals, 6
Optic angle, 209
  calculated with Mallard's constant, 264
  calculation, 210
  chart for estimation, 211
  estimated from curvature of isogyres,
    268
  nomogram, 212
  variation with color of light, 288
Optic axes, dispersion of, 288
  primary, 209
  secondary, 218
Optic-axis figure, biaxial, **266**
  off-center, 286
  use in sign determination, **279**
  curvature of isogyres in biaxial figures,
    268
  uniaxial, **179**

Optic-axis figure, uniaxial, off-center, 181
  use in sign determination, 200
Optic normal, 209
Optic-normal interference figure, 268
Optic orientation, biaxial crystals, 238
  monoclinic crystals, 224
  orthorhombic crystals, 223
  triclinic crystals, 227
  uniaxial crystals, 90
Optic plane, 209
Optic sign, biaxial crystals, 269
  from acute bisectrix figure, 269
  from biaxial optic-axis figure, 279
  from indices of biaxial crystals, 210
  from indices of uniaxial crystals, 196
  from obtuse bisectrix figure, 279
  from uniaxial crystals and cleavage
    fragments, 196, 197
  from uniaxial flash figure, 204
  from uniaxial optic-axis figure, 200
  uniaxial crystals, 196
Optical accessories, 189
  for measurement, of path difference,
    194
    of phasal difference, 194
Optical activity, 155
Optical data, tabulation, 304
Optical examination in immersion
  media, 302
Optical orientation, biaxial crystals, **223**,
  224, 225
  cleavage fragments, 153
  uniaxial crystals, 90
Optical path, 125
Optical path difference, 125
Optical properties, biaxial crystals, **305**
  isotropic substances, 304
  measurement, 301
  tabulation, 304
  uniaxial crystals, 304
Optical sign, biaxial crystals, 269
  uniaxial crystals, 196
Optical system, conoscope, 49
  orthoscope, 47
Optically active crystals, 128, 155
Optically anisotropic media, 30
Optically inactive crystals, 155
Optically isotropic media, 30, 33
Order of interference color, by color
  bands, 143

Order of interference color, by quartz
  wedge, 143
Orders of interference colors, 140
Ordinary rays, 96
Ordinary waves, 89
Orientation, biaxial crystals, 238
  cleavage fragments, 153
  monoclinic crystals, 224
  orthorhombic crystals, 223
  triclinic crystals, 227
  uniaxial crystals, 90
Orthographic projection, 18
Orthorhombic crystals, dispersion, 289
  optic orientation, 223
Orthorhombic dispersion, 289
Orthorhombic system, definition, **4**
Orthoscope, 47
Oscillation, simple harmonic, 26
Ovaloid, uniaxial crystals, 108

Parallel twins, 11, 340
Parameters of crystal faces, **5**
Partial birefringence, 210
Partial compensation, 146
Partial dispersion, 60
Parting, definition, 8
Path difference, 29, 124
  measurement with optical accessories,
    194
  produced by crystal plates, 129
  related to phasal difference, 125
Peacock, M. A., 227
Penetration twins, 11
Perfect crystal, 1
Period of simple harmonic motion, 27
Perpendicular incidence, method of in-
  dex measurement, 82
Petrographic microscope, 45
Phasal difference, 27
  measurement with optical accessories,
    194
  of light waves, 124
  related to path difference, **125**
Phase, definition, 27
Phemister, T. C., 213
Photons, 20
Plane of incidence, 34
Plane of polarization, 109
Plane of symmetry, 6
Plane of vibration, 27, 110

Plane of vibration, from Biot-Fresnel constructions, 260
Plane-polarized light, 27, 109
  by differential absorption, 112
  by double refraction, 110
  by reflection, 114
  by scattering, 115
  composition and resolution, 117
Pleochroic formula, biaxial crystals, 240
  uniaxial crystals, 149
Pleochroism, 149, 240
  biaxial crystals, 240
  uniaxial crystals, 149
Polar, definition, 47
Polar-coordinate equation, for biaxial crystals, 249
  for uniaxial crystals, 94
Polarization, by absorption, 112
  by double refraction, 110
  by reflection, 114
  by scattering, 115
  of light, 109
  plane of, 109
  rotatory, 155
Polarized light, 109
Polarizer, 45
Polarizing microscope, 45
  transmission of light waves, 127
Polaroid, 113
Pole, of crystal face, 13
Polysynthetic twins, 11
Positive biaxial indicatrix, 209
Positive crystals, biaxial, 209
  uniaxial, 90
Positive elongation, 206
Positive uniaxial indicatrix, 90
Posnjak, E., 79
Primary optic axes, 209
Principal section of uniaxial indicatrix, 88, 92
Prism, Nicol, 47
Projection, clinographic, 19
  gnomonic, 17
  orthographic, 18
  rotation of, 341
  spherical, 12
  stereographic, 14
Projection of crystals, 12
Pulfrich refractometer, 84

Quanta, 20
Quarter undulation plate, 192
Quartz, dispersion curves, 92
  optic orientation, 91
  rotation of polarized light, 155
  use in Bertrand ocular, 193
  use in biquartz wedge, 193
Quartz compensator, 194
Quartz crystals, 156
Quartz wedge, 136, 190
  color bands, 139
  use as compensator, 144
  use in determination of order of interference color, 143

Radiation, 20
Radii, conjugate, 216
Ramsden ocular, 53
Rational intercepts, law of, 5
Ray, 29, 87
Ray index of refraction, 96, 216
Ray refractive index, 96, 216
Ray surface, 31
Ray velocity, 31, 87, 218
  biaxial crystals, 214, 223
  uniaxial crystals, 95
Ray-velocity surfaces, 31, 96
  anisotropic media, 32
  biaxial crystals, 214, 223
  derived from indicatrix, 95, 214
  in isotropic substances, 32
  uniaxial crystals, 95
Rays, extraordinary, 96
  ordinary, 96
Rays and wave normals, relationships in biaxial crystals, 219
  uniaxial crystals, 95
Real focus, 42
Real image, 42
Real optic angle, 262
Red of first-order plate, 191
Reflecting goniometer, 13
Reflection, diffuse, 35
  of light, 33
  law of, 33
  regular, 35
  total, 40
Reflectometer, 83
Refraction, 35
  angle of, 35

Refraction, index of, 36, 38
of light by substage condenser, 162
Refractive capacity, 57
Refractive energy, 56
Refractive index, 36, 38, 125
accuracy of measurement, 63
Becke-line method of measurement, 66
calculation, 55
determined from critical angle, 83
dispersion, biaxial crystals, 287
isotropic substances, 62
uniaxial crystals, 92
dispersion methods of measurement, 79
measurement, 55
by Abbe refractometer, 84, 86
by central illumination, 72
by double-variation method, 80
by immersion methods, 62
by method of perpendicular incidence, 82
by Pulfrich refractometer, 84
by total reflectometer, 83
in dark-field immersions, 78
in oblique illumination, 74
using biaxial interference figures, 286
of air, 38
relation to density and composition, 56
Refractive index dispersion, 60
Refractive index liquids, 64
Refractive indices, biaxial crystals, 209
dispersion of, 37
equivalent designations, for biaxial crystals, 209
for uniaxial crystals, 90
measurement, in biaxial crystals, 238
in uniaxial crystals, 151
with one-axis auxiliary stage, 315, 319, 320
temperature dispersion, 61
uniaxial crystals, 88
Refractivity, molecular, 57
specific, 57
Refractometer, Abbe, 84
Pulfrich, 84
Refringence, 38
Regular reflection, 35
Relative dispersion, 60

Relief, 65
apparent, 65
Repeated twins, 11
Resolution of light by crystals, 128
Resolution of light waves in a plane, 115
Resolving power, 52
Retardation, 29
Reversal of image by lens, 42
Rhombic dispersion, 289
Rhombohedral division, hexagonal system, 4
Right-handed crystals, 155
Rosenbusch, H., 232, 246
Rosenfeld, J. L., 312
Rotary inversion, axis of, 6
Rotary polarization, 155
Rotation, of light vectors by condensing lens, 163
of plane-polarized light, 155
of stereographic projections, 341
Rotation methods, 308
Rotatory dispersion, 157
Rotatory polarization, 155
Fresnel mechanization, 157
Rotatory power, 155

Samples, preparation for optical study, 303
Saylor, C. P., 77
Scattering, 115
Schmidt net, 311
Schroeder van der Kolk method, 74
Secondary optic axes, 218
Second-order interference colors, 130
Sensitive tint, 140
Sensitive tint plate, 191
Sign, biaxial crystals, 269
from acute bisectrix figure, 269
from biaxial optic-axis figure, 279
from indices of biaxial crystals, 210
from indices of uniaxial crystals, 196
from obtuse bisectrix figure, 279
from uniaxial crystals and cleavage fragments, 196, 197
from uniaxial flash figure, 204
from uniaxial optic-axis figure, 200
uniaxial crystals, 196
Sign of elongation, 205
Simple harmonic motion, 26
amplitude, 27

Simple harmonic motion, period of, 27
Simple harmonic oscillation, 26
Simple twins, 11
Single-axis stage, 312
Sinusoidal waves, 26, 29
Skiodrome, biaxial, 254, 257
 uniaxial, 173
 uniaxial flash figure, 186
 uniaxial optic-axis figure, 175
Slow component, 144, 189
Slow direction, 190
Snell's law, 37
Solid solution, in crystals, 2
Sources of light, 58
Specific refractive capacity, 57
Specific refractive energy, 56
Specific refractivity, 57
Specific rotation, 155
Spectral lines, 58
Spectrometer, 80
Spectrum, 38
 banded, 140
 channeled, 140
 continuous, 140
 electromagnetic, 22
 from colorless prism, 38
 reference wave lengths, 59
 visible, 23
Spherical aberration, 43
Spherical ellipse, 254
Spherical projection, 12
Stage, auxiliary single-axis, 312
Stage goniometer, 308
 one-circle, 311
Stereographic net, 309
Stereographic projection, 14
Stereographic projections, biaxial crystals, 236, 260, 316, 318, 333
 extinction angles in monoclinic crystal, 235
 uniaxial crystals, 153, 314, 330
Subhedral crystals, 1
Substage condensing lenses, 54
Surface-true nets, 309
Symmetry axis, definition, 6
Symmetry elements, 6
Symmetry plane, definition, 6

Temperature coefficient of refraction, 61

Temperature dispersion of refractive indices, 61
Tetragonal crystals, optic orientation, 90
Tetragonal system, definition, 2
Thickness, by interference color, 142
Third-order interference colors, 138
Tobi, A. C., 265
Total dispersion, 60
Total reflection, 40
Total reflectometer, 83
Tourmaline, absorption, 112, 149
Tourmaline tongs, 149
Transmission coefficient, 112
Transverse waves, 24
Triaxial ellipsoid, 207
Triclinic crystals, dispersion, 300
 optic orientation, 227
Triclinic dispersion, 300
Triclinic system, definition, 4
Trills, 12
Twin, complex, 11, 340
 contact, 11
 measured on universal stage, 339
 normal, 11, 340
 parallel, 11, 340
 penetration, 11
 polysynthetic, 11
 repeated, 11
 simple, 11
Twin axis, 11
Twin plane, 11
Twinned crystals, 9
 on universal stage, 339
Twinning, determined by universal stage, 340
Twins, in crystals, 9

Uniaxial crystals, 88
 birefringence, 92
 dispersion, 92
 Huygenian constructions, 99
 in convergent polarized light, 160
 in plane-polarized light, 126
 interference figures, 165
 isochromatic curves in interference figures, 165, 183
 isogyres in interference figures, 170, 186
 measurement on universal stage, 328

Uniaxial crystals, off-center optic-axis figures, 181
optic-axis figures, 179
optic orientation, 90
optic sign determination, 196
ovaloid, 108
principal section, 92
ray-velocity surfaces, 96
refractive index measurement, 151
relation between rays and wave normals, 93
rotation to measure properties, 313
sign from crystals or cleavage fragments, 197
sign from flash figures, 204
sign from optic-axis figure, 200
stereographic projections, 153
wave-normal-velocity surfaces, 107
wave surfaces, 107
Uniaxial flash figure, 183
use in sign determination, 204
Uniaxial indicatrix, 87, 88
equation, 94
Uniaxial interference figures, isochromatic curves, 165, 183
isogyres, 170, 183
use in sign determination, 200, 204
Uniaxial optic-axis figure, 179
off-center, 181
use in sign determination, 200
Uniaxial ray-velocity surfaces, equation, 98
Uniaxial skiodrome, 173
Unit cell, 1
Units of linear measurement, 23
Universal stage, 195, 308
axis designations, 321
corrections for rotations, 333
determination of anisotropism, 327
determination of isotropism, 327
five-axis, 321
four-axis, 323
measurement, of biaxial crystals, 329
of twinned crystals, 339
of uniaxial crystals, 328
method of plotting crystal planes, 325
multiaxis, 321
one-axis, 311
Upper polar, function, 141

$2V$, 209
calculation, 210
Vector, definition, 115
electric, 21, 26
magnetic, 21
Vector analysis, light waves, 115, 127
uniaxial interference figure, 178
Vector diagrams, 115, 127, 178
Velocity, of electromagnetic waves, 22
of light waves, 22
Vibration, plane of, 27, 110
Virtual focus, 42
Virtual image, 42
Visible spectrum, 23
reference wave lengths, 59
Visual intensities, 139

Wave, 87
Wave front, 23, 24, 31, 87
Wave-front normal, 25, 29, 87
Wave-front-normal velocity, 107
Wave length, 27
Wave-length dispersion, 60
Wave lengths, of light, 24
visible spectrum, 59
Wave movement, in homogeneous medium, 25
Wave normal, 29, 87
Wave-normal velocity, 31, 218
in skiodrome constructions, 174
uniaxial crystals, 95, 108
Wave-normal-velocity surfaces, uniaxial, 107
Wave normals, in biaxial crystals, 215
Wave normals and rays, biaxial crystals, 219
uniaxial crystals, 95
Wave surface, 31
uniaxial, 107
Wave train, 87
Waves, electromagnetic, 21, 23
extraordinary, 89
interference, 115, 117, 129
longitudinal, 24
ordinary, 89
sinusoidal, 26, 29
transverse, 24
Wedge, quartz, 36
West, C. D., 65
White light, 59

White of a higher order, 140
Winchell, H., 265
Wooster, W. A., 244, 246
Wright, F. E., 210, 211, 268

Wright's biquartz wedge, 193
Wülfing, E. A., 232, 246

Zones, in crystals, 13